s

D1452524

Noise Control
in Buildings

Other McGraw-Hill Books Edited by Cyril M. Harris

HARRIS • *Dictionary of Architecture and Construction*
HARRIS • *Handbook of Acoustical Measurements and Noise Control*
HARRIS • *Handbook of Utilities and Services for Buildings*
HARRIS & CREDE • *Shock and Vibration Handbook*

Other McGraw-Hill Books of Interest

AVALLONE & BAUMEISTER • *Marks' Standard Handbook for Mechanical Engineers*
GANIĆ & HICKS • *The McGraw-Hill Handbook of Essential Engineering Information and Data*
GAYLORD & GAYLORD • *Structural Engineering Handbook*
GRIMM & ROSALER • *Handbook of HVAC Design*
HICKS • *Standard Handbook of Engineering Calculations*
KARASSIK ET AL. • *Pump Handbook*
TUMA • *Engineering Mathematics Handbook*
WADSWORTH • *Handbook of Statistical Methods for Engineers and Scientists*
YOUNG • *Roark's Formulas for Stress and Strain*

Noise Control in Buildings

A Guide for Architects and Engineers

Cyril M. Harris, Ph.D. Editor in Chief

*School of Engineering and Applied Science and
Graduate School of Architecture,
Planning and Preservation
Columbia University*

NEW ENGLAND INSTITUTE
OF TECHNOLOGY
LEARNING RESOURCES CENTER

McGraw-Hill, Inc.

New York   San Francisco   Washington, D.C.   Auckland   Bogotá
Caracas   Lisbon   London   Madrid   Mexico City   Milan
Montreal   New Delhi   San Juan   Singapore
Sydney   Tokyo   Toronto

Library of Congress Cataloging-in-Publication Data

Noise control in buildings : a guide for architects and engineers /
  Cyril Manton Harris, editor in chief.
      p.   cm.
  Includes index and bibliographical references.

  ISBN 0-07-028887-8
  1. Soundproofing.   2. Noise control.   I. Harris, Cyril M., date.
  TH1725.N667   1994
  693'.834—dc20   93-19455
                                                           CIP

1 2 3 4 5 6 7 8 9 0   DOC/DOC   9 9 8 7 6 5 4 3

ISBN 0-07-028887-8

*The sponsoring editor for this book was Harold B. Crawford, the
editing supervisor was Peggy Lamb, and the production supervisor was
Suzanne W. Babeuf. This book was set in Century Schoolbook. It was
composed by McGraw-Hill's Professional Book Group composition unit.*

Printed and bound by R. R. Donnelley & Sons Company.

This book is printed on acid-free paper.

Contents

Preface

Noise Control in Buildings is a comprehensive, practical guide to avoiding noise problems in buildings that are still in the design stage and to solving noise problems in existing buildings. This book is especially directed toward architects, engineers, and those engaged in building design, construction, or modernization whose technical background in acoustics is limited. Whenever possible, lucid explanations and simple charts replace derivations of complicated technical equations. Readers who want more complex content will find such material set in smaller type.

Chapters 2 and 4 describe the basic principles of noise control that will be of interest to readers desiring a comprehensive background in this field. However, the material in this book is presented so that readers who are faced with a specific noise problem can turn directly to the relevant chapter for methods of solution.

Chapter 3 provides a description of the properties of acoustical materials and the factors one should consider in selecting such materials. Extensive tables of sound absorption coefficients are required in order to make suitable choices among the large number of commercially available materials. However, no single publication containing such tables has been available in recent years. To fill this significant gap in the literature, the characteristics of acoustical materials manufactured in North America, Europe, and Asia have been assembled as the appendixes to Chapter 3—the most complete collection of such data ever published in book form.

Chapter 5 focuses on the problems of the transmission of airborne noise through partitions. This chapter shows how to select wall constructions to provide adequate sound insulation. The practical application of these principles requires the use of extensive tabular information, which is presented as appendixes to this chapter. The wealth of technical data in these appendixes makes them an invaluable resource. Chapter 6, profusely illustrated, describes the way in which solidborne noise is communicated throughout buildings and how it may be controlled, as, for example, by selecting a floor/ceiling construction so that a tenant in a dwelling below will not be annoyed by the footsteps of occupants above.

Chapter 7 considers the major sources of noise in heating, ventilating, and air-conditioning (HVAC) systems, how noise from these systems is communicated to the rooms being served by them, and how such noise transmission can be controlled. It describes methods for rating and specifying noise produced by HVAC systems, and provides acceptability criteria for background noise in various rooms served by HVAC systems.

Noises in plumbing systems are a common source of complaint in buildings. In general, such problems can be avoided by following the basic procedures outlined in Chapter 8.

Chapter 9 discusses general methods of noise control that are useful in reducing mechanical and electrical noise and do not require modification of the equipment itself. It provides a checklist for the solution of common noise problems, as well as techniques for implementing these solutions. It also describes the principles of vibration control and practical methods for applying these principles to prevent equipment vibration from being communicated to a building structure. Chapter 10 discusses the solutions to noise control problems that involve combinations of the principles described in the various chapters of this book.

Each chapter has been written by an authority who has years of practical experience in the solution of noise control problems, and specific expertise in the subject matter under discussion. Uniform terminology, symbols, and abbreviations are used throughout. Both U.S. Customary units and Standard International units are employed.

I am greatly indebted to the Contributors to the Handbook, who have worked diligently to make every chapter of maximum utility to the reader. Special thanks are due Harold B. Crawford, editor in chief of engineering and technical books at McGraw-Hill, Inc., and to Margaret Lamb, editing manager in McGraw-Hill's Professional Book Group.

Cyril M. Harris

Noise Control
in Buildings

Chapter

1

Introduction to Noise Control in Buildings

Cyril M. Harris

A sonorous melody pouring forth from a radio may be very pleasant to the people in one residence, but in an adjacent residence it may be a nuisance to neighbors who are trying to sleep. It is unwanted. It is noise. By definition, *noise* is unwanted sound.

Consider the results of noise measurements at a suburban building site, shown in Fig. 1.1. The "level" of the noise is shown on an arbitrary scale as a function of time. In this example, noise sources in the immediate vicinity (such as passing automobiles) produce a significant increase in level. More distant sources produce identifiable changes in level only if they are powerful—such as airplanes or heavy trucks. In the absence of any such identifiable sources, there is a relatively steady, pervasive noise (shown as the horizontal dashed line labeled "ambient noise level") below which the noise level does not

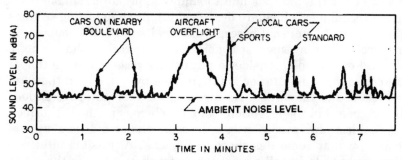

FIG. 1.1 A recording of "noise level" versus time in a residential neighborhood. The "ambient noise level" is represented by the dashed horizontal line. (*D. E. Bishop and P. D. Schomer, Chap. 50 of Ref. 1.*)

fall. *Ambient noise* is the all-encompassing noise associated with any given environment; it is usually a composite of sounds from many sources which reach the location from many directions.

This chapter provides an introduction to the field of noise control in buildings. The general properties and characteristics of sound waves and sound sources are described in the next chapter.

WHAT IS NOISE CONTROL?

By definition, noise control is the technology of obtaining an acceptable noise environment consistent with economic and operational considerations. The use of the term "acceptable noise environment" raises complex questions for which there are usually no unique answers, such as the following:

> Acceptable to whom, and under what conditions? Acceptable to an individual, to a group of people, to an entire community, or to some percentage of a group or community? Acceptable at what time of day or night? The acceptability of a noise environment usually is different at different times during a 24-hour period. For example, in a residential area, during the night when people are sleeping, it is usually required that conditions be quieter than during daylight hours.

Noise Control Is Not the Same As Noise Reduction

In solving a specific noise problem, it is usually advantageous to (1) analyze the problem, (2) determine the most economic solution, and then (3) apply the noise reduction techniques required for its solution in accordance with the principles discussed in Chap. 9. In other cases (for example, where such an analysis is relatively costly or where an immediate solution must be obtained), it may be more sensible to omit the analysis and to simply apply all available noise reduction techniques which are described briefly in following sections of this chapter. In unusual cases, a practical solution to some noise control problems may suggest a noise *increase* rather than a noise reduction. For example, consider a physician's reception room that is separated from his private consultation room by a partition that provides little sound insulation. As a result, his private conversations can be overheard in the reception room. An obvious method of correcting this undesirable condition is to increase the sound insulation of the partition that separates these two spaces. A possible alternate solution might be to install a noise source (such as a fan) in the reception room, thereby making this room noisier. The added noise will make it more difficult to overhear the physician's conversations.

While this latter solution may have its disadvantages,* it is more economical—and therefore should be considered under some circumstances. Thus the terms *noise control* and *noise reduction* are not necessarily synonymous.

THE IMPORTANCE OF NOISE CONTROL

While it is not always possible to state explicit relationships between noise and its effects on humans (or even to provide a rigorous scientific demonstration that some of these effects exist), it is of utmost significance that many businesses and industries are spending considerable amounts of money annually to achieve conditions of quiet.

People are usually annoyed by noise. They are distracted by it. Noise is considered a public nuisance. For these reasons, a considerable effort is being made to achieve quiet conditions in multiple-dwelling housing, offices, and factories:

- To comply with governmental regulations
- To provide greater comfort for those within these buildings

It is estimated that the total annual dollar sales of noise control measures has increased at least eightfold during the past decade in the U.S.A. It may be argued that this increase is simply the result of sales promotional effort; to some extent this is true, as it is with most products. On the other hand, such rapid growth can be fully accounted for only on the basis of the fact that most people do not like noise.

Noise is also a problem of great economic importance in modern society. Thus when the noise level in business offices is high enough to interfere with speech communication, office efficiency may be reduced, resulting in economic losses. Another example of the economical importance of noise is the relationship between noise and property values. The construction of a major roadway through a residential area may reduce the value of the adjacent land for residential housing because of increased noise levels.

HOW MUCH NOISE REDUCTION IS REQUIRED?

In general, the following steps may be taken to determine the amount of noise reduction required for the solution of a specific noise problem:

---

*For example, if a fan is installed in the reception room, the talkers may raise their voices in order to be heard over the fan noise. In that case, the physician may be more likely to hear their conversations.

Step 1. Evaluate the noise environment under existing or expected conditions. Existing noise conditions may be determined from measurements which provide data that are statistically significant. This process requires the appropriate selection of the noise measurement equipment, accurate calibration of the equipment, and correct use of this equipment. Such procedures often are set forth by voluntary or mandatory standards, in governmental regulations, in industrial association codes, or in requirements for environmental impact statements. Expected noise conditions usually can be estimated from empirical engineering formulas or from data derived from similar existing projects.

Step 2. Determine what noise level is acceptable or what noise criterion is to be satisfied. (A noise criterion is defined as a standard or rule for judging the acceptability of noise levels under different conditions and for various purposes.) Acceptable noise levels in buildings are presented in Table 7.12.

Step 3. Obtain the difference between the noise level in Step 1 and the noise level in Step 2. This difference represents the noise reduction that must be provided to obtain an acceptable environment.

HOW NOISE IS TRANSMITTED IN BUILDINGS

Noise usually is communicated to rooms within a building via many different paths, from noise sources elsewhere in the building and/or from noise sources outside the building. It is convenient to classify the most common methods of sound transmission in buildings as follows.

Airborne Sound Transmission

In this type of sound transmission, described in detail in Chap. 5, the noise originates in the air. It is then communicated to the listeners elsewhere in the building:

1. From the source of sound, along a continuous path, to the listener. This mechanism is illustrated in Fig. 1.2 where sound produced by a truck on the street passes through an open window to the bedroom on the second floor. Another example is the transmission of sounds of the bagpipe, communicated along a direct air path via a ventilation duct to the room below.

2. From the source of sound, through the air to a partition which is forced into vibration by the sound waves; the vibrating partition acts as a new source of sound on the other side of the partition. This is because sound waves in air are variations in pressure above and below atmospheric pressure (and *pressure* multiplied by *area* equals *force*); therefore the force causes the partition to

FIG. 1.2 Sound may travel along a continuous air path from a source located in one location to an area elsewhere in the building. For example, sounds of the bagpipe are communicated along a direct air path via a ventilation duct to the room below. Another example shows truck noise communicated along a direct air path, through an open window, to the bedroom on the second floor. Sounds from the bagpipe and a barking dog also travel elsewhere by another mechanism: They strike partitions which forces the partitions into vibration, thereby producing sound on the opposite sides of the partitions. (*Eli King.*[2])

move; even though this movement is relatively small, it generates sound in the adjacent room. This mechanism of sound transmission is illustrated in Fig. 1.2 where the sound waves from a bagpipe and a barking dog strike interior partitions.

Structureborne Sound Transmission

In this type of sound transmission, described in detail in Chap. 6, mechanical energy (in the form of steady vibration or mechanical impacts) is imparted directly to a building structure. Then it is communicated through the structure to other rooms in the building, where a partition or surface is forced into vibration—thereby radiating noise. For example, in Fig. 1.3 the wavy lines with arrowheads indicate paths along which structureborne noise may be transmitted.

In the illustration shown in Fig. 1.3, *vibration* is communicated to the structure by motion of water pipes, by a washing machine in the lower left corner of the illustration, and by the "pin" of a cello which makes direct contact with the floor in the room above. *Mechanical*

FIG. 1.3 Examples of common sources of noise in buildings. The wavy lines with arrowheads indicate some of the paths along which structureborne noise may be communicated. (*After I. L. Vér and D. H. Sturz, Chap. 32 of Ref. 1.*)

impacts are communicated to the structure as a result of footfalls, the dropping of trash down an incinerator chute, and the driving of a nail in the wall.

Block Diagram Representation of Noise Transmission in Buildings

For engineering purposes, it is sometimes convenient to depict the transmission of sound in a building by a block diagram, such as the one shown in Fig. 1.4. The block labeled **source** may represent a sin-

FIG. 1.4 A simplified block diagram representing the transmission of noise from a sound source, along one or more transmission paths, to a listener elsewhere in a building.

gle source or several sources of noise. As indicated above, noise from the source is communicated through the structure along one or more transmission **paths.** The **listener** usually represents one person or a group of people.

METHODS OF CONTROLLING NOISE IN BUILDINGS

This section provides a brief outline of methods of noise control that may be applied in the design of a new building to ensure satisfactory conditions of quiet, and/or in an existing building to reduce existing noise levels within it. Such methods, described in detail through this book, may be classified as:

- Control of noise at the **source**
- Control of noise along its transmission **path** from the source to the listener by increasing the attenuation of sound between the source and the listener
- Control of noise by providing the **listener** with some form of noise protection

Which of these methods, or combination of methods, is most advantageous depends on the required amount of noise reduction, on economic conditions, and on operational considerations. The relative benefit to be gained from the application of each method may be evaluated and compared with its respective cost, as illustrated in Table 9.1.

Control of Noise at Its Source

To control noise at its source:

1. Reduce the amplitude of motion of the source. For example, if the noise source is a vibrating panel of a washing machine, the magnitude of its vibration may be reduced by applying a vibration-damping material on the panel's surface or by modifying the panel's stiffness, mass, or size.

2. Enclose the noise source within solid, heavy walls which are lined with sound absorptive material.
3. Mount the noise source on vibration isolators instead of directly on the floor.
4. Install a resilient floor covering or a floating floor (a "floating floor" is a floor that is supported by the building structure but is completely isolated from it.)

Control of Noise along Its Transmission Path

To control noise along its transmission path the noise source and listener:

1. Position the building on its site so as to minimize noise control measures that would otherwise would be required. For example:

   - Maximize the distance between the building and a nearby highway.
   - Orient the building so that the building (and nearby buildings) shield areas where quiet is required.
   - Use the natural terrain, road cuts, embankments, and artificial barriers to provide additional shielding, as illustrated in Fig. 1.5.

   - Orient buildings to avoid reflections of street noise into areas where quiet is required, as illustrated in Fig. 1.6.

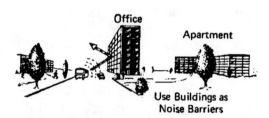

FIG. 1.5 Natural terrain (such as road cuts or embankments), high barriers, or commercial buildings, wherever practical, should be used to shield residential buildings from traffic noise. (*After R. D. Berendt and E. L. R. Corliss.*[3])

Not this

This

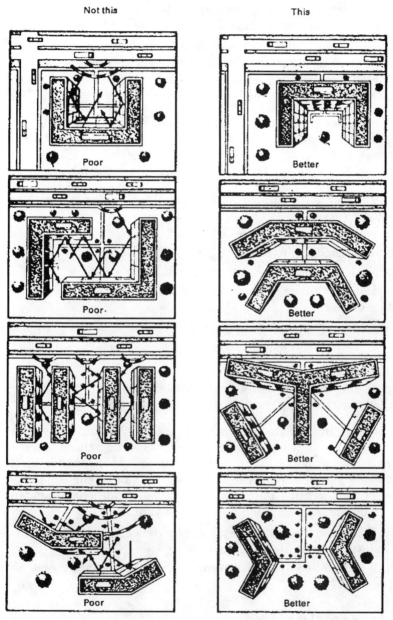

FIG. 1.6 Buildings should be located so as to avoid reflections of street noise to areas where quiet is important. (*R. D. Berendt and E. L. R. Corliss.*[3])

2. Plan the location of rooms within the building to minimize noise control measures that would otherwise be required. For example:

   ■ Locate rooms that contain significant noise sources as far as possible from rooms in which quiet conditions are desired.

3. Seal all openings along airborne paths between the noise source and the listener. For example:

   ■ Seal cracks and openings around conduits, pipes, or ducts that penetrate walls to prevent the transmission of sound along these paths.

4. Improve the sound insulation provided by partitions. For example:

   ■ Add a resiliently-supported gypsum board wall surface to an existing wall.
   ■ Increase the mass of the existing wall.
   ■ Add a second leaf to an existing single-leaf wall.
   ■ Replace existing single glazing with double glazing.
   ■ Install seals (usually in the form of gaskets) around the perimeters of doors.

5. Improve the sound insulation of an existing floor slab. For example:

   ■ Provide a resiliently hung ceiling supported from the structural slab above.

6. Impede the transmission of structureborne noise by breaking the path along which it is communicated. For example:

   ■ Use building expansion joints to impede the transmission of noise through a building structure by locating the sources of noise (such as elevators, mechanical equipment, water lines, toilets, and heavy transformers) on one side of the expansion joint, and locating the areas where quiet conditions are essential on the other side of the expansion joint.

7. Install additional sound-absorptive materials in rooms to lower the noise level [as indicated by Eq. (4.4)].

8. Install partial-height partitions where fully partitioned rooms are impractical.

Control of Noise at the Listener

To control noise at the listener:

1. Furnish the listener with a booth or partial enclosure in which to work. For examples of such enclosures, see Fig. 9.6.

2. Furnish the listener with earplugs.

REFERENCES

1. C. M. Harris (ed.), *Handbook of Acoustical Measurements and Noise Control,* McGraw-Hill, New York, 1991.
2. Eli King, personal communication.
3. R. D. Berendt and E. L. R. Corliss, *N.B.S. Handbook 119,* U.S. Department of Commerce, Washington, D.C., 1976.

Chapter

2

Properties of Sound Waves

Cyril M. Harris

INTRODUCTION

This chapter describes: (1) how sound waves are generated, (2) properties of sound waves, (3) various types of sound levels and the decibel scale, (4) sound-level meters and sound analyzers, and (5) how two or more sound levels can be combined. The appendix to this chapter contains commonly used definitions, symbols, abbreviations, and acronyms.

Chapter 2 describes the basic principles of noise control that will be of interest to readers desiring a comprehensive background in this field. However, the material in this book is presented so that readers who are faced with a specific noise problem can usually skip this chapter and turn directly to the relevant chapter for methods of solution. The more technical material in this chapter (required for the solution of complex noise problems) is presented as extended footnotes or is set in small type.

HOW SOUND WAVES ARE GENERATED

Sound is a physical disturbance (in a medium) that is capable of being detected by the ear.* The medium (such as air, steel, brick, or concrete) in which the sound waves travel must have mass and elasticity. Therefore sound waves will not travel through a vacuum.

Sound waves in air arise from variations in pressure above and below the static value of atmospheric pressure (i.e., the pressure in

---

Sound also may be defined as the hearing sensation excited by a physical disturbance in the medium.

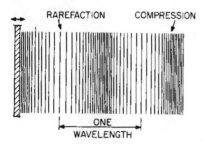

RAREFACTION   COMPRESSION

ONE
WAVELENGTH

FIG. 2.1 The generation of plane sound waves by a flat, vibrating partition (the cross-hatched surface shown at the left). The wavelength λ is equal to the distance between two successive pressure maxima.

the atmosphere when sound waves are not present). These pressure variations may originate in several ways, for example:

- By vibration of a surface, such as a building partition
- By repetitive pulsations in an airstream, such as those produced by rotating fan blades
- By vortices which result when an airstream strikes an obstruction, such as when air flowing through a ventilation duct strikes the louvers of an air outlet
- By the impact of one mass with another

Consider the generation of sound by vibration of the partition shown in Fig. 2.1. A greatly simplified picture of what takes place is as follows: When the partition moves to the right, the layer of air directly adjacent to its right side is compressed, so that the pressure in this compressed layer is higher than the pressure in the undisturbed layer to its right. As a result, the air particles within the compressed layer move to their right, thereby compressing this previously undisturbed layer. Similarly, this newly compressed layer then transmits its motion to the undisturbed layer to *its* right, and so on.

When the partition reverses direction and moves to its left, opposite conditions prevail. Then, the layer of air directly adjacent to its right side is expanded so that the pressure in this expanded layer is lower than the pressure in the undisturbed layer to its right (this is called a *rarefaction*). As a result, the air particles within the undisturbed layer move to their left, thereby creating a rarefaction in this previously undisturbed layer. Similarly, the newly rarified layer then transmits its motion to the undisturbed layer to its right, and so on. Hence, there is a succession of outwardly traveling layers of compression and rarefaction, resulting in *wave motion*. At any point in space, there are alternating increases and decreases in pressure at this point—resulting in sound waves.

PROPERTIES OF SOUND WAVES

Speed of Sound

The speed of sound is the rate at which sound waves travel. At a temperature of 68°F (20°C), the speed of sound in air is approximately 1130 feet per second (344 m/s). The speed increases slightly with increasing temperature. However, this *increase* is very small; for noise control problems in buildings, the speed of sound may be assumed to be independent of temperature, frequency, and humidity.

The speed of sound in solids, such as most structural building materials, is much faster than its speed in air. The speed depends on the density and elasticity of the material. For example, the speed of sound in brick is approximately 11 times faster than the speed of sound in air; the speed of sound in steel is about 15 times faster than the speed of sound in air.

Plane Waves; Spherical Waves

When sound waves have everywhere the same direction of propagation, they are called *plane waves.* This is because the points of maximum compression form plane surfaces. A surface drawn through points of maximum compression (i.e., points of maximum pressure) is called a *wavefront.* The points of maximum rarefaction may also form plane surfaces. As illustrated in Fig. 2.1, these plane surfaces are perpendicular to the direction of propagation of the sound waves, which is indicated by the arrow.

Many sound sources emit sound waves in which the points of maximum compression form concentric spheres. Such waves, called *spherical waves,* are illustrated in Fig. 2.2.

Frequency

By definition, the *frequency* of a periodic phenomenon is the number of times it repeats itself in 1 second. Frequency is usually designated by a number, followed by the unit *hertz (symbol: Hz),* formerly called *cycles per second (symbol: cps).* For example, if a rigid partition vibrates back and forth 100 times a second, it is said to have a frequency of vibration of 100 hertz, that is, 100 Hz. In moving back and forth 100 times a second, the partition generates sound waves having a frequency of 100 Hz. Frequency is a *physical phenomenon* that can be measured by instruments. It is closely related to, but not precisely the same as, *pitch,* which is a *subjective phenomenon.*

Normal young adults usually are capable of hearing sounds in the range of frequencies from about 16 to 20,000 Hz.

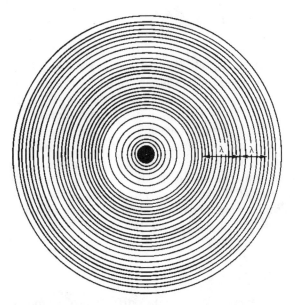

FIG. 2.2 Spherical waves radiated by a point source, i.e., a source whose dimensions are small compared with the wavelength λ of the sound it emits.

Wavelength

The wavelength of a sound is the perpendicular distance between two successive compression maxima (or two successive pressure minima) at a given instant of time, as illustrated in Fig. 2.1. The concept of wavelength is important in many types of noise control problems. For example:

1. The effectiveness of a solid barrier in the open air (in shielding a point on one side of a barrier from a noise source on the other) depends on the ratio of the height of the barrier to the *wavelength* of the sound—the greater this ratio, the more effective the barrier.
2. The directional properties of a noise source depend on the ratio of dimensions of the source to the *wavelength* of the sound radiated by the source—the greater this ratio, the more directional the source.
3. The pattern of sound reflection from a surface depends on the dimensions of the reflecting surface compared with the *wavelength* of the sound which is incident on it.

Wavelength (denoted by the Greek letter lambda λ) is related to the frequency f (in hertz) and the speed of sound c in feet per second (or meters per second) by

$$\lambda = \frac{c}{f} \tag{2.1}$$

Since the speed of sound in air is approximately 1130 feet per second (344 m/s), according to Eq. (2.1), sound having a frequency of 100 Hz has a wavelength of 11.3 feet (3.44 m); sound having a frequency of 1000 Hz has a wavelength of 1.13 feet (0.344 m). For convenience, the relationship between frequency and wavelength, given by Eq. (2.1), is shown graphically in Fig. 2.3.

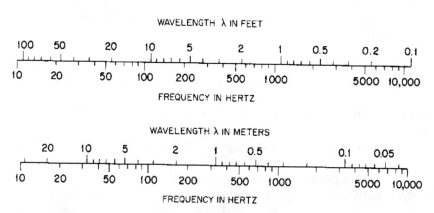

FIG. 2.3 Relationship between wavelength λ and frequency f of sound in air.

Reflection of Sound Waves

When sound waves travel outward from a sound source and strike a surface (such as a wall or ceiling), their direction of travel is changed; i.e., they are *reflected*. For example, Fig. 2.4 illustrates how sound, originating at a source, is reflected from a large, hard, flat surface.

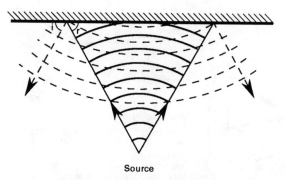

Source

FIG. 2.4 Reflection of sound waves from a surface that is very large compared with the wavelength λ of the incident sound. In this case, the angle of reflection $\angle r$ is equal to the angle of incidence $\angle i$.

The curved *solid* lines represent spherical waves as they spread outward from the source; the curved *dotted* lines represent these waves after they have been reflected from the surface.

Angle of Reflection; Use of Sound Rays.   In most noise control problems, it is usually convenient to indicate the direction of the sound waves by sound rays. A *sound ray* is an imaginary line that is drawn perpendicular to the "wavefronts" which indicates their direction of travel. In Fig. 2.4, the sound rays are shown as straight lines with arrowheads.

Reflection of Sound from a Large, Flat Surface.   Figure 2.4 illustrates the reflection of sound waves from a *flat* surface whose dimensions are large compared to the wavelength λ of the incident sound. Under these conditions, the angle of reflection ∡**r** is equal to the angle of incidence ∡**i**; this relationship is called the *law of reflection*. It is important to emphasize that this law applies *only* when the dimensions of the reflecting surface are large compared to the wavelength. The reflection from surfaces that are not large compared to the wavelength is discussed in Chap. 4 (for example, see Fig. 4.2).

Reflection from a Large Concave Surface.   Figure 2.5 illustrates the reflection of sound rays from a *concave* surface whose dimensions are large compared with the wavelength of the incident sound. Such a surface tends to concentrate the reflected sound. For example, Fig. 2.6 shows a section of an auditorium which has a large concave ceiling. The sound source is on the stage. Sound rays from the source are reflected from the concave ceiling to one area of the balcony—such a focusing of sound in an auditorium is a very undesirable characteristic.

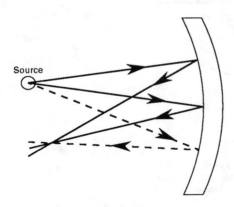

FIG. 2.5   Reflection of sound rays from a concave surface that is very large compared with the wavelength λ of the incident sound. In this case, the reflective surface concentrates the reflected waves.

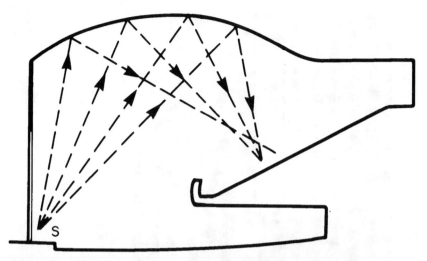

FIG. 2.6 Sound rays from a source on the stage of an auditorium (shown in sections), which are reflected from a large concave ceiling. The sound waves concentrate in one area of the balcony seating area—a very undesirable condition.

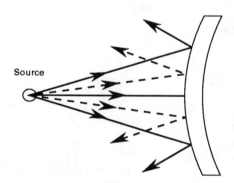

FIG. 2.7 Reflection of sound rays from a convex surface that is very large compared with the wavelength λ of the incident sound. In this case, the reflective surface disperses (i.e., spreads) the reflected waves.

Reflection from a Large Convex Surface.   Figure 2.7 illustrates the reflection of sound rays from a *convex* surface that is large compared with the wavelength of the incident sound. Such a surface tends to disperse the reflected sound. Therefore, large convex surfaces on the walls or ceiling of a room promote a uniform distribution of reflected sound in the room.

Diffraction of Sound

Diffraction is the bending of sound waves (i.e., change in direction of propagation of sound waves other than by reflection) when they strike an object. For example, the bending of sound waves around the edge of a partition, is illustrated in Fig. 2.8. This section considers the

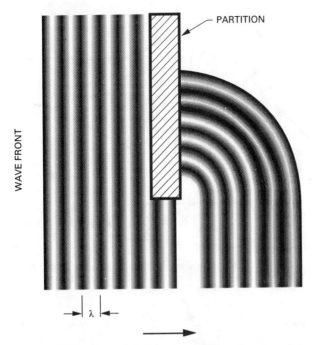

WAVE FRONT

PARTITION

λ

FIG. 2.8 Diffraction of plane waves at the edge of a solid partition.

bending of sound waves as they pass over barriers, as they strike obstacles, and as they are propagated through openings in walls.

Diffraction of Sound over Barriers. When sound waves in the open air strike a solid barrier, such as a wall, the barrier does not cast a sharp "acoustical shadow" because sound will bend over the top (as illustrated in Fig. 2.9) unless the barrier's height is large compared with the wavelength of the incident sound. For example, consider a solid wall between a roadway and homes along the roadway; the wall is intended to reduce the level of automobile noise which is heard in the homes. How effective is a wall 10 feet (3 m) in height? To some extent, the effectiveness depends on the distance of the wall from the roadway and the homes, but for sound having a frequency of 100 Hz [which according to Fig. 2.3 corresponds to a wavelength of about 11 feet (3.3 m)], the wall is not high enough to be effective; the sound waves will bend over the top. In contrast, for sounds having a frequency of 1000 Hz, the height of the wall is approximately 10 times the wavelength of the incident sound; therefore, the wall acts as an effective "sound shield" in casting an acoustical shadow.

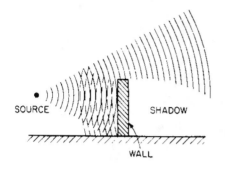

FIG. 2.9 Sound waves striking a solid barrier. Because of diffraction, low-frequency sound bends over the top of the barrier so that the barrier does not cast a sharp "acoustical shadow."

Diffraction of Sound around Obstacles. The manner in which sound is bent around a solid obstacle depends largely on the ratio of the dimensions of the object to the wavelength of the incident sound:

1. If the obstacle's dimensions are much smaller than the wavelength, the sound waves bend around the obstacle, almost as if the obstacle were not there, as illustrated in Fig. 2.10.

2. If the obstacle's dimensions are much larger than the wavelength, then the obstacle reflects the sound waves and casts an acoustical shadow as illustrated in Fig. 2.11. In this illustration, sound waves strike a flat obstacle whose overall dimensions are approximately four times the wavelength of the incident sound.

Diffraction of Sound through a Small Opening. Suppose plane waves of sound waves strike a large, flat wall in which there is a hole. According to Huygens's principle of physics, at any instant of time, each point of a wavefront may be regarded as a new source of "secondary waves." Therefore, if the dimensions of the hole are small compared with the wavelength of the incident sound, the small hole acts as a source from which sound waves spread out spherically, as illustrated in Fig. 2.12. In contrast, if the dimensions of the hole are several times the wavelength of the incident sound, the sound will continue in the shape of a beam.

Simple Harmonic Motion; Pure Tones

Figure 2.13 shows a graphic record produced by a writing stylus that is attached to a tyne (prong) of a tuning fork. As a strip of waxed paper moves past the stylus at constant speed, the stylus produces a record of the tuning fork's motion. In this illustration, the tuning fork undergoes 440 complete oscillations in 1 second, so that its frequency is 440 Hz. The trace obtained when the tuning fork vibrates is called a *sine wave* (illustrated in Fig. 2.14) because the trace may be repre-

FIG. 2.10 Diffraction of sound waves striking an obstacle which is smaller than the wavelength λ of the incident sound. Notice that the waves bend around the obstacle, almost as if it were not there. The source of the spherical sound waves is to the left.

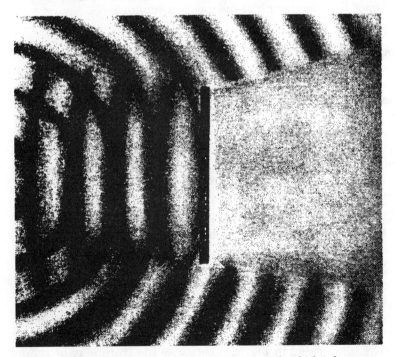

FIG. 2.11 Diffraction of sound waves striking an obstacle which is large compared with the wavelength λ of the incident sound. The source of the spherical sound wave is to the left.

FIG. 2.12 Diffraction of sound passing through a small hole in a partition.

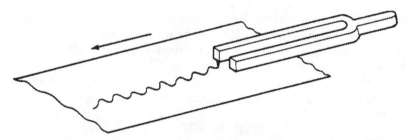

FIG. 2.13 A vibrating tuning fork which has a stylus attached to the end of one of the tynes. A sine wave is traced on waxed paper as the paper moves past the stylus at constant speed. (*T. F. S. Harris,* Handbook of Acoustics, *J. Curwen & Sons, London, 1913.*)

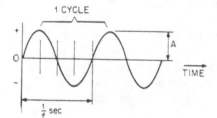

FIG. 2.14 Graphical representation of a sine wave.

sented mathematically by a sine function, i.e., A sin $(2\pi f)t$, where A is the amplitude of motion of the vibrating tyne, f is its frequency of vibration in hertz, and t represents the time in seconds. Thus the motion of the tuning fork is said to be "sinusoidal." The frequency of the sound waves generated by the movement of the tynes is the same frequency as the vibrating tuning fork, that is, 440 Hz. This waveform is *periodic* because it repeats itself, exactly, from one complete oscillation to the next.

The motion described by a sine wave is called *simple harmonic motion* because it is composed of but a single frequency. A sound composed of a single frequency is called a *pure tone*.

Sound Pressure

Consider a point in space. When sound waves are not present, the pressure at this point is equal to the static value of atmospheric pressure P. At a temperature of 32°F (0°C) and at sea level, atmospheric pressure has a value of approximately 14.7 pounds per square inch (10^5 pascals, i.e., 10^5 Pa). When sound waves pass this point, there is an additional oscillating pressure p due to the passage of the sound waves, which is given by

$$p = p_0 \sin (2\pi f)t \qquad (2.2)$$

where p_0 is a constant called the *pressure amplitude*; f is the frequency of the sound wave in hertz (Hz); t is the time in seconds.

Sound pressure usually is expressed in micropascals (μPa); 1 *micropascal* is one-millionth of a pascal. Thus the instantaneous value of the total pressure at the point of observation is equal to the sum of the atmospheric pressure and the sound pressure, i.e.:

$$P + p_0 \sin (2\pi f)t \qquad (2.3)$$

Harmonics

Suppose a rigid partition moves back and forth with sinusoidal motion at a frequency of 100 Hz. The resulting sound waves also have a frequency of 100 Hz. Most partitions are not infinitely rigid—they bend, resulting in oscillations at higher frequencies, often at integral multiples of the basic motion. The lowest frequency generated is called the *fundamental frequency*. In this example, the fundamental frequency is 100 Hz. If the higher frequencies are integral multiples of the fundamental frequency, they are called *harmonics*.

Sound Power

The rate of emission of acoustical energy (i.e., the *sound power*) of a source usually is expressed in watts or in picowatts; 1 picowatt is one-millionth of a millionth of 1 watt (i.e., 1 picowatt is equal to 10^{-12} watt). The *instantaneous power* (the rate at which sound energy is radiated at any instant of time) may fluctuate considerably. The maximum value in any time interval is called the *peak power*. For many types of noise sources, the peak powers may be 100 to 1000 times their average values. The *average power* depends on the time interval over which the average is taken and on the method of averaging.

Table 2.1 shows typical values of sound power emitted by a variety of acoustic sources. These values represent averages taken over a time interval of several seconds. The average power of most sound sources in buildings is small. For example, the average sound power of ordinary conversational speech is only about 0.00001 watt.

Sound Intensity

The passage of sound waves is accompanied by the flow of sound energy. At a given point in a sound field, the *sound intensity* (in a specified direction) is equal to the rate of flow of sound energy through a unit area at that point, the unit area being perpendicular to the specified direction.

TABLE 2.1   The Average Sound Power Level of Various Acoustic Sources

Power, watts (W)	Sound power level, dB re 1 pW	Source
100,000,000	200	Large rocket engine
10,000	160	Aircraft turbojet engine
1,000	150	
100	140	Light airplane, cruising
10	130	
1	120	
0.1	110	Crawler tractor, 150 hp
0.01	100	100-hp electric motor, 2600 r/min
0.001	90	
0.0001	80	Vacuum cleaner
0.00001	70	Highland bagpipe
0.000001	60	
0.0000001	50	Personal computer
0.00000001	40	Whispered speech
0.000000001	30	
0.0000000001	20	Air outlet (0.1m^2), air velocity 1 m/s; open damper, parallel louvers

Example: Consider a sound source whose dimensions are small compared with the wavelength so that it radiates uniformly in all directions. Suppose this source is in a *free field* (i.e., in a space which is distant from all reflecting surfaces) and suppose the source emits a sound power of W watts, as illustrated in Fig. 2.15. Now surround the source by imaginary sphere which has a radius r_o; the surface area of the sphere S is equal to $(4\pi r_o^2)$. Then, the sound intensity in the radial direction is the power per unit area flowing in the radial direction I at the surface of the surface of this sphere. It is equal to

$$I = \frac{W}{S} = \frac{W}{4\pi r_o^2} \qquad \text{watts per square meter} \qquad (2.4)$$

Thus, for a point source in a free field, the intensity (in the radial direction) varies inversely as the square of the distance from the source. This relationship is called the *inverse square law*. Perpendicular to the radial direction, the intensity is zero since no energy flows in a direction perpendicular to the radius. This illustrates that the term *sound intensity* at a given point is meaningful *only* if the direction is specified.

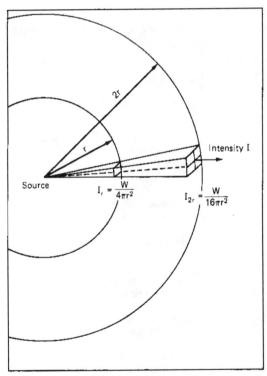

FIG. 2.15 A point source of acoustical power W in a free field. The intensity at any point varies inversely as the square of the distance from the source, so that when the distance is doubled, the intensity is reduced to $1/4$ its value.

LEVELS; SOUND LEVELS

Levels and the Decibel

The range of sound pressures encountered in noise control work is so large that it is convenient to employ a quantity which is proportional to the *logarithm* of the sound pressure. This is because a logarithmic scale has the effect of compressing the range of values considered, as is evident in Fig. 2.16. Sound pressure, expressed in terms of a linear scale, is shown in the right column of this illustration; the logarithm of sound pressure, called *sound pressure level,* is shown on the left.

By definition, *level, expressed in decibels (dB), is 10 times the logarithm of the ratio of two quantities that are proportional to power.*

Sound Power Level: As indicated earlier, sound power of a source (i.e., the rate at which sound is radiated per unit time) is usually expressed in watts or some fraction of a watt. For many purposes it is convenient to express the sound power of a source on a logarithmic scale, called *sound power level.*

The *sound power level,* L_W of a source, in decibels, is given by

$$L_W = 10 \log_{10} \left(\frac{W}{W_o} \right) \quad \text{dB} \tag{2.5}$$

where W = power of the source in watts, and W_o = reference power in watts. The standard reference sound power W_o is 10^{-12} watt, i.e., 1 picowatt (symbol: pW). Substituting this value in Eq. (2.5) yields

$$L_W = 10 \log_{10} \left(\frac{W}{10^{-12}} \right) = (10 \log_{10} W + 120) \quad \text{dB} \tag{2.6}$$

The average sound power levels of a number of typical noise sources are given in Table 2.1.

The term *sound power level* should not be confused with *sound pressure level,* although both are expressed in decibels. The former is a measure of **acoustic power** radiated by the source; it is a characteristic of the source. In contrast, sound pressure level is a measure of the **sound pressure** at any point; it depends not only on the acoustic power of the source, but also on the:

- Distance from the source
- Characteristics of the space surrounding the source

Noise Power Emission Level: To avoid confusing sound power with sound pressure level (since both are expressed in decibels), the sound power of noise sources is sometimes rated in terms of noise power emission level.

Noise power emission level of a sound source is equal to the logarithm (to the base 10) of the ratio of the A-weighted sound power (described below) to the reference power of 1 picowatt; it is expressed in *bels,* where 1 bel = 10 decibels. For example, a typical personal computer has a noise power emission level of 5 bels.

Sound Pressure Level.   The sound pressure level in decibels L_p, corresponding to a sound pressure p, is given by[†]

$$10 \log_{10} \left(\frac{p}{p_0} \right)^2 = 20 \log_{10} \left(\frac{p}{p_0} \right) \qquad dB \qquad (2.7)$$

where p_0 is the reference sound pressure. In air, the reference sound pressure is 20 micropascals (i.e., 20 μPa). Note, in the caption for Fig. 2.16, the label "sound pressure level in decibels re 20 μPa." The letters *re* signify "with reference to." Ordinarily, this reference value is not stated because it has been adopted by international agreement. It approximates the minimum sound pressure that is audible to the normal young adult ear, in the frequency range where the ear is most sensitive, under quiet conditions.

Substituting the reference sound pressure p_0 of 20 micropascals in Eq. (2.7), the *sound pressure level L_p* of sound waves having a sound pressure p micropascals is equal to

$$\text{sound pressure level } L_p = 20 \log_{10} \left(\frac{p}{20} \right) \qquad dB \qquad (2.8)$$

For example, according to this equation, a sound pressure of 20 μPa corresponds to a sound pressure level of 0 dB; and a sound pressure of 200 μPa corresponds to a sound pressure level of 20 dB.

Radiation Pattern of a Sound Source; Sound Pressure Level Versus Angle.
Most noise sources radiate more sound in some directions than in other directions. This is illustrated in Fig. 2.17, which shows the distribution of sound in a horizontal plane around a centrifugal blower in a box. In this illustration, the sound pressure level is shown as a function of angle at a distance of $6\frac{1}{2}$ feet (2 m) from the blower. Such a diagram is called a *radiation pattern*.

Although the radiation patterns for various types of sound sources differ considerably, they usually exhibit the following general characteristics:

1. *When the dimensions of the source are small compared with the wavelength, sound is radiated uniformly in all directions, i.e., the source is nondirectional and is called a "point source."* For example, at 500 Hz in Fig. 2.17, the dimensions of the blower openings are small compared with the wavelength, so the radiation pattern is fairly uniform with angle.

[†]In Eq. (2.7), the ratio p/p_0 is *squared* since pressure *squared* is proportional to sound power for plane waves or spherical waves in a free field. Sound pressure ratios are not always proportional to corresponding power ratios, but it is common practice in acoustics to extend the use of the term *level*, expressed in decibels, to such cases.

2. *When the dimensions of the source are comparable to (or large compared to) the wavelength, the sound radiated from the surface of the source tends to be nonuniform and depends on the geometry of the source.* This is illustrated in Fig. 2.17 by the radiation pattern at 5000 Hz where the dimensions of the blower opening are comparable to the wavelength.

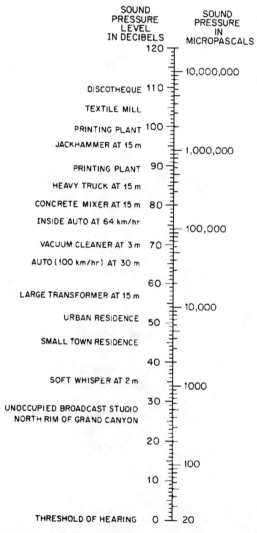

FIG. 2.16 Relation between sound pressure (in pascals) and sound pressure level (in decibels re 20 micropascals). Also shown are typical average values of A-weighted sound levels of various noises.

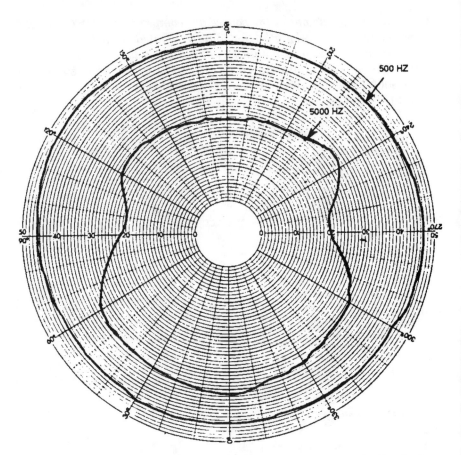

FIG. 2.17 Directional response pattern, i.e., radiation pattern, showing the distribution of sound pressure level (in decibels) versus angle (in degrees), for two different frequencies, around a centrifugal blower. (*Courtesy of M. A. Nobile, IBM Acoustics Lab.*)

Sound Pressure Level Versus Distance from a Sound Source. Consider a point in a *free field* (i.e., far from all reflective surfaces) in which there is a sound source that radiates sound equally in all directions. For these conditions, the only sound that reaches this point comes directly from the source. At a distance r from the source (but not very close to the source), the sound pressure level L_d, is given by

$$L_d = L_W - 20 \log_{10} r - 0.6 \quad \text{dB} \qquad (2.9a)$$

where L_W is the sound power level of the source expressed in decibels re 1 picowatt [see Eq. (2.5)], and r is the distance from the source in feet.

If the distance r is expressed in meters,

$$L_d = L_W - 20 \log_{10} r - 10.9 \qquad \text{dB} \qquad (2.9b)$$

According to this equation, the sound pressure level decreases 6 dB with each doubling of distance from the source and decreases 20 dB for each tenfold increase in distance from the source. (For example, if the sound level is 70 dB at a distance of 30 feet (10 m) from the source, it will be 64 dB at a distance of 60 feet (20 m) from the source. It will be 50 dB at a distance of 300 feet (100 m) from the source.

If the sound source is located in the open air but on (or very close to) a reflective surface (such as on hard ground or pavement), then an adjustment of 3 dB must be added to the sound power level of the source, as indicated in Table 4.3. For example, in the above example if the source is located on the pavement, at a distance of 30 ft (10 m) from the source, the sound level would be 73 dB, rather than 70 dB.

As indicated above, Eq. (2.9) applies only in the open air, far from all reflecting surfaces. In a room, reflections of sound from the walls and ceiling result in a much more complicated spatial distribution around the source; therefore, Eq. (2.9) does not apply within enclosures. This topic is treated in detail in Chap. 4.

Intensity Level: *Sound intensity level* (symbol L_I), in decibels, is equal to 10 times the ratio of a sound intensity I to the reference intensity I_0 of 10^{-12} W/m², that is, 1 picowatt per square meter. Therefore,

$$L_I = 10 \log_{10} \left(\frac{I}{I_0} \right) = 10 \log_{10} \left(\frac{I}{10^{-12} \text{ W/m}^2} \right) \qquad \text{dB} \qquad (2.10)$$

For plane waves or for spherical waves *in a free field,* sound pressure level [given by Eq. (2.8)] and sound intensity level [given by Eq. (2.10)] are numerically equal. For conditions other than a free field, this equality does not hold.

SOUND-LEVEL METERS; WEIGHTED SOUND LEVELS

A sound-level meter is an instrument that provides an indication of the (time-averaged) sound level of sound waves which are incident on its microphone. The sound level usually is displayed either by a pointer that moves across a scale graduated in decibels or by a digital indicator as shown in Fig. 2.18. Most such instruments are small, lightweight, and battery-powered.

Frequency-Weighted Sound Levels; A-Weighted Sound Levels

The ear is not equally sensitive at all frequencies. For this reason, even though the sound pressure level of two different noises may be

FIG. 2.18 A panel view of a commercial sound-level meter having a digital indicator which provides a direct numerical reading of sound level. (*Courtesy of Brüel & Kjær.*)

the same, the first will be judged to be louder than the second if the sound power of the first is concentrated in a frequency region where the ear is more sensitive. For this reason, *frequency weighting* is incorporated in sound-level meters; frequency weighting alters the sensitivity of a sound-level meter with respect to frequency so that the sound-level meter is less sensitive at frequencies where the ear is less sensitive. Most sound-level meters are provided with several (standardized) sensitivity-versus-frequency characteristics. Of these, "A-weighting" is most commonly used;[‡] "C-weighting" is used less fre-

---

[‡]The relative frequency response of a sound-level meter with A-weighting is shown in Table 2.2. According to this table, at 125 Hz, A-weighting reduces the sensitivity of a sound-level meter by 16.1 dB; at 250 Hz, it reduces the sensitivity by 3.2 dB; at 1000 Hz, it has no effect on the sensitivity. For example, suppose two steady tones are measured by a sound-level meter, one tone having a frequency of 1000 Hz and the other tone having a frequency of 125 Hz; both sounds have a sound pressure level of 60 dB. If they are measured with a sound-level meter employing A-weighting, the A-weighted sound level of the 1000-Hz tone is 60 dB(A) since A-weighting does not reduce the sound level at this frequency. In contrast, the A-weighted sound level of the 125-Hz tone is reduced by 16.1 dB, i.e., its sound level is $60 - 16.1 = 43.9$ dB(A).

quently. Sound levels measured on a sound-level meter employing A-weighting are referred to as *A-weighted sound levels*; sound levels measured on a sound-level meter employing C-weighting are referred to as *C-weighted sound levels*. The unit for any weighted sound level is the decibel (symbol: dB). However, when frequency-weighting is used, it is common practice to append the appropriate letter in parentheses after this symbol as a reminder of the type of weighting employed. For example, a measurement of a sound level expressed in dB(A) is a indication that A-weighting was used in the measurement.

Unweighted Sound Levels; Sound Pressure Levels

Some sound-level meters include *flat-weighting*—a response characteristic which is essentially independent of frequency. Sound levels measured using flat-weighting are unweighted, i.e., all frequencies are given equal weight, so they are *sound pressure levels,* expressed in decibels. Flat-weighting usually is employed when the electrical output of the sound-level meter is connected to an auxiliary instrument, such as a magnetic-tape recorder.

Time-Averaging of Sound Levels

As illustrated in Fig. 1.1, sound levels may vary rapidly with time. For this reason, sound-level meters are usually provided with some means of averaging the sound level over a selected time period. Otherwise, for rapidly varying sounds, it would be difficult to read the indicator of a sound-level meter. Most sound-level meters provide a choice of two averaging times (*fast* and *slow*): 0.125 second and 1.0 second, respectively. The appropriate selection of averaging time depends on the rapidity with which the sound level being measured fluctuates, as well as on the applicable measurement standard or test code that must be satisfied. The advent of digital technology in the 1970s led to the development of *integrating-averaging sound-level meters* which provide greater choice in the type and length of averaging time. Such instruments have the added capability of providing sound levels averaged over many minutes or many hours. Such long-time-averages are especially useful in providing time-average sound levels at building sites and in describing community noise.

Spectrum Analyzers; Octave-Band Level; One-Third-Octave-Band Level

An important characteristic of noise is its distribution with respect to frequency over the audible frequency range, for example, whether it is predominantly low-pitched (rumbly), high-pitched (hissy), or neutral sounding (neither rumbly nor hissy). Instruments used to measure such a frequency distribution are called *spectrum analyzers*. The process of determining this distribution is called *spectrum analysis*. Most spectrum analyzers divide the audible frequency range into bands that are each one octave wide. (An *octave* is a frequency interval between two frequencies whose ratio is 2 to 1; for example, the frequency interval between 500 and 1000 Hz is one octave.) An analyzer having bands one octave wide is called an *octave-band analyzer*. The sound pressure level within a band that is one octave wide is called the *octave-band level* (or *octave-band sound pressure level*). In the "Frequency" column of Table 2.2, the numbers shown in boldface are the frequencies of the centers of the octave bands that have been standardized by international agreement. These are the center frequencies used on all commercial octave-band analyzers.

TABLE 2.2   Relative Frequency Response of a
Sound-Level Meter with A-Weighting to Sounds
Arriving at Random Incidence

Frequency, Hz	A-weighting, dB
25	−44.7
31.5	**−39.4**
40	−34.6
50	−30.2
63	**−26.2**
80	−22.5
100	−19.1
125	**−16.1**
160	−13.4
200	−10.9
250	**−8.6**
315	−6.6
400	−4.8
500	**−3.2**
630	−1.9
800	−0.8
1,000	**0.0**
1,250	+0.6
1,600	+1.0
2,000	**+1.2**
2,500	+1.3
3,150	+1.2
4,000	**+1.0**
5,000	+0.5
6,300	−0.1
8,000	**−1.1**
10,000	−2.5

SOURCE: *American National Specifications for Sound Level Meters,* ANSI S1.4–1985, Acoustical Society of America, New York, NY 10017-3483, 1985.

A display of octave-band level versus frequency is called an *octave-band spectrum*. Figure 2.19*a* shows an example of an octave-band spectrum of noise from a fan in an air-conditioning system. In this example, the octave band centered at 63 Hz has an octave-band level of 73 dB.

One-Third-Octave-Band Level

In solving noise problems, when more detailed information is required than can be provided by an octave-band analysis, one-third-octave-band analysis usually is used. As the name implies, a one-third-octave-band analyzer has frequency bands one-third octave wide. The center frequencies of one-third-octave bands that have been standardized by international agreement are shown in the "Frequency" column of Table 2.2.

Figure 2.19*b* shows a one-third-octave-band spectrum for the same fan whose octave-band spectrum is depicted in Fig. 2.19*a*. Notice that the one-third-octave spectrum provides much greater detail than does the octave-band spectrum.

Figure 2.20 shows a panel view of a commercially available analyzer which provides a bar-graph display of one-third-octave-band spectra in real time.

COMBINING LEVELS

Often it is necessary to combine more than one level, for example:

1. To calculate the sound level that results when a combination of noise sources operates simultaneously
2. To determine the combined sound level of a sound source plus background noise
3. To combine octave-band levels or one-third-octave-band levels to obtain their combined levels
4. To calculate the A-weighted sound level from octave-band or one-third-octave-band levels

The level of a combination of levels is *not* the sum of the individual levels. For example, at a given point, if one machine produces a sound level of 60 dB and a second machine also produces a level of 60 dB, when both machines are in operation, their combined sound level is *not* 120 dB. Instead, as shown in this section, their combination is 63 dB. This is because sound level, in decibels, is not a linear scale—it is logarithmic.

To find the combined level of two or more levels, the following procedure may be used:

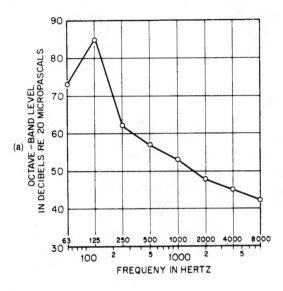

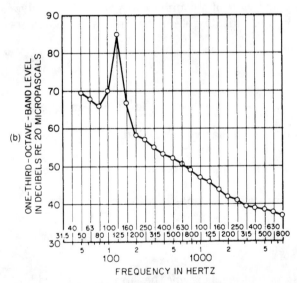

FIG. 2.19 A comparison of (*a*) an octave-band spectrum with (*b*) a one-third-octave-band spectrum for the same noise source—a fan in an air-conditioning system. Connecting lines have been drawn between the experimental data points to provide an indication of the general shape of the spectra. Note that the one-third-octave analysis provides much more detailed information about the frequency content of the noise than does the octave-band analysis.

Step 1. Call L_1 the sound level due to one source, and L_2 the sound level due to a second source. Furthermore, suppose that L_1 is higher than L_2.

Step 2. Subtract the value of L_2 from L_1 and obtain $(L_2 - L_1)$.

Step 3. Using the level difference obtained in Step 2, determine the number of decibels A that must be added to the higher level from Fig. 2.21.

Step 4. The combined level is then equal to $(L_1 + A)$ decibels.

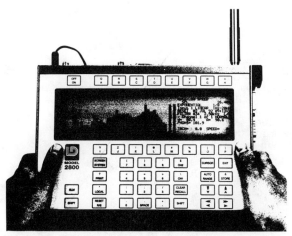

FIG. 2.20 A panel view of a sound analyzer which provides a one-third-octave-band analysis in real time. In this illustration the microphone is attached directly to the instrument; in precision work, the microphone is usually attached to the instrument by means of a cable extension. (*Courtesy of Larson Davis Inc.*)

Example: Combining Several Sound Levels. At a given point, one machine produces a sound level of 60 dB when it is the only machine in operation. At this same point, a second machine produces a sound level of 56.2 dB if it operates alone. A third machine produces a level of 55 dB if it operates alone. What is the sound level when all three machines operate simultaneously?

First combine the levels produced by the first and second machines. This yields a sound level of 61.5 dB. The difference between this combined level and the sound level produced by the third machine is $(61.5 - 55) = 6.5$ dB. According to Fig. 2.21, for a difference of 6.5 dB, 0.9 dB must be added to the higher level. Therefore, the combined level of all three machines is $(61.5 + 0.9) = 62.4$ dB.

Example: Combining the Sound Level of a Source with Background Noise Level.
Measurements show that the sound level at a fixed distance from a machine is 70 dB when the measurements are made under quiet conditions (i.e., when background noise is negligible). What is the value of sound level measured at the same point if the level of the background noise is 65 dB?

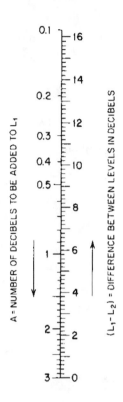

FIG. 2.21 Chart for combining two levels, L_1 and L_2, in decibels; L_1 is the higher level of the two. The left scale shows the number of decibels A to be added to the higher level L_1 to obtain the level, in decibels, of the combination of L_1 and L_2.

The difference between these two levels is 5 dB. Therefore, from Fig. 2.21, the corresponding value of A is 1.2 dB. Thus, 1.2 is added to 70 dB so their combined level is 71.2 dB.

Example: Calculation of A-Weighted Sound Level from Octave-Band Levels.
Consider the octave-band spectrum shown in Fig. 2.19a. If this spectrum is A-weighted, what is the corresponding value of the A-weighted sound level?

These octave-band levels are given in Table 2.3. Below these are shown the values of A-weighting, taken from Table 2.2. On the next line are shown the octave-band levels adjusted for A-weighting. These A-weighted octave-band levels must be combined to determine the value of the A-weighted sound level.

First, combine the levels of the octave bands centered at 4000 and 8000 Hz; the difference between these octave-band levels is 5.1 dB. [In general, it is good practice to combine the lowest lewvels first.] Therefore, according to Fig. 2.21, add 1.2 dB to the higher of the octave-band levels; this yields a combined level of $(46.0 + 1.2) = 47.2$ dB. Now combine this level with that of the octave band centered at 63 Hz; the difference between these levels is $(47.2 - 46.8) = 0.4$ dB. Therefore, add 2.8 dB to 47.2 dB; this yields a combined level of 50.0 dB. Now combine this level with the octave-band level centered at 2000 Hz; the difference between these levels is $(50.0 - 49.2) = 0.8$. Therefore, add 2.6 dB to 50.0 dB; this yields a combined level of 52.6 dB. Now combine this level with that of the octave band centered at 1000 Hz; the difference between these levels is

TABLE 2.3   Octave-Band Levels Corresponding to the Octave-Band Spectrum Shown in Fig. 2.19a. (These Levels Are Adjusted for A-Weighting Using Values of A-Weighting Given in Table 2.2.)

Octave-band center frequency, Hz	63	125	250	500	1000	2000	4000	8000
Octave-band level, dB	73	85	62	57	53	48	45	42
A-weighting, dB	−26.2	−16.1	−8.6	−3.2	0.0	+1.2	+1.0	−1.1
A-weighted octave-band level, dB	46.8	68.9	53.4	53.8	53.0	49.2	46.0	40.9

(53.0 − 52.6) = 0.4 dB. Therefore, add 2.8 dB to 53.0 dB; this yields a combined level of 55.8 dB. Now combine this level with that of the octave band centered at 500 Hz. The difference between these levels is (55.8 − 53.8) = 2 dB. Therefore, add 2.1 dB to 55.8 dB; this yields a combined level of 57.9 dB. Now combine this level with that of the octave band centered at 250 Hz. The difference between these levels is (57.9 − 53.4) = 4.5 dB. Therefore, add 1.3 dB to 57.9 dB; this yields a combined level of 59.2 dB. Finally, combine this level with that of the octave band centered at 125 Hz. The difference between these levels is (68.9 − 59.2) = 9.7 dB. Therefore, add 0.4 dB to 68.9 dB; this yields a combined level of 69.3 dB. This represents the A-weighted sound level of all of these combined octave bands. Thus, the A-weighted sound level for the octave-band spectrum of Fig. 2.19a is 69.3 dB(A).

Example: Combining Sound Power Levels.   Suppose a machine in a room produces a sound power level of 60 dB re 1 picowatt (that is, re 1 pW). A second machine in the room has a sound power level of 56.2 dB re 1 pW. What is their combined sound power level?

The difference between these levels is 3.8 dB. According to Fig. 2.21, the corresponding value of A, the amount that must be added to the higher level, is 1.5 dB. Therefore, their combined level (i.e., the total sound power level) is (60 + 1.5) = 61.5 dB.

APPENDIX 2.1

Definitions of Commonly Used Terms in Noise Control

The definitions that follow are in general agreement with those contained in publications of various professional organizations, including the American National Standards Institute (ANSI); the American Society for Testing and Materials (ASTM); the American Society of Heating, Refrigerating and Air-Conditioning Engineers (ASHRAE); the International Organization for Standardization (ISO); and the International Electrotechnical Commission (IEC). In addition to these definitions, many other terms used in noise control are defined throughout this book; the reader is referred to the index.

Terminology

absorption coefficient: *See* sound absorption coefficient.

acceleration of gravity (*g*):   The acceleration produced by the force of gravity at the surface of the earth. (By international agreement, the value of $g = 32.174$ feet per second per second $= 9.811$ m/s^2).

acoustic; acoustical: *Acoustic* is usually used when the term being qualified designates something that has the properties, dimensions, or physical characteristics associated with sound waves (e.g., acoustic power); *acoustical* is usually used when the term which it modifies does not explicitly designate something that has the properties, dimensions, or physical characteristics of sound (e.g., acoustical material).

acoustical material: A material whose primary function is to absorb sound.

acoustics: (1) The science of sound, including its production, transmission, reception, and effects.   (2) Of a room, those qualities that together determine the room character with respect to human auditory perception.

aerodynamic noise: Noise which results from the flow of air; most often generated when an airstream encounters protuberances, rough surfaces, and/or blunt edges.

air-handling unit; packaged fan equipment: An assembly of air-conditioning components (such as cooling coils, filters, fan humidifiers, and dampers) integrated into a self-contained package and installed as a single unit which is connected to an air distribution system.

ambient noise: The all-encompassing noise associated with a given environment at a specified time, usually being a composite of sound from many sources arriving from many directions, near and far; no particular sound is dominant. [See Fig. 1.1.]

ambient vibration: The all-encompassing vibration associated with a given environment, usually being a composite of vibration from many sources near and far.

anechoic room; free-field room: A room whose boundaries absorb practically all the sound incident thereon, thus providing "free-field" conditions.

angular frequency (ω):   Of a periodic quantity, the frequency *f* multiplied by the quantity (2π). *Unit:* radians per unit time.

atmospheric pressure (*P*):   The steady pressure in the undisturbed atmosphere. At 68°F (20°C), it is equal to 14.7 pounds per square inch (105 pascals).

attenuation: The decrease in level of sound, usually from absorption, divergence, scattering, or the cancellation of the sound waves.

audible sound: (1) Acoustic oscillations of such a character as to be capable of giving rise to the sensation of hearing.   (2) The sensation of hearing excited by sound waves.

average sound level *(L$_{eq}$):*   The level of a steady sound which, in a stated time period and at a stated location, has the same A-weighted sound energy as the time-varying sound. *Unit:* decibel.

A-weighted sound level (L_A): The sound level measured with a sound-level meter using A-weighting. *Unit*: decibel (dB). [Often, the unit symbol is followed by the letter A in parentheses, i.e., dB(A), to indicate that A-weighting has been used in the measurements. Values of A-weighting are given in Table 2.2.]

A-weighted sound power level: Ten times the logarithm to the base 10 of the ratio of a given A-weighted sound power to the reference sound power of 1 picowatt.

background noise: The total noise from all sources other than a particular sound that is of interest (e.g., other than the noise being measured or other than the speech or music being listened to).

bel: A unit of level which denotes the ratio between two quantities proportional to power; the number of bels corresponding to this ratio is the logarithm to the base 10 of this ratio. (1 bel = 10 decibels.)

blade-passage frequency; blade frequency: The lowest frequency of the sound produced by fan blades as they pass a given point; equal to the number of blades times the fan speed in revolutions per second. [See Eq. (7.1).]

break-in: The transfer of acoustic energy from the space surrounding a duct, through the duct walls, to the interior of the duct.

break-out: The transfer of acoustic energy from the interior of a duct, through the duct walls, to the space surrounding the duct.

coincidence effect: Of a panel or a partition, a phenomenon that occurs when the wavelength of the flexural wave in a panel equals that of a wave of the same frequency traveling in the air.

complex tone: Sound waves consisting of sinusoidal components of different frequencies.

continuous spectrum: A sound spectrum whose components are continuously distributed over a specified frequency range. [Random noise has a continuous spectrum because it contains a very large number of frequency components.]

C-weighted sound level (L_C): The sound level measured with a sound-level meter using C-weighting. *Unit*: decibel (dB). [Often, the unit symbol is followed by the letter C in parentheses, i.e., dB(C), to indicate that C-weighting has been used in the measurements.]

cycle: Of a periodic quantity, the complete sequence of values of a periodic quantity that occur during a *period*.

cycles per second (cps): A unit of frequency, now replaced by the term *hertz* (Hz). [*See* frequency.]

dead room: A room containing an unusually large amount of sound absorption.

decay rate: The rate at which the sound level in a room decreases with time, after the source of sound has stopped. *Unit:* decibels per second (dB/s). [See Eq. (4.6).]

decibel (dB): A unit of level which denotes the ratio between two quantities that are proportional to power; the number of decibels correspond to the logarithm (to the base 10) of this ratio. [In many sound fields, the sound pressure ratios are not proportional to the corresponding power ratios, but it is common practice to extend the use of the decibel to such cases. One decibel equals one-tenth of a *bel.*]

diffraction: The change in direction of propagation of sound waves as a result of bending when the sound waves strike an obstacle.

diffuse sound field (diffuse field): In a room, a sound field in which sound waves travel in all directions with equal probability and in which the reflected sound level is approximately everywhere equal—except close to the boundaries of the room.

direct sound level (L_d): The level of the sound that reaches a given location in a direct line from the source, without reflections from any surface.

displacement: The change of position of a body or particle usually measured from its average position or its position of rest.

divergence: The spreading of sound waves from a source; results in a decrease in sound level with increasing distance from the source.

duct silencer: See sound attenuator.

dynamic insertion loss: The *insertion loss* of a sound attenuator when air is flowing through it.

echo: A sound that has been reflected with sufficient time delay (and with sufficient magnitude) to be distinguishable as a repetition of the first sound the listener hears.

effective sound pressure: The root-mean-square (rms) value of the instantaneous sound pressure over a selected time interval. In the case of periodic sound pressures, the interval selected must be (a) long compared to a period, or (b) an integral number of periods. In the case of nonperiodic pressures, the interval should be long enough to make the value obtained essentially independent of small changes in the length of the time interval.

environment: At a given point in time, the aggregate of all conditions and influences to which a system is subject.

equivalent continuous sound level (average sound level) (L_{eq}): The level of a steady sound which, in a stated time period and at a stated location, has the same A-weighted sound energy as the time-varying sound. *Unit*: decibel [dB(A)].

equivalent duct diameter: For a rectangular duct, the diameter of a circular duct having approximately the same cross-sectional area; approximately equal to the square root of the product of the duct's width times its height.

far field: A region that is sufficiently far from a sound source so that the level of the sound coming directly from the source decreases by 6 dB for each doubling of the distance from the source.

flanking path: (1) A path along which sound is communicated that leads to *flanking sound transmission*. [See Fig. 6.1] (2) A path for sound transmission that permits sound to circumvent the element intended to be the only significant sound path between two spaces.

flanking sound transmission: (1) The transmission of sound from one space to an adjacent space by paths other than the common partition between them.   (2) The transmission of sound by a *flanking path*.

floating floor: A floor which is supported by the building structural but is completely isolated from it. [See Fig. 6.2]

flutter echo: A rapid but nearly repetitive succession of sounds originating from a sound source; often occurs as a result of multiple reflections between hard, flat, parallel walls.

free field: A sound field whose boundaries exert a negligible influence on the sound waves.

free-field room (anechoic room):   A room whose boundaries absorb essentially all the sound that is incident on them.

free progressive waves: Waves which are propagated in a *free field*.

frequency (f)**:**   Of a periodic function, the number of times that a quantity repeats itself in one second, i.e., the number of cycles per second. *Unit*: hertz (Hz).

frequency weighting: A standardized frequency response provided in a sound-level meter. [For values of A-weighting, see Table 2.2.]

hemi-anechoic room: A test room having a hard, reflective floor but whose other surfaces absorb essentially all the sound incident on them, thereby providing free-field conditions above the reflective floor surface.

hertz: *See* frequency.

8-hour average sound level (L_{8h})**:**   The (A-weighted) average sound level time-averaged over an 8-hour time period. *Unit:* decibel (dB).

hourly average sound level (L_{1hr})**:**   The (A-weighted) average sound level time-averaged over a 1-hour time period. *Unit:* decibel (dB).

impact: A single collision of one mass in motion with a second mass that may be either at rest or in motion.

impact noise: The noise which results when two masses collide.

impact sound pressure level (L_N)**:**   In a room below a floor under test, the average sound pressure level in a specified frequency band in the room when the floor under test is excited by a standardized impact sound source (e.g., a tapping machine). *Unit:* decibel (dB).

infrasound: Sound having a frequency below the low-frequency limit (approximately below 16 Hz) of audible sound.

insertion loss: Of a sound attenuator, sound barrier, or other element designed to provide sound reduction in a specified frequency band, the decrease in sound power level at the measurement point when this element is inserted in the transmission path between the sound source and the measurement location. *Unit:* decibel (dB).

intensity: *See* sound intensity.

intensity level: *See* sound intensity level.

inverse square law: Far from a sound source in a free field, the sound intensity varies inversely with the square of the distance from the source; this results in a decrease in sound level of 6 dB for each doubling of distance from the source. [See Eq. (2.9).]

isolator: *See* vibration isolator.

live room: A room containing relatively little sound absorption.

loudness: That attribute of auditory sensation in terms of which sounds may be ordered on a scale extending from soft to loud. *Unit:* sone.

masking: (1) The process by which the threshold of hearing for one sound is raised by the presence of another sound.   (2) The amount by which the threshold of hearing for one sound is raised by the presence of another sound. *Unit:* decibel (dB).

maximum A-weighted sound level ($L_{A\,max}$)**:**   The greatest sound level measured on a sound-level meter, during a designated time interval or event, using fast time-averaging and A-weighting. *Unit:* decibel [dB(A)].

metric sabin: *See* sabin.

NC curves (noise criterion curves):   A series of curves of octave-band sound spectra in a system for rating the noisiness of an indoor space; a measured octave-band spectrum is compared with this set of curves to determine the NC level in the space. [See Fig. 7.29.]

noise: Any disagreeable or undesired sound, i.e., unwanted sound.

noise criterion curves: *See* NC curves.

noise level: *Same as* sound level. Usually used to describe the sound level of an unwanted sound.

noise power emission level (L_{NWE})**:**   The logarithm to the base 10 of the ratio of the A-weighted sound power to the reference power of 1 picowatt. *Unit*: bel.

noise reduction (NR)**:**   The difference in sound pressure level between any two points along a path of sound propagation.

noise reduction coefficient (NRC)**:**   A single-number rating of the sound-absorptive properties of an acoustical material; the arithmetic average of the sound absorption coefficients at 250, 500, 1000, and 2000 Hz, rounded to the nearest multiple of 0.05.

normalized impact sound pressure level: The *impact sound pressure level* that has been adjusted by subtracting 10 times the logarithm (to the base 10) of the ratio of an absorption of 10 metric sabins divided by the total sound absorption in the room below the floor under test.

normalized noise isolation class (NNIC):   A single-number rating similar to the *noise isolation class* except that the measured noise reduction values are normalized to a reverberation time of 0.5 second.

octave: The frequency interval between two sounds whose frequency ratio is 2.

octave-band level; octave-band sound pressure level $(L_{1/1})$:   The sound pressure level of the sound contained within an octave band. *Unit*: decibel (dB).

octave-band spectrum: A *spectrum* in which the bands that are displayed as a function of frequency are one octave wide. [For example, see Fig. 2.19*a*.]

one-third-octave-band sound pressure level; one-third-octave-band level; one-third-octave-band sound level $(L_{1/3})$:   The sound pressure level of the sound contained within a 1/3-octave band. *Unit*: decibel (dB). [For example, see Fig. 2.19*b*.]

packaged fan equipment: *See* air-handling unit.

pascal (Pa):   A unit of pressure; 1 Pa = 1 newton per square meter = 1 N/m^2.

peak A-weighted sound level (L_{Apk}):   The maximum instantaneous A-weighted sound level during a stated time period or event. *Unit*: decibel [dB(A)].

peak level: The maximum instantaneous level of a stated kind that occurs during a stated time interval. *Unit:* decibel (dB).

peak sound level: The highest instantaneous value of a standard frequency-weighted sound pressure level, within a stated time interval. *Unit:* decibel (dB).

period: Of a periodic quantity, the smallest increment of the independent variable for which a function repeats itself.

picowatt (pW):   A unit of power equal to one-millionth of one-millionth of one watt (i.e., 10^{-12} W).

plane waves: Waves having *wavefronts* that are planar surfaces; the direction of the displacement of the air particles at each point is perpendicular to the wavefront. [See Fig. 2.1.]

point source: A source whose dimensions are small compared with wavelength of the sound it radiates. Such a source is nondirectional. It radiates sound as if it were emitted from a single point.

power: *See* sound power.

power level: *See* sound power level.

pure tone: Sound waves composed of but one frequency. [See Fig. 2.14.]

random noise: A noise whose magnitude cannot be predicted precisely at any given time.

rate of decay: *Same as* decay rate.

RC curves (room criterion curves): A series of curves of octave-band sound spectra in a system for rating the noisiness of an unoccupied indoor space. [See Fig. 7.31.]

reference sound intensity (I_o): A sound intensity equal to 1 picowatt per square meter.

reference sound power (W_o): A sound power equal to 1 picowatt (that is, 10^{-12} watt).

reference sound pressure (p_o): A sound pressure equal to 20 micropascals.

reflected sound level (L_r): The level of the sound resulting from repeated reflections in a room, excluding sound that travels directly from the source without reflections.

regenerated noise: In an air-conditioning system, noise which is caused by turbulent flow of air, for example, in a *sound attenuator*.

residual sound: The all-encompassing sound (at a specified time and position) which is usually a composite of sound from many sources at many directions, near and far, remaining when all uniquely identifiable discrete sound sources are eliminated or otherwise not included.

reverberant sound field; reverberant field: A sound field in an enclosed or partially enclosed space in which most sound waves have been reflected repeatedly or continuously from the boundaries. [In this type of field in most offices and homes, the sound pressure level close to the source usually decreases approximately 3 dB for each doubling of distance from the source. This is in contrast with conditions in a room with excellent diffusion where the decrease in level is approximately 6 dB for each doubling of distance from the source.]

reverberation: The persistence of sound in an enclosure or partially enclosed space after the source of sound has stopped; the persistence is a result of repeated reflections of sound waves.

reverberation room: A room having a long reverberation time, especially designed to make all surfaces as sound-reflective as possible and to make the sound field within it as uniform as possible.

reverberation time: At a given frequency or frequency band: (1) The time that is required for the sound pressure level in the enclosure to decrease by 60 dB after the source has stopped. [See Eq. (4.5).] (2) The time is seconds given by $T_{60} = 60 \text{ dB}/R$, where R is the rate of decay of sound in the room expressed in decibels per second. *Unit:* second.

room absorption (A): The total sound absorption within a room due to absorption by surfaces and furnishing and due to absorption of sound by air within the room. *Unit*: sabin or metric sabin. [See Eq. (4.1).]

room criterion curves: *See* RC curves.

sabin: A unit of measure of sound absorption; a measure of the sound absorption of a surface. One *sabin* is the equivalent of 1 square foot of a perfectly absorptive surface; a *metric sabin* is the equivalent of 1 m^2 of a perfectly absorptive surface.

Sabine absorption: The sound absorption defined by the Sabine reverberation time equation, Eq. (4.5).

scattering: The irregular diffraction of sound in many directions.

seismic restraint: *See* snubber.

simple harmonic motion: Motion that is a sinusoidal function of time. [See Fig. 2.14.]

sine wave: A wave that may be represented mathematically by the sine function: $A \sin (2\pi f)t$, where A is the amplitude of motion, and f is the frequency in hertz. [See Fig. 2.14.]

single-degree-of-freedom: Descriptive of a mechanical system that requires only one coordinate to define its configuration completely, at any instant of time.

snubber: A component that limits the motion of a vibration isolator.

solidborne sound: *See* structureborne sound.

sone: The unit of loudness. One sone is the loudness of a pure tone presented to a listener facing the source of plane progressive waves in a free field at a frequency of 1000 Hz and a sound pressure level of 40 dB.

sound: (1) A change in air pressure that is capable of being detected by the human ear. (2) The hearing sensation excited by a change in air pressure.

sound absorption: The process of converting sound waves into heat.

sound absorption coefficient (α): (1) Ideally, the fraction of the randomly incident sound power that is absorbed (or otherwise not reflected) by a material. (2) A measure of the sound-absorptive property of a material as approximated by ASTM Method C423.

sound analyzer: An apparatus for the determination of a *sound spectrum*.

sound attenuator: A device that is inserted into an air duct to provide more attenuation than an acoustically lined duct of equivalent length and cross section.

sound field: A region containing sound waves.

sound insulation: The capacity of a material or structure to prevent sound from reaching a selected location. Sound energy is not necessarily absorbed; it may be reflected back toward the source.

sound intensity (I)**:**   In a specified direction at a point, the average rate of sound energy transmitted in the specified direction through a unit area normal to this direction at the point considered. *Unit*: watts per square meter (W/m^2). [See Eq. (2.4).]

sound intensity level (L_I)**:**   Ten times the common logarithm (i.e., to the base 10) of a given sound intensity to a reference sound intensity of one picowatt (i.e., 1 pW/m). *Unit*: decibel (dB). [See Eq. (2.10).]

sound level: Ten times the logarithm to the base 10 of the square of the ratio of the frequency-weighted (and time-averaged) sound pressure to the reference sound pressure of 20 micropascals. The frequency-weightings and time-weighting employed should be specified; if they are not specified, it is understood that A-frequency-weighting is used and that an averaging time of 0.125 is used. *Unit:* decibel (dB).

sound-level meter: An instrument for the measurement of *sound level.*

sound power (W)**:**   The rate per unit time at which sound source radiates energy. *Unit*: watt (W).

sound power level (L_W)**:**   Ten times the logarithm (to the base 10) of the ratio of a given sound power to the reference sound power of 10^{12} W. *Unit*: decibel (dB). [See Eq. (2.6).]

sound pressure: (1) The additional oscillating pressure due to the passage of sound waves.   (2) Variations in pressure, above and below atmospheric pressure, which give rise to a physical disturbance capable of being detected by the ear.

sound pressure level (L_p)**:**   In air, 10 times the logarithm (to the base 10) of the square of the ratio of the given sound pressure to a reference sound pressure of 20 micropascals. *Unit*: decibel (dB). [See Eq. (2.8).]

sound spectrum: A representation of the magnitude of the components of a complex sound as a function of frequency. [For example, an octave-band spectrum is shown in Fig. 2.19a.]

sound transmission class (STC)**:**   A single-number rating used to compare the sound insulation properties of walls, floors, ceilings, windows, or doors. [For example, see Fig. 5.2]

sound transmission loss: *See* transmission loss.

sound trap: *See* sound attenuator.

source room: A room that contains a noise source or sources.

spherical waves: Waves having wavefronts that are concentric circles. [For example, see Fig. 2.2.]

static pressure (P)**:**   At a point in the atmosphere, the pressure that would exist at that point in the absence of sound waves. *Unit*: pascal (Pa).

structureborne sound: Sound that is propagated through a solid structure.

tapping machine: A mechanical device sometimes used in rating different floor constructions against impacts; it produces 10 impacts per second on the floor under test.

third-octave-band level: *See* one-third-octave-band level.

time-average sound level: *See* equivalent-continuous sound level.

transmission loss (TL): A rating of the sound insulation value of a partition, for a specified frequency band. [Equivalent to the difference between the average sound pressure levels in the reverberant source room and receiving room plus 10 times the logarithm to the base 10 of the ratio of the area of the common partition to the total absorption in the receiving room.] *Unit:* decibel (dB). [For example, see Fig. 5.1.]

vibration isolator, vibration mount: A resilient support (on which equipment may be supported or from which it may be hung) designed to reduce the vibration transmitted to the supporting structure.

wave: A disturbance that is propagated in air so that at any point the quantity serving as measure of the disturbance is a function of time; at any instant, the displacement at a point is a function of the position of the point.

wavefront: Of a progressive wave in space, a continuous surface where the phase is the same at a given instant.

wavelength (λ): The perpendicular distance between the maxima in two successive wavefronts. [See Fig. 2.1.]

weighting: *See* frequency weighting.

Symbols, Abbreviations, and Acronyms

A	total sound absorption in a room
ADC	Air Diffusion Council
AHU	air-handling unit
AMC	Air Movement and Control Association
ANSI	American National Standards Institute
ARI	Air Conditioning and Refrigeration Institute
ASA	Acoustical Society of America
ASHRAE	American Society of Heating, Refrigerating and Air-Conditioning Engineers
ASTM	American Society for Testing and Materials
c	speed of sound
CAC	ceiling attenuation class
cfm	cubic feet per minute
CMU	concrete masonry unit
cps	cycles per second (same as *hertz*)
dB	decibel
dB(A)	decibel [The (A) indicates use of A-weighting.]
dB(C)	decibel [The (C) indicates use of C-weighting.]
f	frequency

FPT	fan-powered terminal
FSTC	field sound transmission class
g	acceleration of gravity
HUD	U.S. Department of Housing and Urban Development
HVAC	heating, ventilating, and air conditioning
Hz	hertz
I	sound intensity
I_o	reference sound intensity (1 picowatt per square meter)
IEC	International Electrotechnical Commission
IIC	impact isolation class
INCE	Institute of Noise Control Engineering
INR	impact noise rating
ISO	International Organization for Standardization
kg	kilogram
kHz	kilohertz
L_a	vibration acceleration level
L_A	A-weighted sound level
L_{AI}	A-weighted impulse sound level
L_{AIeq}	A-weighted impulse equivalent-continuous sound level
$L_{A\,max}$	maximum A-weighted sound level
L_{Apk}	peak A-weighted sound level
L_C	C-weighted sound level
L_{8h}	8-hour average sound level
L_d	day average sound level
L_d	direct sound level
L_{dn}	day-night average sound level
L_{eq}	equivalent-continuous sound level; average sound level
L_I	sound intensity level
L_N	calculated loudness level
L_{NWE}	noise power emission level
L_p	sound pressure level
L_{pT}	time-average sound (pressure) level
L_W	sound power level
L_{pA}	A-weighted sound power level
$L_{1/1}$	octave-band sound pressure level
L_r	reflected sound level
$L_{1/3}$	one-third-octave-band sound pressure level
L_{10}	*fast* A-weighted sound level exceeded 10% of the time

L_{50}	*fast* A-weighted sound level exceeded 50% of the time
L_{90}	*fast* A-weighted sound level exceeded 90% of the time
LR	level reduction
m	meter
N	newton
NC	noise criterion level
NEMA	National Electrical Manufacturers Association
NEPA	National Environmental Policy Act
NIC	noise isolation class
NII	noise impact index
NNIC	normalized noise insulation class
NPEL	noise power emission level
NR	noise reduction
NRC	noise reduction coefficient
NRR	noise reduction rating
NVLAP	National Voluntary Laboratory Accreditation Program
OBL	octave-band level
OITC	outdoor-indoor transmission class
OSHA	Occupational Safety and Health Administration
p	sound pressure
p_o	reference sound pressure (20 micropascals)
Pa	pascal
PNR	product noise rating
psi	pounds per square inch
psf	pounds per square foot
PWL	sound power level
r	radius; distance from a source
RC	room criterion level
rms	root-mean-square
RTU	rooftop unit
s	second
SA	sound attenuator
SI	Standard International; International Standard
SMACNA	Sheet Metal and Air Conditioning Contractor's National Association
SPL	sound pressure level
STC	sound transmission class
STI	sound transmission index

t	time
T_{60}	reverberation time
TL	transmission loss
VAV	variable air volume
W	sound power
W_0	reference sound power (1 picowatt, i.e., 10^{-12} watt)
α	sound absorption coefficient
λ	wavelength

Chapter

3

Sound-Absorptive Materials

Ron Moulder

INTRODUCTION

When sound waves strike the surface of a material, a fraction of the incident acoustical energy is absorbed by conversion into heat. In most acoustical materials, this conversion of acoustical energy into heat is primarily a result of friction generated by the motion of air particles within the pores of a highly porous material. The pores may be formed by felted mineral or fiberglass fibers, by the interstices between small granules, or by a foamed composition in which the cells interconnect throughout the material. Some sound energy also may be absorbed by the flexure of the tiles or panels that are forced into vibration by the sound waves; the resulting flexural vibrations dissipate a small amount of the incident sound energy by its conversion into heat.

All materials absorb sound to some extent. *Acoustical materials* are those materials whose primary function is to absorb sound; they usually absorb a large fraction of the acoustical energy which strikes them.

This chapter describes:

- How sound-absorptive materials are rated

- Basic characteristics of sound-absorptive materials and constructions

- Types of acoustical materials and constructions including acoustical tiles, acoustical boards, acoustical blankets, assemblies of perforated facings and acoustical blankets, sound-absorptive wall panels and office dividers, acoustical roof decks, and acoustical sprayed-on materials

- Special types of sound absorbers, including suspended absorbers, drapes, carpet, and Helmholtz resonators. (The absorption of sound in air and the sound absorption provided by auditorium chairs is discussed in Chap. 4.)

An extensive Appendix is provided of commercially available acoustical materials. Comprehensive information is provided not only of the sound adsorption coefficients of the materials but also other characteristics that are important in the selection of acoustical materials, such as their physical characteristics and weight per unit area.

SOUND ABSORPTION RATINGS

Sound Absorption Coefficients

The *sound absorption coefficient* of a material is the fraction (expressed as a decimal number) of the randomly incident sound energy that is absorbed or otherwise not reflected by the material. It is a measure of the sound-absorptive property of the material. For example, a sound absorption coefficient of 0.65 indicates that 65 percent of the incident acoustical energy which strikes a material is absorbed. A sound absorption coefficient of 0.00 indicates complete reflection; a sound absorption coefficient of 1.00 represents complete absorption. Because of limitations in the test method used to determine sound absorption coefficients, values in excess of 1.00 are sometimes reported. (For design purposes, any such values should be reduced to 1.00.) The sound absorption coefficient of every material varies with frequency. It is common practice to list the coefficients of a material at frequencies of

125, 250, 500, 1000, 2000, and 4000 Hz

or at frequencies of

100, 125, 160, 200, 250, 315, 400, 500, 630, 800, 1000,

1250, 1600, 2000, 2500, 3150, 4000, and 5000 Hz

At a given frequency, the absorption coefficient of any material varies with the angle of incidence of the sound waves. For this reason, published values of absorption coefficients of materials represent the coefficients *averaged over all angles of incidence*. This type of average coefficient is required in most noise control problems in buildings since sound waves in rooms strike materials at many different angles.*

---

*Values of sound absorption coefficients (averaged over all angles) are measured in a *reverberation room* (i.e., a test chamber whose characteristics include a very long reverberation time) in which sound waves strike the material from all angles with nearly equal probability. In North America an ASTM Test Standard[1] is used; in Europe, an ISO Test Standard[2] is used. At a given test frequency, the difference between the reverberation times in the room [see Eq. (4.5)] with and without the material under test is determined. From this information and a knowledge of the volume of the room and the size of the test sample, the absorption coefficient at the test frequency is determined.

It is important to differentiate between a material's *sound-absorptive* characteristics and its *sound insulation properties*. As explained in Chap. 5, a good absorber of sound does not necessarily provide good insulation against the transmission of airborne sound through the material, and vice versa. For example, in the mid-frequency range, the sound absorption provided by a fiberglass acoustical blanket 4 inches (10 cm) thick is excellent. In contrast, the sound insulation it provides is very poor—sound can travel from one side of the blanket to the other, with little attenuation. Conversely, in the mid-frequency range, a solid concrete wall provides little sound absorption, but the airborne sound insulation it provides is very high.

Noise Reduction Coefficient

The *noise reduction coefficient* (NRC) of a material is the average value of the absorption coefficients of the material at the frequencies of 250, 500, 1000, and 2000 Hz; this average is rounded off to the nearest multiple of 0.05. For example, suppose a material has the following sound absorption coefficients:

Frequency, Hz	Absorption coefficient
125	0.07
250	0.26
500	0.70
1000	0.99
2000	0.99
4000	0.98

Then the noise reduction coefficient for this material is

$$\frac{0.26 + 0.70 + 0.99 + 0.99}{4} = 0.735$$

Rounding this number off to the nearest multiple of 0.05 yields a noise reduction coefficient of 0.75. (Because *measured values* of sound absorption coefficients can be greater than 1.00, NRC values also can be greater than 1.00.)

In preparing specifications for acoustical materials used for noise control in buildings, it often is convenient to make use of the noise reduction coefficient since it is but a single number. However, if the sound absorption at very low or very high frequencies is an important consideration, it is usually better practice to compare the sound absorption coefficients of the two materials rather than their noise reduction coefficients (NRCs). For example, suppose an acoustical material is required to reduce the level of low-frequency noise (say, in the region of 125 Hz—a frequency that is not considered in determining the NRC of a material). In this case, the use of NRCs may lead to a poor choice of materials if the material having the higher NRC has a lower sound absorption coefficient at 125 Hz.

Effect of Mounting on Absorption Coefficients

The sound absorption coefficients of an acoustical material usually depend on how it is mounted or installed. For this reason several standard mountings have been established so that data on various acoustical materials can be compared for the same mounting conditions. When the absorption coefficients for an acoustical material are given, usually one of the following mounting conditions, illustrated in Fig. 3.1, is specified:

Type A Mounting: Laid directly against a rigid solid surface with no air space.

Type B Mounting: Spot-cemented to gypsum board with a $\frac{1}{8}$-inch (20-mm) air space.

Type C Mounting: In a perforated faced material backed with sound-absorptive material, the number following the letter C represents the depth of the space (in mm) behind the perforated facing.

Type D Mounting: Nailed to wood furring strips. The number following the letter D represents the thickness of the furring strips.

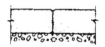

Type A mounting
Laid directly on surface

Type B mounting
Cemented to gypsum board

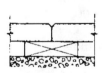

Type D-20 mounting
Nailed to nominal 3/4 X 11/2-in (20- X 40-mm)
wood furring

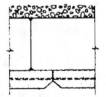

Type E–400 mounting
Suspended with 16-in (400-mm)
airspace

FIG. 3.1 Standard mountings for testing acoustical materials.

Type E Mounting: Supported from a hard surface (such as a ceiling) by a metal suspension system, with an air space above the acoustical material. A number following the letter *E* represents the number of millimeters from the face of the acoustical material to the hard surface above.

Type F Mounting: Supported by a reinforced sheet metal with an airspace behind the sheet metal. A number following the letter *F* represents the number of millimeters between the sheet metal and hard surface supporting the sheet metal.

Other mounting conditions may be used as specified in test standards published by the American Society for Testing and Materials[1,3] or published by the International Organization for Standardization.[2]

Figure 3.2 shows sound absorption coefficients for the same material for three different mounting conditions. Note that sound absorption increases significantly at low frequencies if the material is furred out or suspended from the ceiling. Thus when comparing the sound absorption provided by two different materials, the data must be compared for the same mounting conditions. For example, it is meaningless to compare the sound-absorptive properties of a material whose coefficients have been measured for a Type A mounting with a second material whose coefficients have been measured for a Type E-400 mounting.

Effect of Thickness on Sound Absorption Coefficients

In general, the sound absorption coefficients of acoustical materials increase with increasing thickness of material except at the higher frequencies, where the increase may not be significant. For example,

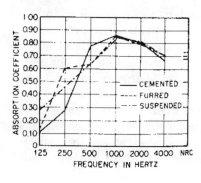

FIG. 3.2 Comparison of the sound absorption coefficients of the same acoustical tile for cemented, furred, and suspended mountings.

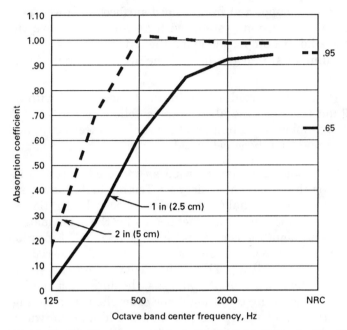

FIG. 3.3 Sound absorption coefficients for two thicknesses of a fiber-glass board having a density of 6 pounds per cubic foot (9.6 kg/m³) for a Type A mounting. (*Courtesy of Owens-Corning Corp.*)

Fig. 3.3 shows sound absorption coefficients versus frequency for two thicknesses of a fiberglass board for the same mounting conditions. Note that the increase in absorption is primarily at the frequencies below 1000 Hz and is greatest at frequencies below 250 Hz.

Effect of Density on Sound Absorption Coefficients

The sound absorption of a material, such as fiberglass board, usually increases with increasing density up to densities of 6 to 9 pounds per cubic foot (9.6 to 14.4 kg/m³). Above these densities the interconnecting air cells in the material are very small so that little acoustical energy is dissipated due to air friction. Figure 3.4 shows the sound absorption coefficients versus frequency for fiberglass boards having the same thickness but different densities.

Because materials may be composed of fibers or pores having different diameters (and this, in turn, affects their physical characteristics), the thickness and density of a sound-absorptive material may not always provide an accurate basis of comparison of their sound-absorptive properties.

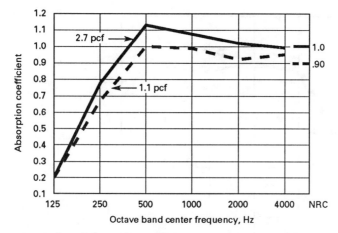

FIG. 3.4 Sound absorption coefficients versus frequency for fiberglass boards 2 inch (5 cm) thick which have two different densities: 1.1 pounds per cubic foot (17.6 kg/m³) and 2.7 pounds per cubic foot (43 kg/m³). These data are for a Type A mounting.

Effect of an Airspace behind a Sound-Absorptive Material

If a porous material is spaced away from a hard wall or ceiling, its sound absorption is increased significantly at frequencies below 1000 Hz compared with its sound absorption if the same material is cemented to a wall or ceiling. This effect is illustrated in Fig. 3.5 for a fiberglass board with and without an airspace behind it. At frequencies above 250 Hz, there is usually no significant change in sound absorption of a material if it has an airspace behind it.[†]

GENERAL CHARACTERISTICS OF ACOUSTICAL MATERIALS

In the Appendix to this chapter, the acoustical characteristics of commercially available sound-absorptive materials and constructions used for the control of noise in buildings are tabulated according to the following classification system; other details are provided for each of these classifications, sequentially, in the sections that follow:

[†]A porous, sound-absorptive material that is spaced away from a hard surface (such as a wall or ceiling) provides increased sound absorption because the velocity of the air particles through the material is higher when it is spaced away from the wall. At a hard surface, the velocity of the air particles is zero because the particles cannot penetrate the surface. The magnitude of the energy converted into heat (and hence sound absorption) depends on the square of the velocity of the air particles.

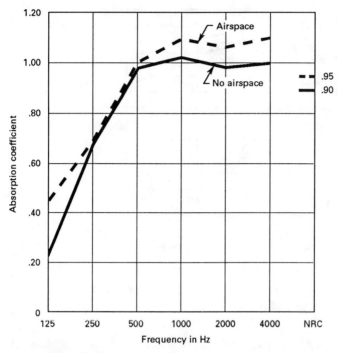

FIG. 3.5 Sound absorption coefficients versus frequency for fiberglass boards having a density of 6 pounds per cubic foot (9.6 kg/m³) and a thickness of 2 inches (5 cm). The data are shown for the fiberglass boards with and without a 14-inch (35-cm) airspace behind the sound-absorptive material. (*Courtesy of Owens-Corning Corp.*)

1. Acoustical tiles and lay-in panels
2. Duct liners
3. Foam materials
4. Acoustical boards, blankets, and batts
5. Acoustical panels
6. Acoustical roof decks
7. Sprayed-on materials
8. Sound-rated masonry units (Helmholtz resonators)
9. Unit absorbers and hanging panels; suspended absorbers
10. General building materials and furnishings

In addition to its sound-absorptive properties, other properties of a material should be considered when selecting an acoustical treatment, including:

- Appearance
- Compatibility with other materials and components (such as lighting fixtures)
- Cost
- Ease of installation
- Ease of repair if the material is damaged
- Maintenance and cleanability
- Paintability
- Space available for acoustical installation
- Susceptibility to damage by high humidities
- Weight

Other less obvious properties are discussed below.

Mechanical Strength and Mechanical Abuse

The mechanical strength of most acoustical materials is usually low (i.e., they are easily damaged when struck). For this reason, the surface of an acoustical material that is subject to abuse may be protected by a facing of perforated metal, plywood, or hardboard, or by a metal screen or strips of wood. For example, see Fig. 3.6.

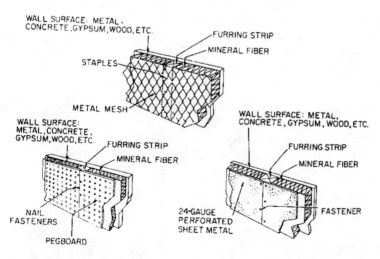

FIG. 3.6 Examples showing how the surface of an acoustical material can be protected from abuse.

Dimensional Stability

An acoustical material is said to be dimensionally stable if its physical dimensions do not change significantly with changes in humidity and/or temperature. The dimensional stability of an acoustical material depends on the fiber of which it is fabricated (inorganic materials are more dimensionally stable than organic materials) and the binder that holds the fibers together (water-resistant binders are more stable than non–water-resistant binders).

Effects of Humidity

As noted in the above paragraph, the dimensional stability of some acoustical materials may be affected by conditions of high humidity. In fact, some materials may even disintegrate when exposed to high humidities (say, 90 percent or higher) over prolonged periods of time—either as a result of damage to the fibers or to the binder which holds the fibers together. For this reason, for installations in swimming pool areas, or the like, it is advisable to check with the material's manufacturer to ensure that the material is guaranteed for such applications. Acoustical materials are available for application in these environments.

Sound Insulation Properties of Acoustical Ceilings; STC Range

In many offices, partitions extend upward only as high as a suspended acoustical ceiling. Sound from a source in one room may travel up through the suspended acoustical ceiling into the overhead plenum area, over the top of the partition, and then down through the suspended acoustical ceiling into the adjacent room, as illustrated in Fig. 3.7. In order to reduce the amount of sound that passes through

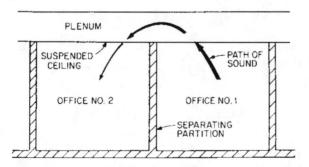

FIG. 3.7 How sound may be transmitted from one room to an adjacent room through a suspended acoustical ceiling.

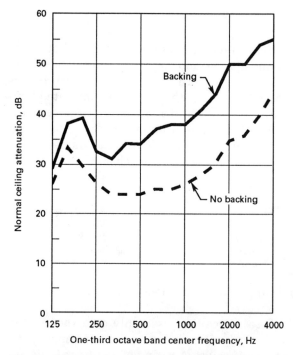

FIG. 3.8 The sound insulation (expressed in terms of "normalized ceiling attenuation") of a ³/₄-inch (2-cm) thick ceiling tile with and without an impervious backing. The backing increases the sound insulation of the tile but reduces its sound absorption. (*Courtesy of U.S. Gypsum Co.*)

acoustical ceilings, many acoustical tiles and/or acoustical boards are fabricated with a back coating or foil. This seals the back of the porous material, thereby improving its sound insulation but reducing its sound absorption. For example, Fig. 3.8 shows the sound insulation of an acoustical tile, expressed in terms of normalized ceiling attenuation with and without a foil backing. (The *normalized ceiling attenuation* is a measure of the effectiveness of the suspended ceiling in attenuating sound between the two adjacent rooms, as described in Chap. 5.) The effectiveness of this sound insulation varies with frequency. Therefore, to facilitate comparison between various suspended acoustical ceiling constructions, the sound insulation may also be expressed as a single number, called the *ceiling attenuation class* (CAC); the higher this number, the greater the sound insulation which the construction provides. Most manufacturers of acoustical ceilings list a CAC range for their products. The ranges usually are 20 to 24, 25 to 29, 30 to 34, 35 to 39, 40 to 44, and 45 to 49.

Flame-Spread Index, Fire Class, and Fire Endurance

Specifications for acoustical materials usually require that these materials be rated for flame spread and fire endurance. The *flame-spread index* of a material[4] is a measure of the rate at which flames will travel across the exposed surface of the material. Untreated lumber has a designated value of 100, and noncombustible cement-asbestos board has a value of 0. Ranges of performance are more significant than individual numerical values. Thus, the flame-spread index usually is expressed as one of the following classes:

Class	Flame-spread index	Fire class designation (ASTM E1264)[5]
I	0–25	Class 25
II	26–75	Class 75
III	76–200	Class 200
IV	Over 200	—

Most acoustical materials are included in Class I, which are relatively noncombustible.

The *fire endurance*[6] of a floor-ceiling assembly or a roof-ceiling assembly (of which an acoustical ceiling is but one of the components) is rated in hours or fractions of hours. A rating of one hour indicates that after one hour of exposure to a specified flame, (a) the top of the floor/ceiling or roof-ceiling assembly did not exceed a specified temperature, (b) there was no passage of flame through the assembly, or (c) the assembly did not fail structurally.

Light Reflectance

The light reflectance of a material, a measure of the fraction of incident light that is reflected from its surface, may be determined from ASTM Standard E1477, "Luminous Reflectance Factor of Acoustical Materials by Use of Integrating Sphere Reflectometer." Most acoustical materials used in ceiling installations have a light reflectance value of 0.75 or higher. Because the accumulation of dirt or dust on an acoustical material reduces light reflectance from its surface, exact values of reflectance are usually not supplied by manufacturers. Instead, they provide data on light reflectance that is characterized by a letter having the following significance:

Letter designation	Light reflectance
a	0.75 or more
b	0.70 to 0.74
c	0.65 to 0.69
d	0.60 to 0.64

The face of an acoustical ceiling material must be cleanable or paintable in order to maintain a high light reflectance.

ACOUSTICAL TILES, LAY-IN PANELS, ACOUSTICAL BOARDS   (SEE APPENDIX 3.1)

An acoustical tile or board is an integral, rigid, self-supporting material furnished in prefabricated units of fixed size and thickness. The distinction between an acoustical tile and/or acoustical board is only one of size; boards are larger than tiles. In North America, tiles commonly range in size from 12 × 12 inches to 24 × 24 inches, whereas acoustical boards commonly range from 2 × 4 feet to 4 × 14 feet. In Europe, tiles commonly range in size from 30 × 30 cm to 60 × 60 cm, whereas acoustical boards commonly range from 60 to 180 cm.

Acoustical tiles and boards usually range in thickness from $1/2$ to 2 inches (1.25 to 5 cm) and in density from 3 to about 8 pounds per cubic foot (5.0 to about 12.8 kg/m^3).

The various types of acoustical tiles or acoustical boards differ widely in composition and surface characteristics; hence they differ widely in their sound absorption characteristics as well as other properties, such as appearance, architectural style, cleanability, paintability, light reflectance, flame resistance, dimensional stability, and methods of application.

Types of commercial tiles and boards include: perforated felted mineral fiber, fiberglass or rock wool tile or board; smooth or textured felted mineral-fiber tile; fissured mineral-fiber tile or board; fiberglass board faced with glass-cloth; and, membrane-faced mineral-fiber tile or board. Mineral fiber is similar to fiberglass except the fibers are made from basalt or iron slag. Photographs showing the appearance of various types of surfaces are given in Fig. 3.9.

Installation

One advantage of acoustical tile and acoustical board is that such materials can be installed by a variety of methods. For example, acoustical tile may be applied by means of:

- Adhesive cement (to surfaces such as plaster, concrete, or gypsum board)

- Nails, staples, or screws (to wood furring, roof deck, or gypsum board)

Various methods of mounting acoustical tiles and acoustical boards are illustrated in Figs. 3.10 to 3.13. Figure 3.10 shows an acoustical tile cemented to a solid backing such as a gypsum board ceiling or

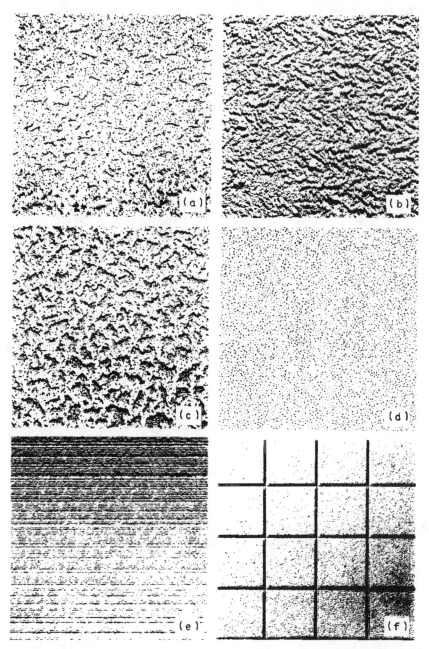

FIG. 3.9 Photographs (half-scale) showing the surface appearance of various types of prefabricated acoustical ceiling tiles: (*a*) fissured; (*b*) rough textured; (*c*) randomly textured; (*d*) pin perforated; (*e*) linear patterned; (*f*) score patterned. (*Courtesy of U.S.G. Interiors, Inc.*)

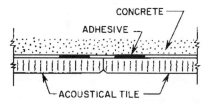

FIG. 3.10 An acoustical tile cemented to a solid backing such as a concrete slab or gypsum board.

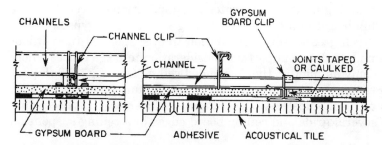

FIG. 3.11 The application of acoustical tile to a gypsum board suspended ceiling. The gypsum board reduces the transmission of sound through the acoustical ceiling.

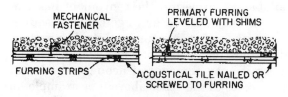

WOOD FURRING TO CONCRETE

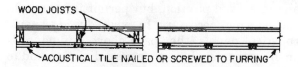

DIRECT TO WOOD JOISTS

FIG. 3.12 An acoustical tile or board applied to furring strips or joists using nails or mechanical fasteners.

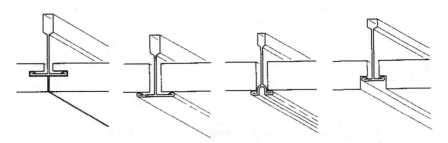

FIG. 3.13 Cross-section views showing suspension details at edges of several types of acoustical tiles and panels. (*Courtesy of U.S. Gypsum Interiors, Inc.*)

concrete slab. Figure 3.11 illustrates the application of acoustical tile to a gypsum board in a suspended ceiling system. The gypsum board provides much greater sound insulation than suspended tile without the gypsum board—an important consideration in large offices where walls are only as high as the suspended ceiling (see Fig. 3.7). Figure 3.12 shows acoustical tiles or boards applied to furring strips or joists by nails or mechanical fasteners. Figure 3.13 shows cross-sectional views of several grids and ceiling board edges in a ceiling suspension system.

Most acoustical tiles and boards may be installed so as to form a complete ceiling by suspending them from metal members which support the edges of the tiles. The maximum unsupported span of acoustical boards which is allowable depends on the deflection characteristics of the particular material used. A number of mechanical suspension systems are available which permit the convenient installation of some combination (in any desired arrangement) of sound-absorptive ceiling surfaces with luminaries, air-conditioning outlets, loudspeakers, and/or radiant-heating elements. Some suspension systems are designed to permit easy removal of acoustical tiles or acoustical boards, allowing access to the space above. For example, in some metal-pan systems (described in a following section), the pans are fabricated with flanges which snap into special T-bars, thereby securing the metal pans in a fixed position, but permitting the individual panels to be removed when necessary. In exposed-grid systems employing "lay-in" acoustical panels, the space above any panel is accessible merely by pushing the panel in an upward direction and to one side. Figure 3.14 shows a concealed-grid system which provides accessibility to the space above.

Acoustical tiles and acoustical boards may both be applied to wall surfaces if they are not subject to abuse. When used as a wall treatment, the exposed edges of acoustical tiles or boards are usually protected by a wood or metal frame.

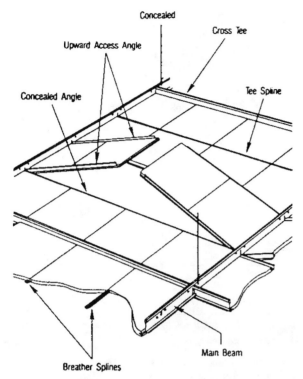

FIG. 3.14   One type of accessible ceiling tile suspension system. (*Courtesy of Armstrong World Industries.*)

Effects of Tile Thickness on Sound Absorption

As indicated earlier, the sound absorption coefficients of acoustical materials increase with increasing thickness except at the higher frequencies, where the increase may not be significant. For example, Fig. 3.15 shows sound absorption coefficients versus frequency for several thicknesses of a fiberglass ceiling panel. These data show that an increase in thickness increases the absorption primarily at the frequencies below 1000 Hz. At 125 Hz, the sound absorption coefficient is roughly proportional to thickness.

Effects of Airspace behind a Board on Its Sound Absorption

As indicated in Fig. 3.5, the presence of an airspace behind an acoustical material increases the sound absorption of the material significantly at low frequencies. For an acoustical board, this effect is

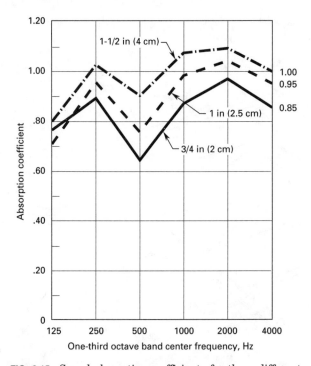

FIG. 3.15 Sound absorption coefficients for three different thicknesses of a fiberglass ceiling panel in a suspended grid system.

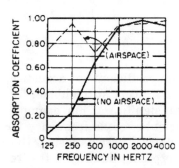

FIG. 3.16 Sound absorption coefficients of a 1-inch (2.5-cm) thick fiberglass ceiling board with and without an airspace behind the acoustical material. These data illustrate that the presence of a 16-inch (400-mm) airspace (Type E-400 mounting) increases the sound absorption markedly at 125 and 250 Hz.

illustrated in Fig. 3.16, which shows the sound absorption coefficients of the material with and without an airspace behind it. Note that the presence of the airspace increases the absorption markedly at 125 and 250 Hz. For most materials, this increase in absorption with increasing depth of airspace shows no further significant increase in absorption when the airspace is increased beyond about 16 inches (40 cm), except at very low frequencies. If the back surface of the tile is relatively impervious, there is less of an effect than if the back surface is porous—particularly at low frequencies.

Paintability; Effects of Paint in Reducing Sound Absorption

Most acoustical tiles and acoustical boards are supplied with a factory-applied paint finish (often, a washable finish) having a value of light reflectance of 0.70 to 0.80. Usually it is desirable to maintain the light reflectance of an acoustical material close to its initial value, either by washing or repainting the surface. It is imperative that such maintenance not reduce the sound-absorptive properties of the material.

If an acoustical tile or acoustical board is not properly repainted, its sound-absorptive properties will be reduced significantly. Depending on the type of acoustical tile or board and its surface appearance, the sound absorption coefficients (especially at the middle and high frequencies) can be reduced by as much as 40 percent. Tiles or boards whose surfaces are perforated or slotted usually may be repainted a number of times without significant loss of sound absorption if the paint does not bridge (i.e., close the perforations). Tiles or boards with no large surface openings that depend entirely on the surface porosity of the material to provide sound absorption usually cannot be repainted without loss of sound absorption. In general, such materials are furnished with a factory-applied paint finish which provides satisfactory light reflectance while retaining a porous surface.

Fissured materials that have an impervious factory-applied paint coating covering the surface between the fissured openings must be repainted with care. Characteristically, the fissures differ widely in size and depth, even within a single tile. Repainting tends to close the smaller and shallower openings, which has negligible effect on sound absorption. In repainting, care must be taken to avoid filling the larger fissures.

When it is necessary to repaint any acoustical tile or board, it should be painted using a sprayer, preferably at an angle with respect to the surface. A brush or roller tends to put too much paint on a tile or board. A nonbridging paint must be used and applied at a rate of 400 to 450 square feet per gallon (9.7 to 11.0 m^2/L). Ceiling tiles or acoustical boards that are painted in place may sag or wrap. Therefore, there is some advantage to removing the ceiling tiles or boards and laying them on a flat surface when the paint is applied—if this is practical. Before repainting any acoustical material, the manufacturer of the product should be consulted concerning the best type of paint to use and the proper method of application.

Simple check to determine if a coat of paint will reduce the sound absorption: Place your mouth on the unpainted surface and blow. Next place your mouth against a sample of the painted surface. If it is much more difficult to blow through the newly painted surface, there is a high probability that the newly applied layer of paint has reduced the sound-absorptive properties of the material.

Specifications for an Acoustical Tile Ceiling

Most manufacturers provide typical specifications for their particular products that can be used by an owner or architect, including requirements such as the following:

Acoustical material shall be (name of product) as manufactured by (name of company). It shall be (thickness and size), and have an NRC of ____ for a type ____ mounting. A ____-year written guarantee of dimensional stability against warping, buckling, or sagging shall be issued by the manufacturer to the Owner.

The suspension system shall be formed of cold rolled steel electro-galvanized which meets the requirements of ASTM C635. Specification of Metal Suspension Systems for Acoustical Tile and Lay-In Panel Ceilings. The suspension shall be installed in accordance with ASTM C636 Recommended Practice for Installation of Metal Ceiling Suspension Systems for Acoustical Tile and Lay-In Panels.

Other requirements may depend on the environmental conditions to which the acoustical material will be subject, for example, humidity, or on a specified fire-rating.

ACOUSTICAL DUCT LINERS (SEE APPENDIX 3.2)

The properties of acoustical materials used as lining in ducts for a heating, ventilating, and air-conditioning (HVAC) system may be different than those required for quieting rooms. Duct liners (1) must not be combustible, (2) must have sufficient mechanical strength to prevent particles of the material from being carried off by the airstream, (3) must offer little resistance to airflow over the surface of the material, and (4) should be moisture resistant. In general, duct lining usually is fabricated of mineral fiber, such as fiberglass, held together by a binder that does not support combustion. To obtain low resistance to the flow of air over its surface, one surface is either sprayed by a fine coating of a neoprene compound (this coating is so thin that it has no significant effect on the material's absorptive characteristics) or is covered with a very thin layer of fiberglass cloth that is adhered to the surface. It is this surface that is exposed to the airflow.

Because the exposed surface of duct lining material usually is black and resists the "dusting off" of fiber materials, it is often used in noise control applications in buildings. Sound absorption coefficients for such materials are given in App. 3.2. In calculating, these values should not be used since these data represent sound absorption coefficients averaged over all angles of incidence, whereas noise that travels down the duct grazes the surface of the material. For the application of duct lining material in HVAC systems, see Table 7.6, which takes these factors into account.

FOAM MATERIALS   (SEE APPENDIX 3.3)

Certain types of open-cell foam materials, such as polyurethane and polyester foams, can be used as sound-absorptive materials. (An *open-cell material* is one in which the cells of the materials interconnect so that it is possible to blow through the material.) Closed-cell foams are not sound-absorptive. Foams have the advantage of being very lightweight, can be formed in many different sizes and thicknesses, and are easy to handle. Foams have the disadvantage of being combustible and giving off toxic fumes. Some acoustical foam materials are treated with a fire-retardant material or fabricated of special foams that do not burn. Before using any type of foam in building construction, its long-term flame-spread properties should be determined.

ACOUSTICAL BLANKETS (GLASS FIBER AND MINERAL FIBER)   (SEE APPENDIX 3.4)

Acoustical blankets, usually composed of glass fibers or mineral fibers, are similar to acoustical boards, with one important difference—rigidity. An acoustical board has greater rigidity as a result of its higher density; if a piece of acoustical board is held upright by one edge, it will remain erect. In contrast, a blanket has little rigidity as a result of its relatively low density; if a piece is held upright, it will bend over. Acoustical blankets are usually similar in characteristics to duct lining materials and may or may not have a facing that minimizes the resistance of airflow across the material's surface and the "dusting off" of particles from the material's surface.

Fiberglass blankets may be available in rolls having the following densities: $3/4$, 1, $1^1/2$, 2, and/or 3 pounds per cubic foot (12, 16, 24, 32, and/or 48 kg/m^3). These acoustical blankets range in thickness from $1^1/2$ to 4 inches (1.25 and 10 cm). Figure 3.17 shows the sound absorp-

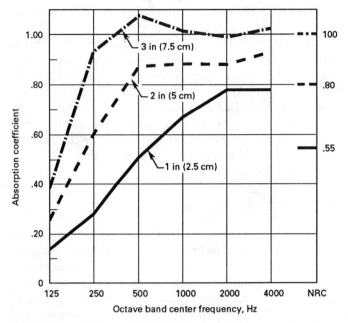

FIG. 3.17 Sound absorption coefficients versus frequency for three different thicknesses of a 0.75-pound-per-cubic-foot (1.2-kg/m²) density fiberglass blanket in a Type A mounting. (*Courtesy of Owens-Corning Corp.*)

tion coefficients versus thickness for three different thicknesses of fiberglass blankets. Blankets of greater thickness and blankets containing an internal septum (for increased low-frequency absorption) are available for special applications.

ASSEMBLIES OF PERFORATED FACINGS AND ACOUSTICAL BLANKETS (SEE APPENDIX 3.5)

The values of the absorption coefficients provided by acoustical boards or acoustical blankets covered with a perforated facing depends on the:

- Size of the perforations
- Percentage of open area of the perforation compared with the total area
- Density of the sound-absorptive material
- Thickness of the sound-absorptive material
- Depth of airspace behind the sound-absorptive material

Perforated Facings

The chief function of a perforated panel, used in combination with an acoustical blanket or acoustical board, is to provide a rigid, durable surface of good appearance that is relatively acoustically transparent over much of the range of frequencies. The panel also protects the acoustical material from mechanical damage. Such facings include:

- Perforated sheet metal
- Perforated hardboard
- Wire-mesh screen
- Strips of wood

Figure 3.18 shows the sound absorption coefficients versus frequency for an acoustical board:

a. *Without a Facing:*   This curve is fairly typical for a fiberglass board.

b. *With a Perforated Facing:*   Values are presented for two percentages of open area. At high frequencies, the effect of the perforated panel is to decrease the absorption; the amount of this decrease depends on the percentage of open area—the less the open area, the greater the decrease in sound absorption. At low frequencies, the absorption usually increases in proportion to the thickness of

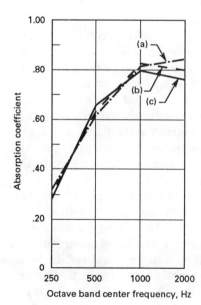

FIG. 3.18 Sound absorption coefficients versus frequency for a fiberglass board with and without a perforated facing. (*a*) No facing; (*b*) 5 percent open-area facing; (*c*) 13 percent open-area facing. (*Courtesy of Owens-Corning Corp.*)

the material and increases with the depth of the airspace between the material and the surface from which it is spaced. At the high frequencies, the sound absorption usually depends on the percentage of open area (if covered by a perforated facing). In the middle-frequency range, where there is usually a maximum, the absorption depends on the resistance to airflow through the material. If the highest frequency for which effective sound absorption is required is 4000 Hz, a perforated surface should have an open area of not less than 15 percent. The perforations should be small and numerous rather than large and few in number.

Membrane-Covered Acoustical Materials.   Acoustical tiles and acoustical boards may be covered by an air-impervious, relatively "sound-transparent" membrane to improve their cleanability. Such a membrane is so light [usually no more than 0.33 ounces per square foot (90 g/cm^2)] that it is practically transparent except at high frequencies. Thus the sound waves that impinge on it are transmitted to the acoustical material it covers, where a fraction of the sound waves are absorbed. At high frequencies, the inertia of the membrane reduces its ability to transmit the sound waves to the material, so there is a decrease in sound absorption. Figure 3.19 shows the effect of an impervious-membrane facing on the sound absorption properties of a fiberglass board.

Perforated Metal Pans with Fiberglass or Mineral-Fiber Pads

Figure 3.20 illustrates an assembly consisting of a metal pan of perforated steel or aluminum, which is backed with a fiberglass or mineral-fiber pad. A *metal pan* (also called a *perforated metal pan*) is the exposed finish portion of an acoustical ceiling assembly, which contains and protects a separate pad or layer of sound-absorptive material. Such metal pans have a baked-enamel finish, particularly suitable for ceiling installations where frequent washing is necessary; they are available in a variety of perforated patterns. In North America, a typical size of tiles is 12 × 24 inches, with a crease in the metal surface designed to provide the appearance of two 12- × 12-inch tiles. The metal pans usually have upturned flanges which snap into special T bars, thereby securing the metal pans in a fixed position but permitting the individual panels to be removed when necessary. The sound-absorptive pads, fabricated of fiberglass or mineral fiber, are usually 1$\frac{1}{2}$ inch (3.8 cm) thick and are wrapped in lightweight flame-proof paper or a thin plastic membrane to prevent small particles from dusting off the material and falling through the

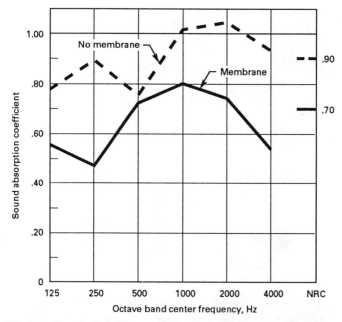

FIG. 3.19 Sound absorption coefficients of a fiberglass ceiling board with and without an air impervious membrane facing.

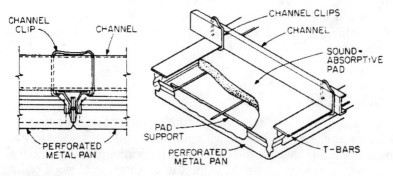

FIG. 3.20 An assembly consisting of metal pans (fabricated of perforated steel or aluminum) with mineral-fiber sound-absorptive pads.

perforations. The pads, placed in the metal pans during installation, are held away from direct contact with the metal pans by spacers. This facilitates repainting and washing operations and increases the sound absorption.

In addition to relatively small sizes of perforated metal pan, large sheets of perforated, corrugated, or ribbed metal are used in ceiling assemblies, such as those shown in Fig. 3.21. Such perforated sheets

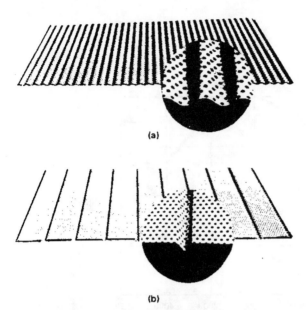

FIG. 3.21 Illustrations of (a) corrugated and (b) ribbed perforated metal used in ceiling assemblies with an acoustical blanket. (*Courtesy of Alpro Structural Systems Corp., Acoustic Division.*)

(usually aluminum) are self-supporting in one direction and supported by exposed metal members in the other direction; a light-weight fiberglass blanket is laid on top of the corrugated metal to provide sound absorption.

Perforated Hardboard with an Acoustical Blanket

Hardboard is a building material manufactured of a fiber (such as wood fiber) and, with a binder, compressed into sheets. Perforated hardboard is often used in combination with a fiberglass or mineral-wool blanket or acoustical board behind it. In the case of wood ceiling joists, the perforated facing, fastened to the joists, supports the blanket.

Protective Facing Consisting of Wood Strips

Wood battens or strips may be used to protect fiberglass or mineral-wool blankets and boards. They provide a durable and attractive facing. Figure 3.22 shows such a construction detail. The vertical battens may be curved to provide a contoured surface. The metal wire

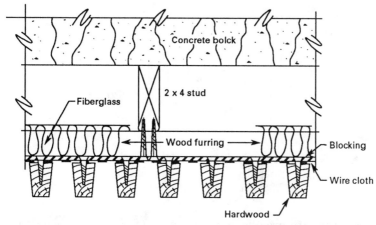

FIG. 3.22 Plan view of a highly absorptive wall treatment employing a fiberglass blanket. Decorative hardwood battens and wire cloth are used to protect the fiberglass blanket. Here, 2- × 4-inch (5- × 10-cm) wood studs hold the 2-inch (5-cm) layer of fiberglass away from the wall, thereby providing significantly increased sound absorption at low frequencies.

cloth at the interface between the wood battens and the fiberglass protect this sound-absorptive blanket from damage. Spacing the blanket from the wall provides a significant improvement in sound absorption at low frequencies.

ACOUSTICAL WALL PANELS AND OFFICE DIVIDERS   (SEE APPENDIX 3.5)

Acoustical wall panels and partial-height partitions are used extensively in both commercial and industrial noise control applications because they are an excellent means of placing sound absorption near a noise source (where it is most effective). In many installations it is impractical or uneconomical to install an acoustical ceiling because of obstructions on the ceiling or because the acoustical ceiling is so high that its effectiveness will be reduced. Then, commercially available, acoustical wall panels may be applied to vertical surfaces in the room. Acoustical wall panels are usually fabricated of fiberglass board or a felted mineral-fiber board which is covered with a decorative or abuse-resistant facing. In North America, wall panels are usually 48 × 96 inches (122 × 244 cm) in size and ³/₄ to 2 inches (2 to 5 cm) thick. In Europe, wall panels are usually 120 × 240 cm in size and may be 20 to 50 mm thick. Figure 3.23 shows several methods of attaching sound-absorptive panels to a wall.

Partial-height partitions (also called *office dividers*) are widely used

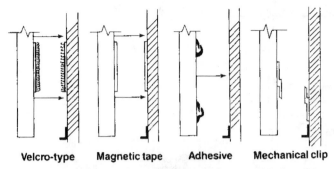

| Velcro-type | Magnetic tape | Adhesive | Mechanical clip |

FIG. 3.23 Several different methods of attaching sound-absorptive panels to a wall. (*Courtesy of ESSI Acoustical Products Co.*)

in open-plan offices to provide some measure of visual and acoustical privacy between work positions. These partitions are usually 60 to 90 inches (150 to 250 cm) high. To be effective, the material of which the partition is fabricated should have a noise reduction coefficient (NRC) of at least 0.80 and sound transmission loss values of 20 to 30 dB in the frequency range from 200 to 4000 Hz. Further information on partial height partitions is given in Chap. 10.

Carpet is widely used as a covering for both acoustical wall panels and office dividers because of its durability and cleanability. As indicated in a subsequent section, carpet can provide significant additional absorption at the middle and high frequencies. If the carpeting has a porous backing and it is spot-cemented or tacked to the acoustical wall panel, it will not change the sound-absorptive properties of the panel significantly. In fact, it may provide additional sound absorption in the middle- and high-frequency ranges. However, if the carpet is adhered to the panel with adhesive that covers the entire surface of the panel, the sound-absorptive properties of the panel may be reduced substantially.

ACOUSTICAL ROOF DECKS (SEE APPENDIX 3.6)

A *roof deck* is a structural material, laid on roof supports, which is used as a base for the roof-covering system; it may be fabricated of metal, concrete, wood, gypsum, or some combination of these and similar materials. An *acoustical roof deck* uses acoustical materials as an integral part of the roof deck, forming the lower surface of the roof structure. This type of construction is used primarily in one-story buildings, such as industrial plants, where the underside of the roof deck forms the exposed ceiling surface of the space below. The following acoustical roof decks are in common usage.

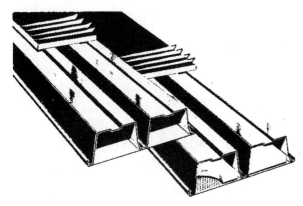

FIG. 3.24 A typical sound-absorptive steel roof-deck assembly.

Perforated Roof Deck Panels

This type of acoustical roof deck consists of a hollow steel-deck panel, the lower surface of which is perforated; a mineral-fiber sound-absorptive material is laid over the perforated surface. One type of structure is illustrated in Fig. 3.24. Roof insulation and build-up roofing are installed over the steel deck in the usual manner. The noise reduction coefficients for such constructions usually range from 0.65 to 0.85, depending on the type of sound-absorptive material and on the depth of the airspace behind the sound-absorptive material.

Acoustical Form Boards for Poured Roof Decks

A *form board* is a board or sheet of wood used in construction to contain wet concrete while it is cast and while it is setting. An *acoustical form board* is a form board, having sound-absorptive properties, which is fabricated from an acoustical board in special sizes and thicknesses. It is usually supported by steel subpurlins. A layer of gypsum or concrete is then poured on top of the acoustical form board to a thickness of 2 to 3 inches (5 to 7.5 cm). The noise reduction coefficients of assemblies of this type usually are in the range from 0.55 to 0.70.

Structural Roof Insulation as Roof Decking

Structural roof insulation is a type of roof deck consisting of large sheets of porous thermal insulation having sound-absorptive properties. Such sheets must be sufficiently thick and rigid to support a layer of gypsum or light-weight concrete that is poured on top of it. Some materials of this type are fabricated of wood excelsior with a cement binder, compressed into a rigid slab; to provide effective sound absorption, the bottom surface must be left exposed. Typically, the noise reduction coefficient for a thickness of 3 inches (7.5 cm) usually is between 0.70 and 0.85.

SPRAYED-ON ACOUSTICAL MATERIALS (SEE APPENDIX 3.7)

Sprayed-on acoustical materials are low-density sound-absorptive materials consisting of a fibrous material with a binder. The fibrous material may be either organic or inorganic. Most commercial products use fiberglass or cellulose fibers. Sprayed-on materials provide a continuous surface so they may be applied to curved surfaces to provide visual continuity. Sprayed-on materials are also used to provide thermal insulation. They may be sprayed on a solid material (such as a metal deck or concrete block wall) or on metal lath spaced away from a solid surface.

The proper ratio of fibrous material to binder is critical. A material with not enough binder may not have the required mechanical strength and fall off. In contrast, a material with too much binder will not provide sufficient sound absorption.

If damaged, a sprayed-on acoustical material may be difficult to repair. Figure 3.25 shows a sprayed-on material being applied. Typically, the NRC of a material that is sprayed on to a thickness of 1 inch (2.5 cm) on a solid surface has an NRC value of 0.75.

FIG. 3.25 Application of an acoustical sprayed-on material with a spray gun. (*Courtesy of Isotalek International.*)

SLOTTED MASONRY BLOCKS; HELMHOLTZ RESONATORS   (SEE APPENDIX 3.8)

A *Helmholtz resonator* (sometimes called a *cavity resonator*) is an enclosed volume of air that is connected to a short, open neck. When sound waves strike the neck of the resonator, they set the air within it in motion; in the low-frequency range, the air in the neck behaves somewhat like a solid plug which moves back and forth, compressing the air in the enclosed volume of the resonator. As the plug moves back and forth, acoustic energy is converted to heat as a result of friction of the movement of air along the walls of the neck. Additional sound absorption will result if a light, porous material (such as fiberglass) is placed within the enclosed volume of the resonator. Maximum sound absorption occurs at the resonance frequency of the resonator which is determined by the combination of: (a) the mass of air in the neck and (b) the "spring" furnished by the air which is compressed in the enclosed volume.

The resonance frequency f of a Helmholtz resonator f is given by

$$f = \frac{2160S}{(\nu V)^{1/2}}$$

where V is the enclosed volume of the resonator, S is the cross-sectional area of the neck, and ν is the volume of the neck, and where all dimensions are expressed in inches.

The corresponding equation in metric units is given by

$$f = \frac{5500S}{(\nu V)^{1/2}}$$

where all dimensions are expressed in centimeters.

Helmholtz resonators can provide very high values of absorption at resonance, although the absorption is primarily within a narrow frequency range, as indicated by the absorption versus frequency curve shown in Fig. 3.26. The placement of a sound-absorptive material within the cavity decreases the absorption at resonance but increases

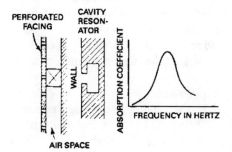

FIG. 3.26 Sound absorption versus frequency for a Helmholtz resonator. A perforated board placed away from a solid wall is also a Helmholtz resonator.

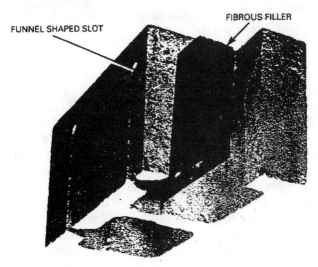

FIG. 3.27 Photograph of a "slotted" masonry unit that is a Helmholtz resonator. (*Courtesy of Proudfoot Company.*)

the absorption on both sides of the resonance frequency. Helmholtz resonators are available commercially which are specially fabricated, hollow concrete blocks; a slot or hole in the face of the block provides the "neck" of the resonator. Figure 3.27 is a photograph of a concrete block that is designed to act as a Helmholtz resonator.

SUSPENDED ACOUSTICAL ABSORBERS; UNIT ABSORBERS; HANGING PANELS; HANGING CURTAINS   (SEE APPENDIX 3.9)

Suspended acoustical absorbers (also called *unit absorbers*) are individual units which are hung from the ceiling of a room or hung from wires or cables fastened to walls of the room. They may be flat sheets or boards of sound-absorptive material, or they may be hollow boxlike or tubular units (or the like). In general, they provide a high value of sound absorption. Suspended acoustical absorbers are sometimes used in areas where ceiling treatment of the conventional type is impractical or where considerable sound absorption is required as a temporary measure. In contrast to the installation of a conventional ceiling treatment, such sound absorbers can be installed by individuals having little or no construction experience.

Figure 3.28 shows an installation of one type of suspended acoustical absorber, composed of a sheet of fiberglass blanket covered with a thin, impervious, washable plastic membrane. The plastic is so light

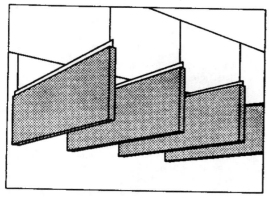

FIG. 3.28   A typical layout of suspended acoustical absorbers. These units are suspended from wires spaced 4 feet (1.2 m) apart.

that it is essentially acoustically transparent at most frequencies. Such absorbers usually are suspended in continuous rows spaced 4 to 8 feet (1.2 to 2.4 m) apart.

The sound-absorptive properties of suspended absorber are expressed in terms of sabins. A *sabin* is a unit of sound absorption equivalent to 1 square foot of a perfectly absorptive surface. A *metric sabin* is equivalent to 1 m^2 of a perfectly absorptive surface (the equivalent of 10.8 sabins in U.S. Customary units).

The absorption furnished by an acoustical material, in sabins, is equal to the area of the surface of the material multiplied by its sound absorption coefficient, as indicated by Eq. (4.2). In contrast, the sound absorption of a suspended absorber is expressed in terms of the number of sabins (or metric sabins) of absorption furnished *per suspended unit*. The sound absorption furnished by each suspended absorber depends on how closely it is spaced to adjacent units, as illustrated in Fig. 3.29. These data are for suspended absorbers hung in continuous rows in one direction.

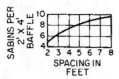

FIG. 3.29   Sound absorption per unit versus spacing between continuous rows of 2- × 4-feet (61- × 122-cm) suspended absorbers. (*Courtesy of Owens-Corning Corp.*)

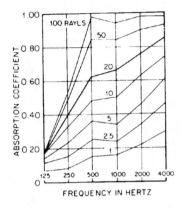

FIG. 3.30 Sound absorption coefficients for drapes having various densities of weave (i.e., different values of resistance to airflow, expressed in *rayls*). These data are for drapes hung with 100 percent fullness and spaced 3 inches (7.5 cm) from a wall. Shear drapes have a low resistance to airflow (i.e., small rayl value) and heavy drapes have a high value. (*After data of Owens-Corning Corp.*)

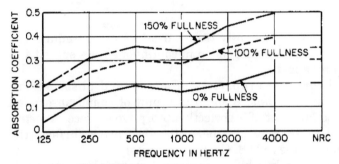

FIG. 3.31 Sound absorption coefficients for drapes of the same material but hung with different percentages of fullness. (*After data of Owens-Corning Corp.*)

Drapes

The sound absorption coefficients of drapes depend on the resistance to the flow of air through the drapery material (a function of the density or closeness of weave), the distance of the drapes from the wall or window, and the percent fullness of the drape. (*Percent fullness* is the percent by which the width of the material exceeds the span of the hung drape; the greater the fullness, the greater the number and depth of folds. For example, 100 percent fullness indicates that the width of the material is twice the span of the drape.)

Figure 3.30 shows the sound absorption coefficients for drapes made of cloth woven of glass fibers (for 100 percent fullness) having different densities of weave. Figure 3.31 shows that the absorption by drapes increases with increasing fullness. The effect of spacing

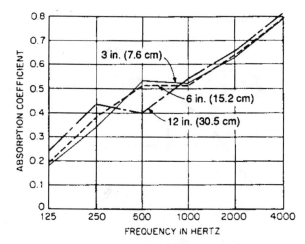

FIG. 3.32 Sound absorption of a porous drapery material (100 percent fullness) hung at different distances from a wall.

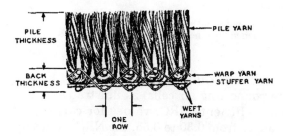

FIG. 3.33 Construction of a typical carpet.

drapes away from a wall is illustrated in Fig. 3.32, which shows the absorption coefficients of a curtain at different distances from a wall. Note that at low frequencies there is a significant increase in sound absorption when the drape is spaced away from the wall.

Carpet

The construction of a typical carpet is shown in Fig. 3.33. The sound absorption coefficients of carpet[8] depend on the pile height, pile (face) weight per unit area, type of pile (i.e., whether the pile is looped or cut), and type of backing material. In general, a carpet having cut pile provides greater absorption than a loop pile of otherwise identical construction. The type of pile fiber (i.e., whether it is nylon or wool, for example) has no significant effect on sound absorption. The sound absorption provided by a carpet can be increased significantly by lay-

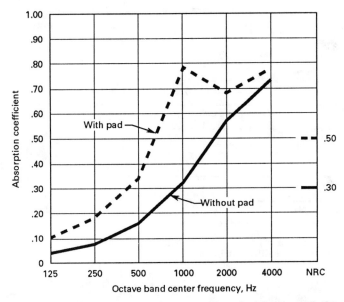

FIG. 3.34 Sound absorption of a carpet with and without a pad; this carpet had a tufted loop pile, and weighed 20 ounces per square yard (0.7 kg/m²).

ing it over a pad, called *underlayment* (usually fabricated of hair or foamed plastic having interconnecting air cells) as illustrated in Fig. 3.34. The noise reduction coefficient (NRC) values for carpet laid directly on bare concrete ranges from 0.30 to 0.55; the NRC values for carpet laid on underlayment weighing 40 ounces per square yard (1.4 kg/m²) usually range from about 0.40 to 0.70. To be an effective sound absorber, the pad underlayment must be porous, i.e., it must be of open-cell construction so that one is able to blow through it. For example, a carpet and pad which consist of a tufted carpet with a pile weight of a 43 ounces per square yard (1.5 kg/m²) and a pile height of ¹/₂ inch (13 mm), laid on a pad has an NRC of 0.70. Most carpeting and pads used in commercial offices have an NRC in the range from 0.30 to 0.45.

REFERENCES

1. *Sound Absorption and Sound Absorption Coefficients by the Reverberation Room Method,* ASTM C423, American Society for Testing and Materials, Philadelphia, PA 19103 (revised periodically).
2. *Measurement of Sound Absorption in a Reverberation Room,* ISO 354, International Organization for Standardization, CH-1211 Geneva 20, Switzerland (revised periodically).
3. *Mounting Test Specimens During Sound Absorptive Tests,* ASTM E795 (revised periodically).

4. *Surface Burning Characteristics of Building Materials,* ASTM E84 (revised periodically). Also see *Fire Resistance Directory,* Underwriters' Laboratories, Inc. (revised periodically).
5. *Standard Classification for Acoustical Materials,* ASTM E1264 (revised periodically).
6. *Fire Tests of Building Construction and Materials,* ASTM E119 (revised periodically).
7. *Method of Test for Airborne Attenuation Between Rooms Sharing a Common Ceiling and Plenum,* ASTM E1414 (revised periodically).
8. *Laboratory Measurement of Room-to-Room Airborne Sound Insulation of a Suspended Ceiling With a Plenum Above It,* ISO 140/9 (revised periodically).
9. *Carpet Specifier's Handbook,* Chap. 9, American Carpet and Rug Institute, Dalton, GA 30722.

Appendix

3

Tables of Sound Absorption Coefficients

Cyril M. Harris

Ron Moulder

LIST OF TABLES IN THIS CHAPTER APPENDIX

HOW TO USE THE TABLES IN THIS APPENDIX

NRC (Noise Reduction Coefficient). The average value of a material's absorption coefficient at the frequencies of 250, 500, 1000, and 2000 Hz is called its *noise reduction coefficient* (NRC). This average is rounded off to the nearest multiple of 0.05.

Mounting Types. **The sound absorption furnished by an acoustical material depends significantly on the way in which it is mounted. Therefore, a comparison of the sound absorption coefficients of materials is meaningful only if the data are compared for identical mounting conditions.** The various types of mounting, designated by a letter (see Fig. 3.1), are:

Type A Mounting: The acoustical material is laid directly against a rigid solid surface with no airspace between the acoustical material and the solid surface.

Type B Mounting: The acoustical material is spot-cemented to gypsum board with a ¹/₈-inch (20-mm) airspace behind the material.

Type C Mounting: The acoustical material is covered with a perforated facing; an airspace separates the material from a rigid surface such as a ceiling. A number following the letter C represents the depth of the airspace (in millimeters) between the perforated facing and the rigid surface.

Type D Mounting: The acoustical material is nailed to wood furring strips. A number following the letter D represents the thickness (in millimeters) of the furring strips.

Type E Mounting: The acoustical material is supported from a hard surface (such as a ceiling) by a metal suspension system, with an airspace above the acoustical material. A number following the letter E represents the number of millimeters from the face of the acoustical material to the hard surface above.

Type F Mounting: The acoustical material is supported by a reinforced sheet metal with an airspace behind the sheet metal. A number following the letter F represents the number of millimeters between the sheet metal and hard surface supporting the sheet metal.

Company Codes. In this appendix, data are grouped according to company or manufacturer, using the following abbreviations or acronyms:

Alpro	Alpro Structural Systems Corp.; New Orleans, LA 70150
ASCPac	ASC Pacific, Inc.; West Sacramento, CA 95691-3493
AWI	Armstrong World Industries, Inc.; Lancaster, PA 17604
BHS	B. Hitz Söhne AG; 8610 Uster, Switzerland
BradIns	Bradford Insulation; North Sydney, NSW 2059, Australia

CA	Commercial Acoustics; Phoenix, AR 85034
Conweb	Conweb Bonded Fiber; Riverdale, NJ 08075
CTeed	CertainTeed Corp.; Valley Forge, PA 19482
Drupa	Drupa, S.A.; 28220 Majadahonda, Madrid
E-A-R	E-A-R Specialty Composites; Indianapolis, IN 46268
EAS	Empire Acoustical Systems; Mansfield, OH 44906
Epic	Epic Metals Corp.; Rankin, PA 15104
Flumroc	Flumroc A.G.; CH-8890, Flums, Switzerland
Forbol	Forbo Industries, Inc.; Hazelton, PA 18201
FSKG	Ferdinand Schad KG; 7790 Messkirch, Germany
G+H	G+H Isover; 6802 Ladensburg/Neckar, Germany
IAC	Industrial Acoustics Company; Bronx, NY 10462
ICC	International Cellulose Corp.; Houston, TX 77045
ImiTech	Imi-Tech Corp.; Elk Grove Village, IL 60007
INC	Industrial Noise Control; Addison, IL 60101
Isover	Isover AG; 8155 Niedershasli, Switzerland
Knauf	Knauf Fiber Glass; Shelbyville, IN 46176
MartinF	Martin Fireproofing Georgia, Inc.; Elberton, GA 30635
MvL	Manville; Post Office Box 5108, Denver, CO 80217-5108
OC	Owens-Corning Corp.; Toledo, OH 43659
PAVAROC	PAVAfibre SA; Fribourg, Switzerland
Peer	Peer, Inc.; Wheeling, IL 60090
Perdue	Perdue Acoustics; Amarillo, TX 79121
PI	Pyrok, Inc.; Brooklyn, NY 11215
PolyTech	Polymer Technologies, Inc.; Newark, DE 19702
PR	Preform Raumgliederungssysteme GmbH; 8805 Feuchtwangen, Germany
Prdfoot	Proudfoot Co.; Botsford, CT 06404-0338
PuV	Prod. u. Vertriebs, GmbH; 4300 Essen, Germany
Rockfon	Rockfon A/S; DK-2640, Hedehusene, Denmark
RPG	RPG Diffusor Systems, Inc.; Upper Marlboro, MD 20772
SeigK	Siegfried Keller; CH-8036, Brüttisellen, Switzerland
Sonex	Sonex Division, Illbruck, Inc.; Minneapolis, MN 55412
Soning	Soning; Prague 6, Czech Republic
Stark	Stark Ceramics, Inc.; East Canton, OH 44730
TCeram	Thermal Ceramics; Augusta, GA 30903
Tectum	Tectum, Inc.; Newark, OH 43055
USG	USG Interiors, Inc.; Chicago, IL 60606

Test Lab.   The following abbreviations represent the laboratories where the acoustical materials were tested:

AS	Acoustic Systems
AWI	Armstrong World Industries
BI	Bauphysicalisches Institut; Switzerland
CAE	Center for Applied Engineering
CK	Cedar Knolls
EMPA	E.M.P.A.; Dübendorf, Switzerland
G&H	Geiger & Hamme
G+H	G+H Montage GmbH; Labor Akustik
HL	Hufcor Co. Laboratories
IA	Instituto de Acustica, CSIC; Madrid 6, Spain
IfL	Institute für Lärmschutz; Switzerland
Int	Intest
LC	Louis A. Challis & Associates; Australia
LI	Lydteknisk Institut; DK-2800, Denmark
MTC	Mountain Technical Center; Manville R&D Center
NGC	National Gypsum Co. Laboratory
OC	Owens-Corning Corp. Lab.
RAL	Riverbank Acoustical Lab.
TCT	Twin City Testing Laboratory
VPC	Vipac Laboratories Pty, Ltd; Australia
Vzrt	Vuzort; Czech Republic
WEAL	Western Electro-Acoustical Lab.

APPENDIX 3.1 Ceiling Tiles; Lay-in Panels

NRC	Company Trade name	Description	Thickness, inches (mm)	Mounting type	Unit size, inches	Sound absorption coefficients, Hz 125	250	500	1000	2000	4000	Weight, lb/ft² (kg/m²)	Test lab
0.80	USG Orion	Ceiling panel with laminated textured surface	1/2	E-400	24 × 48	0.69	0.76	0.65	0.86	0.83	0.75	0.7	RAL
0.95	USG Orion	Ceiling panel with laminated textured surface	1	E-400	24 × 48	0.74	0.82	0.82	1.05	1.06	1.09	1.3	RAL
0.85	USG Orion	Same as above but with impervious backing	1	E-400	24 × 24	0.42	0.43	0.82	1.13	1.09	1.02	1.3	RAL
0.75	USG Glacier	Rough textured tile and panels	3/4	E-400	12 × 12	0.56	0.76	0.57	0.80	0.94	1.00	1.4	RAL
0.70	USG "F"	Fissured ceiling tile	3/4	E-400	12 × 12	0.49	0.53	0.53	0.75	0.92	0.99	1.3	RAL
0.65	USG Acoustone Chex/16	Foil-backed tiles and panels	3/4	E-400	24 × 24	0.22	0.29	0.66	0.80	0.83	0.89	1.3	RAL
0.75	USG Acoustone Glacier	Foil-backed tiles and panels	3/4	E-400	24 × 24	0.37	0.33	0.61	1.00	0.96	1.03	1.3	RAL
0.75	USG Acoustone "F"	Fissured, foil-backed tiles and panels	3/4	E-400	24 × 24	0.52	0.38	0.67	0.97	0.98	1.02	1.3	RAL
0.75	USG Acoustone "F" Firecode	Fissured tiles and panels, fire-rated	3/4	E-400	24 × 24	0.52	0.50	0.67	0.95	0.94	0.99	1.4	RAL
0.55	USG Auratone	Fissured acoustical panels	5/8	E-400	24 × 48	0.42	0.34	0.44	0.72	0.67	0.64	0.81	RAL
0.65	USG Auratone	Fissured acoustical panels	3/4	E-400	24 × 48	0.34	0.36	0.71	0.85	0.68	0.64	1.3	RAL

APPENDIX 3.1 Ceiling Tiles; Lay-in Panels (Continued)

NRC	Company Trade name	Description	Thick-ness, inches (mm)	Mount-ing type	Unit size, inches	Sound absorption coefficients, Hz						Weight, lb/ft² (kg/m²)	Test lab
						125	250	500	1000	2000	4000		
0.65	USG Auratone	Fissured acoustical panels	3/4	E-400	24 × 48	0.34	0.36	0.71	0.85	0.68	0.64	1.3	RAL
0.60	USG Auratone Firecode	Fissured, fire-rated acoustical tiles and panels	5/8	E-400	24 × 48	0.34	0.30	0.53	0.78	0.73	0.69	1.2	RAL
0.55	USG Auratone	Fissured acoustical tile	5/8	E-400	12 × 12	0.42	0.29	0.52	0.68	0.64	0.69	0.9	RAL
0.65	USG Auratone	Fissured acoustical tile	3/4	E-400	12 × 12	0.50	0.36	0.76	0.73	0.69	0.72	1.2	RAL
0.60	USG Auratone Firecode	Fissured acoustical tile	5/8	E-400	12 × 12	0.59	0.33	0.45	0.70	0.79	0.70	1.2	RAL
0.90	USG Nubby	Fiberglass lay-in panels	1	E-400	24 × 48	0.55	0.89	0.73	1.03	1.11	1.07	0.5	RAL
0.55	AWI Type 769	Fissured mineral fiber, "Cortega" lay-in panel	5/8	E-400	24 × 48	0.31	0.32	0.51	0.72	0.74	0.77	0.60	AWI
0.55	AWI Type 704	Fissured mineral fiber, "Cortega" lay-in panel	5/8	E-400	24 × 48	0.35	0.27	0.47	0.65	0.74	0.82	0.65	AWI
0.55	AWI Type 775	Surfaced-textured, mineral, "Minatex" lay-in panel	5/8	E-400	24 × 48	0.30	0.28	0.43	0.64	0.76	0.68	0.70	AWI
0.55	AWI Type 737	Surface-textured, mineral, "Minatex" lay-in panel	5/8	E-400	24 × 48	0.36	0.28	0.47	0.65	0.76	0.82	0.70	AWI
0.60	AWI Type 821	Mineral fiber, lay-in, with with polymeric membrane	5/8	E-400	24 × 48	0.29	0.54	0.30	0.79	0.78	0.60	1.05	AWI

	AWI Type	Description	Thickness		Size								
0.60	AWI Type 602	Ceramic and mineral fiber, noncombustible, lay-in panel	$5/8$	E-400	24 × 48	0.23	0.24	0.50	0.77	0.91	0.86	1.4	AWI
0.60	AWI Type 823	Fissured mineral fiber, fire-resistive lay-in panel	$5/8$	E-400	24 × 48	0.33	0.36	0.50	0.78	0.84	0.84	1.0	AWI
0.60	AWI Type 537	Fissured mineral fiber, fire-resistive lay-in panel	$5/8$	E-400	24 × 48	0.35	0.34	0.48	0.69	0.88	0.92	1.15	AWI
0.65	AWI Type 863	Vinyl-faced aluminum surface mineral fiber, lay-in panel	$5/8$	E-400	24 × 48	0.35	0.36	0.55	0.90	0.74	0.46	1.00	AWI
0.65	AWI Type 2907	Vinyl-faced fiberglass with vinyl film facing	$5/8$	E-400	24 × 48	0.53	0.37	0.50	0.82	0.82	0.72	0.25	AWI
0.75	AWI Type 2906	Fiberglass panel with perforated vinyl film facing	$5/8$	E-400	24 × 48	0.68	0.68	0.67	0.84	0.86	0.71	0.25	AWI
0.60	AWI Type 584	Mineral fiber lay-in panel with factory-applied paint	$3/4$	E-400	24 × 48	0.29	0.33	0.53	0.73	0.86	0.92	1.25	AWI
0.75	AWI Type 3301	Cloth-faced, fiberglass lay-in panel, painted	$3/4$	E-400	24 × 48	0.48	0.35	0.71	0.96	1.05	1.04	0.40	AWI
0.85	AWI Type 3101	Cloth-faced, fiberglass lay-in panel, painted	$3/4$	E-400	24 × 48	0.71	0.87	0.62	0.86	0.96	1.07	0.35	AWI
0.70	AWI Type 2925	Vinyl-film-faced, fiberglass lay-in panel	1	E-400	24 × 48	0.55	47	0.72	0.80	0.74	0.54	0.20	AWI
0.90	AWI Type 2946	Microperforated vinyl film-faced fiberglass panel	1	E-400	24 × 48	0.77	0.89	0.75	1.01	1.04	0.93	0.20	AWI
0.95	AWI Type 3103	Woven glass fibers adhered to fiberglass board, painted	1	E-400	24 × 48	0.70	0.95	0.75	0.99	1.04	1.01	0.40	AWI
0.80	AWI Type 2921	Vinyl membrane facing over fiberglass lay-in panel	$1\frac{1}{2}$	E-400	24 × 48	0.57	0.79	0.77	0.90	0.71	0.47	0.30	AWI

APPENDIX 3.1   Ceiling Tiles; Lay-in Panels   (Continued)

NRC	Company Trade name	Description	Thickness, inches (mm)	Mounting type	Unit size, inches	Sound absorption coefficients, Hz						Weight, lb/ft² (kg/m²)	Test lab
						125	250	500	1000	2000	4000		
0.95	AWI Type 2942	Fiberglass lay-in panel with microperforated vinyl facing	1½	E-400	24 × 48	0.62	0.83	0.90	1.10	1.06	0.94	0.30	AWI
1.00	AWI Type 3105	Cloth-faced fiberglass lay-in panel, factory painted	1½	E-400	24 × 48	0.74	0.97	0.85	1.03	1.05	1.00	0.70	AWI
0.75	Sonex Vision	Wedge-shaped, melamine foam, ceiling tile	2	A	24 × 24	0.08	0.24	0.73	0.96	0.98	0.99	0.12	TCT
0.75	Sonex Contour	Wedge-shaped, melamine foam, ceiling tile	2	A	24 × 24	0.08	0.26	0.76	0.96	0.97	1.01	0.12	TCT
0.75	Sonex Spectrum	Wedge-shaped, melamine foam, ceiling tile	2	A	24 × 24	0.12	0.33	0.83	0.97	0.98	0.95	0.12	TCT
0.75	Sonex Panorama	Wedge-shaped, melamine foam, ceiling tile	2	A	24 × 24	0.22	0.29	0.79	0.93	0.94	1.00	0.12	TCT
0.75	Sonex Trim	Flat, melamine foam, ceiling tile	1	A	24 × 24	0.08	0.17	0.60	0.88	0.88	0.93	0.06	TCT
0.85	Tectum Classic	Prefinished Nubby lay-in board	¾	E-400	24 × 48	0.33	0.47	0.89	0.97	1.07	0.94	0.19	RAL
0.95	Tectum Classic	Prefinished Nubby lay-in board	1	E-400	24 × 48	0.83	0.88	0.80	1.05	1.06	1.08	0.25	RAL
1.00	Tectum Classic	Prefinished Nubby lay-in board	1½	E-400	24 × 48	0.71	0.87	0.97	1.10	1.07	1.03	0.38	RAL
0.85	Tectum Classic	Painted Linear lay-in board	¾	E-400	24 × 48	0.27	0.80	0.65	0.98	1.00	0.90	0.19	G&H

0.95	Tectum Classic	Painted Linear lay-in board	1	E-400	24 × 48	0.37	0.83	0.82	1.07	1.02	0.94	0.25	G&H
1.00	Tectum Classic	Painted Linear lay-in board	1½	E-400	24 × 48	0.71	0.83	0.82	1.07	1.02	0.94	0.38	G&H
0.85	Tectum Classic	Painted Nubby lay-in board	¾	E-400	24 × 48	0.33	0.47	0.89	0.97	1.07	0.94	0.19	RAL
1.00	Tectum Classic	Film-faced lay-in board	1½	E-400	24 × 48	0.29	0.80	0.74	0.92	0.85	0.52	0.38	RAL
0.80	Tectum Classic	Ultimate Nubby lay-in board	1⅜	E-400	24 × 48	0.21	0.47	0.68	1.03	1.09	1.06	0.34	RAL
0.65	PAVAROC Fissura	Acoustical panels, lay-in	(16)	E-300	62.5cm × 62.5cm	0.38	0.44	0.50	0.77	0.98	1.08	(5.5)	EMPA
0.65	PAVAROC Orion	Acoustical panels, lay-in	(16)	E-300	62.5cm × 62.5cm	0.33	0.53	0.52	0.68	0.82	0.80	(5.5)	EMPA
0.55	PAVAROC Stria 2	Acoustical panels, lay-in	(16)	E-300	62.5cm × 62.5cm	0.52	0.43	0.49	0.65	0.71	0.61	(5.5)	EMPA
0.45	Rockfon Dekor	Textured, white-painted acoustic tiles	(12)	E-200	60cm × 120cm	0.52	0.45	0.40	0.41	0.49	0.57	(4.0)	LI
0.65	Rockfon Cadral	Smooth, white-painted acoustic tiles	(12)	E-200	60cm × 120cm	0.48	0.60	0.65	0.57	0.73	0.82	(2.7)	LI
0.70	Rockfon Sonar	White-painted acoustic tiles	(18)	E-200	60cm × 120cm	0.53	0.61	0.65	0.65	0.85	0.95	(4.4)	LI
0.85	Rockfon Classic	White-painted acoustic panels	(18)	E-200	60cm × 120cm	0.43	0.65	1.03	0.72	0.90	0.94	(1.5)	LI
0.80	Rockfon Polar	White-painted acoustic panels	(20)	E-200	60cm × 120cm	0.47	0.72	0.92	0.70	0.89	0.93	(1.7)	LI
0.85	Rockfon Fibral	White-painted acoustic panels	(25)	E-200	60cm × 120cm	0.40	0.76	1.01	0.76	0.96	0.97	(1.9)	LI

APPENDIX 3.1 Ceiling Tiles; Lay-in Panels (Continued)

NRC	Company Trade name	Description	Thickness, inches (mm)	Mounting type	Unit size, inches	Sound absorption coefficients, Hz						Weight, lb/ft² (kg/m²)	Test lab
						125	250	500	1000	2000	4000		
0.85	Rockfon Koral	White-painted acoustic panels	(25)	E-200	60cm × 120cm	0.53	0.81	0.88	0.82	0.93	0.87	(2.2)	LI
0.85	Rockfon Paral	White-painted acoustic panels	(20)	E-200	60cm × 120cm	0.35	0.76	0.99	0.70	0.88	0.93	(1.4)	LI
0.90	Rockfon Hygienic	White-painted industrial panels	(40)	E-200	60cm × 120cm	0.38	0.87	1.01	0.82	0.88	0.88	(2.3)	LI
0.90	Rockfon Foil	Black plastic, industrial panels	(50)	E-200	60cm × 120cm	0.46	0.88	1.03	0.84	0.85	0.75	(2.0)	LI
0.85	SiegK Pyramid-Platte	Acoustical panels	(50)	A	98cm × 98cm	0.15	0.40	0.90	1.00	1.10	1.10	(1.4)	EMPA

APPENDIX 3.2 Fiberglass Duct Liners

NRC	Company Trade name	Description	Thickness, inches (mm)	Mounting type	Unit size, inches	Sound absorption coefficients, Hz						Weight, lb/ft² (kg/m²)	Test lab
						125	250	500	1000	2000	4000		
0.60	CTeed Ultralite	Fiberglass duct liner with surface coating	1	F-25	roll	0.34	0.42	0.47	0.84	0.80	0.79	0.12	RAL
0.75	CTeed Ultralite	Fiberglass duct liner with surface coating	1½	F-25	roll	0.29	0.55	0.72	0.85	0.89	0.89	0.18	RAL
0.85	CTeed Ultralite	Fiberglass duct liner with surface coating	2	F-25	roll	0.32	0.71	0.83	0.91	0.95	1.01	0.24	RAL
0.65	CTeed Ultralite	Fiberglass duct liner with surface coating	1	F-25	roll	0.23	0.47	0.57	0.74	0.85	0.87	0.17	RAL
0.80	CTeed Ultralite	Fiberglass duct liner with surface coating	1½	F-25	roll	0.33	0.57	0.79	0.91	0.92	0.89	0.25	RAL
0.90	CTeed Ultralite	Fiberglass duct liner with surface coating	2	F-25	roll	0.39	0.69	0.92	0.98	0.93	1.00	0.34	RAL
0.70	CTeed Ultralite	Fiberglass duct liner with surface coating	1	F-25	roll	0.23	0.47	0.61	0.79	0.88	0.91	0.25	RAL
0.85	CTeed Ultralite	Fiberglass duct liner with surface coating	1½	F-25	roll	0.37	0.63	0.80	0.90	0.89	0.90	0.37	RAL
0.95	CTeed Ultralite	Fiberglass duct liner with surface coating	2	F-25	roll	0.36	0.79	0.96	0.99	0.93	0.97	0.50	RAL
0.60	CTeed Ultralite	Fiberglass duct liner with surface coating	1	A	roll	0.10	0.28	0.50	0.70	0.82	0.83	0.12	RAL
0.70	CTeed Ultralite	Fiberglass duct liner with surface coating	1½	A	roll	0.20	0.40	0.71	0.86	0.91	0.85	0.18	RAL

APPENDIX 3.2   Fiberglass Duct Liners   (Continued)

NRC	Company Trade name	Description	Thickness, inches (mm)	Mounting type	Unit size, inches	Sound absorption coefficients, Hz						Weight, lb/ft² (kg/m²)	Test lab
						125	250	500	1000	2000	4000		
0.80	CTeed Ultralite	Fiberglass duct liner with surface coating	2	A	roll	0.22	0.49	0.83	0.89	0.89	0.91	0.24	RAL
0.60	CTeed Ultralite	Fiberglass duct liner with surface coating	1	A	roll	0.10	0.29	0.59	0.72	0.83	0.84	0.17	RAL
0.75	CTeed Ultralite	Fiberglass duct liner with surface coating	1½	A	roll	0.20	0.42	0.80	0.93	0.93	0.88	0.25	RAL
0.85	CTeed Ultralite	Fiberglass duct liner with surface coating	2	A	roll	0.24	0.57	0.90	0.95	0.95	0.96	0.34	RAL
0.60	CTeed Ultralite	Fiberglass duct liner with surface coating	1	A	roll	0.05	0.25	0.57	0.78	0.87	0.89	0.25	RAL
0.80	CTeed Ultralite	Fiberglass duct liner with surface coating	1½	A	roll	0.20	0.46	0.82	0.94	0.95	0.91	0.37	RAL
0.95	CTeed Ultralite	Fiberglass duct liner with surface coating	2	A	roll	0.27	0.72	1.04	1.02	0.96	0.92	0.50	RAL
0.65	Knauf Type M	Duct liner, matte facing	1	A	roll	0.17	0.35	0.59	0.81	0.90	0.94	0.12	RAL
0.80	Knauf Type M	Duct liner, matte facing	1½	A	roll	0.35	0.51	0.83	0.93	0.97	0.96	0.18	RAL
0.90	Knauf Type M	Duct liner, matte facing	2	A	roll	0.34	0.64	0.96	1.03	1.00	1.03	0.24	RAL
0.45	Knauf Type M	Duct liner, matte facing	½	A	roll	0.09	0.14	0.40	0.60	0.73	0.82	0.08	RAL

0.70	Knauf Type M	Duct liner, matte facing	1	A	roll	0.25	0.35	0.69	0.89	0.96	1.01	0.17	RAL
0.85	Knauf Type M	Duct liner, matte facing	1½	A	roll	0.27	0.55	0.87	0.99	1.00	0.98	0.25	RAL
0.65	Knauf	Rigid plenum liner	1	A	24 or 48 × 36 to 120	0.13	0.24	0.56	0.83	0.92	0.98	0.25	RAL
0.85	Knauf	Rigid plenum liner	1½	A	24 or 48 × 36 to 120	0.19	0.41	0.89	1.02	1.03	1.04	0.37	RAL
0.95	Knauf	Rigid plenum liner	2	A	24 or 48 × 36 to 120	0.33	0.67	1.07	1.07	1.03	1.06	0.50	RAL
0.75	Knauf Type EL475	Air duct board, one side faced with foil-scrim-Kraft vapor retarder	1	A	48 × 96 48 × 120	0.27	0.46	0.64	0.90	0.98	0.96	0.35	RAL
0.80	MvL SuperDuct	Type 475 FSK, coated duct board	1	A	to 48 × 120	0.11	0.29	0.81	1.05	1.09	1.01	0.37	MTC
0.75	MvL SuperDuct	Type 800 FSK, coated duct board	1	A	to 48 × 120	0.09	0.22	0.78	1.00	1.08	1.02	0.42	MTC
0.95	MvL SuperDuct	Type 800 FSK, coated duct board	1½	A	to 48 × 120	0.17	0.61	1.03	1.12	1.02	0.89	0.47	MTC
0.80	MvL SuperDuct	Type 475 FSK, coated duct board	1	F-25	to 48 × 120	0.52	0.40	0.74	1.03	1.06	1.02	0.37	MTC
0.80	MvL SuperDuct	Type 800 FSK, coated duct board	1	F-25	to 48 × 120	0.52	0.37	0.70	1.01	1.07	1.01	0.42	MTC
0.95	MvL SuperDuct	Type 800 FSK, coated duct board	1½	F-25	to 48 × 120	0.54	0.58	1.02	1.14	1.01	0.92	0.47	MTC
0.65	MvL Micro-Aire	Type 475 FSK, coated duct board	1	A	to 48 × 120	0.06	0.22	0.61	0.86	1.00	1.04	0.35	MTC
0.75	MvL Micro-Aire	Type 800 FSK, coated duct board	1	A	to 48 × 120	0.01	0.23	0.67	0.98	1.05	1.06	0.42	MTC

APPENDIX 3.2 Fiberglass Duct Liners (Continued)

NRC	Company Trade name	Description	Thickness, inches (mm)	Mounting type	Unit size, inches	Sound absorption coefficients, Hz						Weight, lb/ft² (kg/m²)	Test lab
						125	250	500	1000	2000	4000		
0.90	MvL Micro-Aire	Type 800 FSK, coated duct board	1½	A	to 48 × 120	0.11	0.45	0.99	1.11	1.09	1.07	0.47	MTC
0.70	MvL Micro-Aire	Type 475 FSK coated duct board	1	F-25	to 48 × 120	0.46	0.30	0.58	0.85	1.00	1.03	0.35	MTC
0.80	MvL Micro-Aire	Type 800 FSK, coated duct board	1	F-25	to 48 × 120	0.29	0.42	0.70	1.00	1.06	1.08	0.42	MTC
0.95	MvL Micro-Aire	Type 800 FSK, coated duct board	1½	F-25	to 48 × 120	0.46	0.58	0.95	1.10	1.08	1.09	0.47	MTC
0.65	MvL Linacoustic	Mat-faced, smooth, duct liner	1	A	rolls	0.08	0.26	0.58	0.84	0.96	0.99	0.22	MTC
0.85	MvL Linacoustic	Mat-faced, smooth, duct liner	1½	A	rolls	0.17	0.53	0.87	0.99	1.00	0.95	0.19	MTC
0.95	MvL Linacoustic	Mat-faced, smooth, duct liner	2	A	rolls	0.22	0.69	1.02	1.08	1.05	1.08	0.22	MTC
0.70	MvL c Linacoustic	Mat-faced, smooth, HP duct liner	1	A	rolls	0.05	0.29	0.61	0.87	0.98	0.98	0.18	MTC
0.70	MvL Linacoustic	Mat-faced, smooth, R duct liner	1	A	rolls	0.09	0.32	0.68	0.88	0.97	1.03	0.23	MTC
0.90	MvL Linacoustic	Mat-faced, smooth, R duct liner	1½	A	rolls	0.07	0.52	0.94	1.02	1.02	1.04	0.31	MTC
0.70	MvL Linacoustic	Permacote, coated, smooth duct liner	1	A	rolls	0.99	0.09	0.67	0.89	1.03	0.99	0.13	MTC
0.90	MvL Linacoustic	Permacote, coated, smooth duct liner	1½	A	rolls	0.16	0.51	0.90	1.05	1.06	1.01	0.19	MTC

NRC	Manufacturer	Product	Thickness	Mounting	Form	125	250	500	1000	2000	4000		Test
1.00	MvL Linacoustic	Permacote, coated, smooth duct liner	2	A	rolls	0.23	0.73	1.05	1.13	1.06	1.07	0.22	MTC
0.75	MvL Linacoustic	Permacote, coated, smooth HP duct liner	1	A	rolls	0.09	0.31	0.69	0.91	1.02	1.03	0.18	MTC
0.80	MvL Linacoustic	Permacote, coated, smooth R-300 duct liner	1	A	rolls	0.08	0.32	0.72	0.99	1.07	1.00	0.25	MTC
0.95	MvL Linacoustic	Permacote, coated, smooth R-300 duct liner	1½	A	rolls	0.15	0.63	1.01	1.07	1.01	0.88	0.38	MTC
1.05	MvL Linacoustic	Permacote, coated, smooth R-300 duct liner	2	A	rolls	0.27	0.81	1.11	1.13	1.06	1.05	0.50	MTC
0.80	MvL Linacoustic	Permacote, coated, smooth R-300 duct liner	1	F-25	rolls	0.53	0.39	0.70	1.00	1.09	1.01	0.25	MTC
0.90	MvL Linacoustic	Permacote, coated, smooth R-300 duct liner	1½	F-25	rolls	0.60	0.58	1.01	1.09	1.01	0.90	0.38	MTC
1.05	MvL Linacoustic	Permacote, coated, smooth R-300 duct liner	2	F-25	rolls	0.67	0.77	1.13	1.14	1.09	1.06	0.50	MTC
0.55	OC Aeroflex Plus Type 150	Fiberglas duct liner with surface coating	1	A	rolls	0.18	0.19	0.48	0.65	0.78	0.88	0.13	OC
0.70	OC Aeroflex Plus Type 150	Fiberglas duct liner with surface coating	1½	A	rolls	0.21	0.35	0.66	0.81	0.89	0.95	0.20	OC
0.80	OC Aeroflex Plus Type 150	Fiberglas duct liner with surface coating	2	A	rolls	0.25	0.47	0.76	0.94	0.95	0.98	0.26	OC
0.60	OC Aeroflex Plus Type 200	Fiberglas duct liner with surface coating	1	A	rolls	0.07	0.25	0.54	0.73	0.83	0.95	0.17	OC
0.75	OC Aeroflex Plus Type 200	Fiberglas duct liner with surface coating	1½	A	rolls	0.17	0.39	0.72	0.88	0.95	0.96	0.25	OC
0.85	OC Aeroflex Plus Type 200	Fiberglas duct liner with surface coating	2	A	rolls	0.24	0.53	0.83	0.99	0.98	1.00	0.34	OC

APPENDIX 3.2 Fiberglass Duct Liners (Continued)

NRC	Company Trade name	Description	Thickness, inches (mm)	Mounting type	Unit size, inches	Sound absorption coefficients, Hz						Weight, lb/ft² (kg/m²)	Test lab
						125	250	500	1000	2000	4000		
0.60	OC Aeroflex Plus Type 300	Fiberglas duct liner with surface coating	1	A	rolls	0.10	0.25	0.55	0.79	0.86	0.96	0.25	OC
0.65	OC Duct Board	Fiberglas duct liner board	1	A	24 × 48 48 × 96	0.03	0.22	0.60	0.84	0.98	0.97	0.25	OC
0.85	OC Duct Board	Fiberglas duct liner board	1½	A	24 × 48 48 × 96	0.16	0.39	0.91	1.01	1.01	1.01	0.37	OC
1.00	OC Duct Board	Fiberglas duct liner board	2	A	24 × 48 48 × 96	0.24	0.79	1.13	1.13	1.04	1.05	0.50	OC
0.70	BradIns Fibertex R4	Duct liner	(25)	A	120cm × 150cm	0.18	0.29	0.69	0.86	1.05	1.20	(1.5)	LC
0.95	BradIns Fibertex R4	Duct liner	(50)	A	120cm × 150cm	0.29	0.70	1.20	1.04	1.14	1.06	(3.0)	LC
0.75	BradIns Fibertex R4	Duct liner, perforated foil facing	(25)	A	120cm × 150cm	0.36	0.21	0.30	0.97	1.06	0.67	(1.5)	LC
0.90	BradIns Fibertex R4	Duct liner, perforated foil facing	(50)	A	120cm × 150cm	0.31	0.83	1.15	0.99	0.90	0.78	(3.0)	LC
0.75	BradIns Fibertex R6	Duct liner	(25)	A	120cm × 150cm	0.11	0.20	0.80	1.10	1.02	1.12	(2.0)	LC
1.00	BradIns Fibertex R6	Duct liner	(50)	A	120cm × 150cm	0.36	0.91	1.19	1.20	1.07	1.05	(3.0)	LC
0.75	BradIns Fibertex R6	Duct liner, perforated foil facing	(25)	A	120cm × 150cm	0.12	0.27	0.80	1.17	1.16	0.80	(1.5)	LC
0.95	BradIns Fibertex R6	Duct liner, perforated foil facing	(50)	A	120cm × 150cm	0.26	0.91	1.10	1.00	1.08	0.85	(3.0)	LC

NRC	Company Trade name	Description	Thickness, inches (mm)	Mounting type	Unit size, inches	Sound absorption coefficients, Hz						Weight, lb/ft² (kg/m²)	Test lab
						125	250	500	1000	2000	4000		
0.70	E-A-R Tufcote	Type E-100SM polyether urethane foam, Al. polyester surface	1	A	54 × 22ft	0.20	0.81	0.61	0.73	0.71	0.69	0.17	RAL
0.70	E-A-R Tufcote	Type E-100CM polyether urethane foam, 1 mil clear polyester surface	1	A	54 × 22ft	0.17	0.74	0.63	0.78	0.69	0.73	0.17	RAL
0.70	E-A-R Tufcote	Type E-100RM polyether urethane foam, reinforced polyester surface	1	A	54 × 22ft	0.21	0.52	0.71	0.87	0.75	0.66	0.17	RAL
0.80	E-A-R Tufcote	Type E-100SF polyether urethane foam, textured surface	1	A	54 × 22ft	0.17	0.25	0.73	1.14	0.99	1.02	0.17	RAL
0.85	ImiTech Solimide AC-403	Polimide foam	2	A	96 × 96	0.23	0.51	0.96	1.04	0.93	0.96	0.25	RAL
0.80	ImiTech Solimide TA-301	Polimide foam	2	A	96 × 96"	0.30	0.49	0.89	0.97	0.84	0.88	0.5	RAL
0.55	INC K-10M	Aluminized mylar-faced polyether foam	1	A	1 × 54 100ft	0.10	0.57	0.57	0.39	0.68	0.35	0.17	RAL
0.70	Sonex	Wedge-shaped polyurethane foam panels	2	A	24 × 48 48 × 48	0.08	0.25	0.61	0.92	0.95	0.92	0.34	Intest
0.85	Sonex	Wedge-shaped polyurethane foam panels	3	A	24 × 48 48 × 48	0.14	0.43	0.98	1.03	1.00	1.00	0.51	Intest

APPENDIX 3.3 Foam Materials (Continued)

NRC	Company Trade name	Description	Thickness, inches (mm)	Mounting type	Unit size, inches	Sound absorption coefficients, Hz						Weight, lb/ft² (kg/m²)	Test lab
						125	250	500	1000	2000	4000		
0.95	Sonex	Wedge-shaped polyurethane foam panels	4	A	24 × 48 48 × 48	0.20	0.70	0.98	1.06	1.01	1.00	0.67	Intest
0.80	Sonex 1	Wedge-shaped melamine foam panels	2	A	24 × 48	0.16	0.34	0.81	1.00	0.99	0.97	0.7	Intest
0.80	Sonex 1 Hypalon	Wedge-shaped melamine foam panels	2	A	24 × 48	0.18	0.65	1.04	0.73	0.68	0.56	0.7	Intest
1.10	Sonex Super-Sonex 1	Wedge-shaped melamine foam panels	6	A	12 × 12	0.11	0.86	1.22	1.24	1.14	1.20	0.7	TCT
1.15	Sonex Sonex	Wedge-shaped polyurethane foam panels	6	A	12 × 12	0.38	0.99	1.19	1.21	1.14	1.38	1.0	TCT
0.65	Sonex Mini-Sonex 1	Wedge-shaped melamine foam panels	1½	A	24 × 48	0.14	0.21	0.61	0.80	0.89	0.92	0.7	TCT
0.60	Sonex Mini-Sonex 200	Wedge-shaped melamine foam panels	1½	A	24 × 48	0.16	0.13	0.40	0.85	0.95	0.93	0.5	TCT

APPENDIX 3.4 Acoustical Boards, Blankets, and Batts

NRC	Company Trade name	Description	Thickness, inches (mm)	Mounting type	Unit size, inches	Sound absorption coefficients, Hz						Weight, lb/ft² (kg/m²)	Test lab
						125	250	500	1000	2000	4000		
0.75	CTeed IB150	Unfaced fiberglass board, bonded with thermosetting resin	1	A	24 × 48	0.19	0.62	0.72	0.82	0.88	0.89	0.13	NGC
0.75	CTeed IB200	Unfaced fiberglass board, bonded with thermosetting resin	1	A	24 × 48	0.15	0.55	0.73	0.86	0.92	0.94	0.17	NGC
0.75	CTeed IB250	Unfaced fiberglass board, bonded with thermosetting resin	1	A	24 × 48	0.25	0.52	0.71	0.83	0.89	0.95	0.21	NGC
0.75	CTeed IB300	Unfaced fiberglass board, bonded with thermosetting resin	1	A	24 × 48	0.19	0.49	0.69	0.87	0.92	0.94	0.29	NGC
0.75	CTeed IB420	Unfaced fiberglass board, bonded with thermosetting resin	1	A	24 × 48	0.33	0.40	0.70	0.94	1.00	0.98	0.35	NGC
0.75	CTeed IB600	Unfaced fiberglass board, bonded with thermosetting resin	1	A	24 × 48	0.12	0.52	0.68	0.87	0.93	0.99	0.50	NGC
0.80	CTeed IB150	Unfaced fiberglass board, bonded with thermosetting resin	1½	A	24 × 48	0.19	0.51	0.82	0.86	0.95	0.97	0.19	NGC
0.90	CTeed IB150	Unfaced fiberglass board, bonded with thermosetting resin	2½	A	24 × 48	0.41	0.78	0.96	0.94	0.93	0.97	0.31	NGC

APPENDIX 3.4 Acoustical Boards, Blankets, and Batts (Continued)

NRC	Company Trade name	Description	Thickness, inches (mm)	Mounting type	Unit size, inches	Sound absorption coefficients, Hz						Weight, lb/ft² (kg/m²)	Test lab
						125	250	500	1000	2000	4000		
0.95	CTeed IB150	Unfaced fiberglass board, bonded with thermosetting resin	2½	F-25	24 × 48	0.54	0.85	0.97	0.96	0.93	0.97	0.31	NGC
0.70	CTeed IB250	Unfaced fiberglass board, bonded with thermosetting resin	1	A	24 × 48	0.08	0.33	0.69	0.81	0.92	0.97	0.21	NGC
1.00	CTeed IB250	Unfaced fiberglass board, bonded with thermosetting resin	3	A	24 × 48	0.44	0.91	1.07	0.99	1.02	0.99	0.63	NGC
0.85	CTeed IB420	Unfaced fiberglass board, bonded with thermosetting resin	1½	A	24 × 48	0.09	0.45	0.91	0.99	1.02	0.96	0.53	NGC
1.00	CTeed IB420	Unfaced fiberglass board, bonded with thermosetting resin	3	A	24 × 48	0.54	1.01	1.05	0.98	1.01	0.97	1.1	NGC
1.00	CTeed IB600	Unfaced fiberglass board, bonded with thermosetting resin	2½	A	24 × 48	0.53	0.99	1.02	0.84	1.00	0.94	1.3	NGC
0.35	CTeed Ultralite	Unfaced fiberglass blanket	1	A	roll	0.06	0.20	0.29	0.40	0.50	0.54	0.10	NGC
0.50	CTeed Ultralite	Unfaced fiberglass blanket	1	A	roll	0.09	23	0.453	0.61	0.70	0.76	0.12	NGC
0.55	CTeed Ultralite	Unfaced fiberglass blanket	1	A	roll	0.12	0.31	0.50	0.68	0.77	0.79	0.17	NGC

	Manufacturer/Product	Description	Thickness	Mounting	Size	125	250	500	1000	2000	4000		Source
0.60	CTeed Ultralite	Unfaced fiberglass blanket	1	A	roll	0.06	0.25	0.54	0.75	0.84	0.90	0.25	NGC
0.95	CTeed WP16	Unfaced semirigid fiberglass board	3	A	24 × 48	0.43	0.83	1.02	0.95	0.97	0.99	0.42	NGC
0.95	CTeed MBP	Fiberglass blanket, flexible, unfaced	3½	A	rolls	0.38	0.90	1.00	0.93	0.94	0.99	0.58	NGC
1.05	CTeed MBP	Fiberglass blanket, flexible, unfaced	5	A	rolls	0.68	1.11	1.06	0.94	1.00	0.97	0.83	NGC
1.05	CTeed MBP	Fiberglass blanket, flexible, unfaced	6	A	rolls	0.88	1.19	1.03	0.96	1.02	1.00	1.0	NGC
0.95	CTeed Ultracoustic	Fiberglass blanket with flexible internal septum	3	A	roll	0.43	0.91	0.99	0.98	0.95	0.93	0.3	NGC
0.55	Knauf	Fiberglass insulation board, unfaced	¾	A	48 × 96 / 48 × 120	0.00	0.15	0.48	0.72	0.86	0.97	0.19	RAL
0.70	Knauf	Fiberglass insulation board, unfaced	1	A	48 × 96 / 48 × 120	0.10	0.26	0.60	0.85	0.99	0.96	0.25	RAL
0.85	Knauf	Fiberglass insulation board, unfaced	1½	A	48 × 96 / 48 × 120	0.35	0.46	0.86	0.98	1.02	1.04	0.38	RAL
0.95	Knauf	Fiberglass insulation board, unfaced	2	A	48 × 96 / 48 × 120	0.18	0.59	1.03	1.14	1.06	0.99	0.50	RAL
0.70	Knauf	Fiberglass insulation board, unfaced	1	A	48 × 96 / 48 × 120	0.07	0.24	0.69	0.88	0.98	1.03	0.33	RAL
0.80	Knauf	Fiberglass insulation board, unfaced	1	A	48 × 96 / 48 × 120	0.19	0.32	0.71	0.98	1.10	0.98	0.50	RAL
0.55	Knauf Type KN	Fiberglass acoustical blanket, max width: 96", max length: 125'	1	A	roll	0.12	0.18	0.51	0.72	0.78	0.86	0.75	RAL

APPENDIX 3.4 Acoustical Boards, Blankets, and Batts *(Continued)*

NRC	Company Trade name	Description	Thickness, inches (mm)	Mounting type	Unit size, inches	Sound absorption coefficients, Hz						Weight, lb/ft² (kg/m²)	Test lab
						125	250	500	1000	2000	4000		
0.75	Knauf Type KN	Fiberglass acoustical blanket, max width: 96", max length: 125'	1½	A	roll	0.20	0.42	0.82	0.87	0.94	0.91	0.75	RAL
0.65	Knauf Type KN	Fiberglass acoustical blanket, max width: 96", max length: 125'	1	A	roll	0.17	0.24	0.62	0.79	0.88	0.96	0.08	RAL
0.85	Knauf Type KN	Fiberglass acoustical blanket, max width: 96", max length: 125'	1½	A	roll	0.31	0.50	0.89	0.98	1.01	1.01	0.13	RAL
0.65	Knauf Type KN	Fiberglass acoustical blanket, max width: 96", max length: 125'	1	A	roll	0.03	0.28	0.56	0.82	0.90	0.94	0.13	RAL
0.90	Knauf Type KN	Fiberglass acoustical blanket, max width: 96", max length: 125'	1½	A	roll	0.21	0.51	0.97	1.08	1.07	1.06	0.19	RAL
0.70	Knauf Type KN	Fiberglass duct wrap	1½	F-25	roll	0.35	0.64	0.69	0.76	0.79	0.81	0.25	RAL
0.85	Knauf Type KN	Fiberglass duct wrap	2	F-25	roll	0.43	0.74	0.83	0.87	0.88	0.88	0.38	RAL
0.80	Knauf Type KN	Fiberglass duct wrap	1½	F-25	roll	0.41	0.69	0.77	0.86	0.90	0.85	0.13	RAL
0.85	Knauf Type KN	Fiberglass duct wrap	2	F-25	roll	0.45	0.78	0.88	0.90	0.91	0.91	0.17	RAL
0.80	Knauf Metal bldg. insulation	Fiberglass blanket, max width: 72", max length: 150'	2	A	roll	0.25	0.48	0.81	0.90	0.97	0.94	0.11	RAL

0.95	Knauf Metal bldg. insulation	Fiberglass blanket, max width: 72", max length: 150'	3	A	roll	0.36	0.76	1.04	0.94	0.98	1.00	0.16	RAL
1.00	Knauf Metal bldg. insulation	Fiberglass blanket, max width: 72", max length: 150'	4	A	roll	0.59	1.01	0.97	0.96	1.06	1.08	0.22	RAL
1.15	Knauf Metal bldg. insulation	Fiberglass blanket, max width: 72", max length: 150'	6	A	roll	1.18	1.36	1.02	1.02	1.12	1.07	0.33	RAL
0.60	MvL Microlite	Fiberglass blanket	1	A	roll	0.12	0.31	0.56	0.73	0.83	0.88	0.05	MTC
0.80	MvL Microlite	Fiberglass blanket	1½	A	roll	0.19	0.53	0.81	0.91	0.94	0.98	0.08	MTC
0.90	MvL Microlite	Fiberglass blanket	2	A	roll	0.23	0.65	0.90	0.98	0.98	1.01	0.10	MTC
0.65	MvL Microlite	Fiberglass blanket	1	A	roll	0.08	0.34	0.59	0.75	0.86	0.81	0.08	MTC
0.70	MvL Microlite	Fiberglass blanket	1	A	roll	0.11	0.30	0.66	0.88	1.00	1.01	0.17	MTC
0.80	MvL Microlite	Fiberglass blanket	1	A	roll	0.11	0.35	0.77	1.01	1.04	1.05	0.25	MTC
0.65	MvL Microlite	Fiberglass blanket	1	F-25	roll	0.17	0.59	0.57	0.65	0.75	0.83	0.05	MTC
0.75	MvL Microlite	Fiberglass blanket	1½	F-25	roll	0.24	0.66	0.72	0.81	0.89	0.93	0.08	MTC
0.90	MvL Microlite	Fiberglass blanket	2	F-25	roll	0.27	0.80	0.88	0.96	1.01	1.05	0.10	MTC
1.00	MvL Microlite	Fiberglass blanket	3	F-25	roll	0.41	1.02	1.03	1.02	1.02	1.10	0.15	MTC
0.70	MvL Microlite	Fiberglass blanket	1	F-25	roll	0.12	0.57	0.60	0.73	0.86	0.93	0.08	MTC
0.75	MvL Microlite	Fiberglass blanket	1	F-25	roll	0.11	0.57	0.69	0.87	0.96	1.02	0.13	MTC
0.80	MvL Microlite	Fiberglass blanket	1	F-25	roll	0.15	0.59	0.74	0.93	1.01	1.06	0.17	MTC
0.65	MvL Microlite	Fiberglass blanket	1	F-405	roll	0.30	0.38	0.61	0.80	0.89	0.97	0.05	MTC
0.80	MvL Microlite	Fiberglass blanket	1½	F-405	roll	0.30	0.53	0.79	0.93	0.98	1.03	0.08	MTC
0.90	MvL Microlite	Fiberglass blanket	2	F-405	roll	0.48	0.66	0.92	0.98	1.00	1.07	0.10	MTC

APPENDIX 3.4 Acoustical Boards, Blankets, and Batts (Continued)

NRC	Company Trade name	Description	Thickness, inches (mm)	Mounting type	Unit size, inches	Sound absorption coefficients, Hz						Weight, lb/ft² (kg/m²)	Test lab
						125	250	500	1000	2000	4000		
0.70	MvL Microlite	Fiberglass blanket	1	F-405	roll	0.26	0.39	0.62	0.81	0.88	0.84	0.08	MTC
0.75	MvL Microlite	Fiberglass blanket	1	F-405	roll	0.33	0.40	0.70	0.92	0.99	1.06	0.13	MTC
0.75	MvL Microlite	Fiberglass blanket	1	F-405	roll	0.27	0.37	0.67	0.92	1.02	1.09	0.17	MTC
0.80	MvL Microlite	Fiberglass blanket	1	F-405	roll	0.25	0.36	0.79	1.03	1.09	1.13	0.25	MTC
0.70	MvL Tuf-Skin	Semirigid fiberglass blanket	1	A	roll	0.10	0.34	0.64	0.85	0.98	1.04	dual density	MTC
1.00	MvL Tuf-Skin	Semirigid fiberglass blanket	2	A	roll	0.19	0.71	1.02	1.14	1.07	1.05	dual density	MTC
0.70	MvL Spin-Glas	Fiberglass board	1	A	various	0.07	0.30	0.71	0.96	1.03	1.05	0.25	MTC
0.80	MvL Spin-Glas	Fiberglass board	1	A	various	0.04	0.43	0.86	1.00	0.99	1.00	0.50	MTC
1.00	MvL Spin-Glas	Fiberglass board	2	A	various	0.32	0.89	1.06	1.01	1.04	1.06	1.0	MTC
1.05	MvL Spin-Glas	Fiberglass board, Precipitator series	2	A	various	0.20	0.85	1.11	1.11	1.07	1.07	0.40	MTC
1.10	MvL Spin-Glas	Fiberglass board, 1000 Series	2	A	various	0.24	1.05	1.16	1.12	1.08	1.07	0.50	MTC
1.10	MvL Spin-Glas	Fiberglass board, 1000 Series	3	A	various	0.58	1.21	1.11	1.08	1.07	1.08	0.75	MTC
0.70	OC Type 701	Flexible insulation board	1	A	24 × 48	0.17	0.33	0.64	0.83	0.90	0.92	0.13	OC

0.90	OC Type 701	Flexible insulation board	2	A	24 × 48	0.22	0.67	0.98	1.02	0.98	1.00	0.25	OC
1.15	OC Type 701	Flexible insulation board	3	A	24 × 48	0.43	1.17	1.26	1.09	1.03	1.04	0.38	OC
1.15	OC Type 701	Flexible insulation board	4	A	24 × 48	0.73	1.29	1.22	1.06	1.00	0.97	0.50	OC
0.70	OC Type 701	Flexible insulation board	1	E-405	24 × 48	0.32	0.41	0.70	0.83	0.93	1.02	0.13	OC
0.95	OC Type 701	Flexible insulation board	2	E-405	24 × 48	0.44	0.68	1.00	1.09	1.06	1.10	0.25	OC
1.10	OC 1 Type 701	Flexible insulation board	3	E-405	24 × 48	0.77	1.08	1.16	1.09	1.05	1.18	0.38	OC
1.20	OC Type 701	Flexible insulation board	4	E-405	24 × 48	0.87	1.14	1.24	1.17	1.18	1.28	0.50	OC
0.70	OC Type 703	Semirigid insulation board	1	A	24 × 48	0.11	0.28	0.68	0.90	0.93	0.96	0.25	OC
1.00	OC Type 703	Semirigid insulation board	2	A	24 × 48	0.17	0.86	1.14	1.07	1.02	0.98	0.50	OC
1.10	OC Type 703	Semirigid insulation board	3	A	24 × 48	0.53	1.19	1.21	1.08	1.01	1.04	0.75	OC
1.15	OC Type 703	Semirigid insulation board	4	A	24 × 48	0.84	1.24	1.24	1.08	1.00	0.97	1.0	OC
0.75	OC Type 703	Semirigid insulation board	1	E-405	24 × 48	0.32	0.32	0.73	0.93	1.01	1.10	0.25	OC
1.00	OC Type 703	Semirigid insulation board	2	E-405	24 × 48	0.40	0.73	1.14	1.13	1.06	1.10	0.50	OC
1.05	OC Type 703	Semirigid insulation board	3	E-405	24 × 48	0.66	0.93	1.13	1.10	1.11	1.14	0.75	OC

APPENDIX 3.4 Acoustical Boards, Blankets, and Batts (Continued)

NRC	Company Trade name	Description	Thickness, inches (mm)	Mounting type	Unit size, inches	Sound absorption coefficients, Hz						Weight, lb/ft² (kg/m²)	Test lab
						125	250	500	1000	2000	4000		
1.10	OC Type 703	Semirigid insulation board	4	E-405	24 × 48	0.65	1.01	1.20	1.14	1.10	1.16	1.0	OC
0.65	OC Type 705	Rigid insulation board	1	A	24 × 48	0.02	0.27	0.63	0.85	0.93	0.95	0.50	OC
0.95	OC Type 705	Rigid insulation board	2	A	24 × 48	0.16	0.71	1.02	1.01	0.99	0.99	1.0	OC
1.10	OC Type 705	Rigid insulation board	3	A	24 × 48	0.54	1.12	1.23	1.07	1.01	1.05	1.5	OC
1.10	OC Type 705	Rigid insulation board	4	A	24 × 48	0.75	1.19	1.17	1.05	0.97	0.98	2.0	OC
0.70	OC Type 705	Rigid insulation board	1	E-405	24 × 48	0.30	0.34	0.68	0.87	0.97	1.06	0.50	OC
1.00	OC Type 705	Rigid insulation board	2	E-405	24 × 48	0.39	0.63	1.06	1.13	1.09	1.10	1.0	OC
1.05	OC Type 705	Rigid insulation board	3	E-405	24 × 48	0.66	0.92	1.11	1.12	1.10	1.19	1.5	OC
1.10	OC Type 705	Rigid insulation board	4	E-405	24 × 48	0.59	0.91	1.15	1.11	1.11	1.19	2.0	OC
0.85	TCeram Kawool	Ceramic fiber blanket	1	A	48 × 107	0.10	0.29	1.00	1.04	0.99	0.98	1.33	RAL
0.85	TCeram Kawool	Ceramic fiber blanket	2	A	48 × 107	0.42	0.80	0.72	0.86	0.92	1.02	2.67	RAL

	Manufacturer	Product			Size	0.15	0.50	0.92	0.91	0.91	0.94	0.67	RAL
0.80	TCeram Kawool	Ceramic fiber blanket	1	A	48 × 107	0.15	0.50	0.92	0.91	0.91	0.94	0.67	RAL
0.45	TCeram Type M	Ceramic fiber board	1	A	36 × 48	0.26	0.41	0.40	0.47	0.58	0.65	1.67	RAL
0.95	BradIns	Glasswool building blanket	(50)	A	120cm × 15m	0.68	0.75	1.05	1.04	1.05	1.11	(0.55)	LC
1.00	BradIns	Glasswool building blanket with perforated foil facing	(50)	A	120cm × 15m	0.55	0.69	1.07	1.07	0.99	1.00	(0.55)	LC
0.65	BradIns	Glasswool building blanket with foil facing	(50)	A	120cm × 15m	0.56	1.03	0.93	0.41	0.21	0.14	(0.55)	LC
1.00	BradIns	Glasswool building blanket with perforated foil facing	(75)	A	120cm × 10m	0.47	0.87	1.09	1.03	0.97	0.86	(0.83)	LC
1.05	BradIns	Glasswool building blanket with perforated foil facing	(100)	A	120cm × 10m	0.75	0.93	1.14	1.04	1.03	0.97	(1.1)	LC
0.70	BradIns Flexitel	Glasswool building blanket	(25)	A	120cm × 15m	0.33	0.28	0.61	0.89	1.01	1.05	(0.60)	LC
0.80	BradIns Flexitel	Glasswool building blanket with perforated foil facing	(25)	A	120cm × 15m	0.03	0.33	0.68	1.04	1.15	0.95	(0.60)	LC
0.90	BradIns Flexitel	Glasswool building blanket	(50)	A	120cm × 15m	0.42	0.64	0.92	1.07	0.98	1.02	(1.2)	LC
1.05	BradIns Flexitel	Glasswool building blanket with perforated foil facing	(50)	A	120cm × 15m	0.39	0.84	1.08	1.20	1.06	1.01	(1.2)	LC

APPENDIX 3.4 Acoustical Boards, Blankets, and Batts (Continued)

NRC	Company Trade name	Description	Thickness, inches (mm)	Mounting type	Unit size, inches	Sound absorption coefficients, Hz						Weight, lb/ft² (kg/m²)	Test lab
						125	250	500	1000	2000	4000		
1.05	BradIns	Glasswool building blanket with perforated foil facing	(75)	A	120cm × 15m	0.47	0.96	1.11	1.05	1.01	0.88	(1.8)	LC
0.75	BradIns Supertel	Glasswool blanket	(25)	A	120cm × 240cm	0.12	0.41	0.63	0.90	1.01	0.99	(0.8)	LC
0.80	BradIns Supertel	Glasswool blanket with perforated foil facing	(25)	A	120cm × 240cm	0.08	0.39	0.73	1.02	1.12	0.84	(0.8)	LC
0.70	BradIns Supertel	Glasswool blanket with perforated metal facing	(25)	A	120cm × 240cm	0.13	0.32	0.59	0.83	0.99	0.97	(0.8)	LC
0.80	BradIns Supertel	Glasswool blanket with 23μm Mylar film facing	(25)	A	120cm × 240cm	0.15	0.45	0.67	1.07	1.08	0.71	(0.8)	LC
0.85	BradIns Supertel	Glasswool blanket with 50μm Mylar film facing	(25)	A	120cm × 240cm	0.13	0.44	0.92	1.14	0.82	0.45	(0.8)	LC
1.00	BradIns Supertel	Glasswool blanket with 23μm Mylar film facing	(50)	A	120cm × 240cm	0.20	0.55	1.20	1.15	1.04	0.83	(1.6)	LC
0.90	BradIns Supertel	Glasswool blanket with 59μm Mylar film facing	(50)	A	120cm × 240cm	0.30	0.60	1.16	1.07	0.85	0.59	(1.6)	LC
0.70	BradIns Fibertex 350	Rockwool blanket	(25)	A	90cm × 150cm	0.18	0.29	0.69	0.86	1.05	1.20	(1.5)	LC
0.95	BradIns Fibertex 350	Rockwool blanket	(50)	A	90cm × 150cm	0.29	0.70	1.19	1.04	1.14	1.06	(3.0)	LC

1.05	BradIns Fibertex 350	Rockwool blanket	(75)	A	90cm × 150cm	0.60	1.03	1.13	0.99	1.07	1.01	(4.5)	LC
0.70	Flumroc Ecco	Dämmplatte, rockwool fiber	(30)	A	6cm × 10cm	0.08	0.34	0.81	0.97	1.02	0.98	(2.5)	EMPA
0.95	Flumroc Ecco	Dämmplatte, rockwool fiber	(50)	A	6cm × 10cm	0.18	0.77	1.01	1.04	0.97	0.97	(4.3)	EMPA
1.00	Flumroc Ecco	Dämmplatte, rockwool fiber	(100)	A	6cm × 10cm	0.60	0.97	1.00	1.00	0.99	1.00	(8.5)	EMPA
0.80	Flumroc Iglu	Dämmplatte, rockwool fiber	(30)	A	6cm × 10cm	0.08	0.38	0.85	0.98	0.99	1.00	(3.3)	EMPA
0.90	Flumroc Iglu	Dämmplatte, rockwool fiber	(50)	A	6cm × 10cm	0.22	0.81	0.95	0.95	0.96	0.94	(5.5)	EMPA
0.90	Flumroc Iglu	Dämmplatte, rockwool fiber	(100)	A	6cm × 10cm	0.60	0.84	0.90	0.95	0.97	0.99	(11.0)	EMPA
0.75	Flumroc 341	Dachdämmplatte, rockwool fiber	(60)	A	6cm × 10cm	0.40	0.66	0.73	0.81	0.85	0.91	(9.9)	EMPA
0.80	Flumroc 341	Dachdämmplatte, rockwool fiber	(80)	A	6cm × 10cm	0.49	0.66	0.78	0.89	0.92	0.97	(13.2)	EMPA
0.75	Flumroc 341	Dachdämmplatte, rockwool fiber	(100)	A	6cm × 10cm	0.47	0.59	0.72	0.81	0.86	0.89	(16.5)	EMPA
0.55	G+H Isover	Type P3/V mineral wool	(200)	A	various	0.10	0.26	0.53	0.71	0.84	0.96	—	G+H
0.90	G+H Isover	Type P3/V mineral wool	(50)	A	various	0.26	0.60	0.95	1.07	1.01	1.04	—	G+H
0.65	G+H Isover	Type P4/V mineral wool	(20)	A	various	0.07	0.21	0.56	0.85	0.97	1.07	—	G+H
1.00	G+H Isover	Type P4/V mineral wool	(50)	A	various	0.26	0.80	1.07	1.13	1.01	1.06	—	G+H

APPENDIX 3.4 Acoustical Boards, Blankets, and Batts (Continued)

NRC	Company Trade name	Description	Thickness, inches (mm)	Mounting type	Unit size, inches	Sound absorption coefficients, Hz						Weight, lb/ft² (kg/m²)	Test lab
						125	250	500	1000	2000	4000		
0.90	G+H Isover	Type P4/TRHV 50 mineral wool	(50)	A	various	0.19	0.58	0.95	1.01	0.98	0.96	—	G+H
0.95	G+H Isover	Type P4/TRHV 100 mineral wool	(50)	A	various	0.23	0.70	1.05	1.05	1.02	1.04	—	G+H
0.95	G+H Isover	Type P4/TRHV 120 mineral wool	(50)	A	various	0.29	0.75	0.98	1.02	1.01	0.98	—	G+H
0.95	G+H Isover	Type P6 mineral wool	(50)	A	various	0.25	0.73	1.03	1.13	1.01	1.05	—	G+H

APPENDIX 3.5 Acoustical Panels (Also See Appendix 3.4)

NRC	Company Trade name	Description	Thickness, inches (mm)	Mounting type	Unit size, inches	Sound absorption coefficients, Hz						Weight, lb/ft² (kg/m²)	Test lab
						125	250	500	1000	2000	4000		
0.85	Alpro Flat Baf	Perforated steel panel, 1½ pcf fiberglass backing 2" thick, covered by ¾ mil PVC	2	A	24 × 108	0.44	0.62	0.94	0.99	0.79	0.59	1.5	RAL
1.00	Alpro Flat Baf	Perforated steel panel, 1½ pcf fiberglass backing 2" thick	2	A	24 × 108	0.21	0.66	1.13	1.14	1.00	0.90	1.5	RAL
1.00	Alpro Flat Baf	Perforated Al. panel, with corrugations ⅝" deep, 1½ pcf 2" fiberglass backing	2	E-400	36 × 96	0.72	0.98	1.00	1.07	1.02	0.84	1.0	RAL
0.55	CA	Perforated steel panel backed by 4" layer of 3½ pcf USG Thermafiber in Mylar	4¼	A	48 × 108	0.52	0.37	0.64	0.60	0.56	0.29	5	RAL
1.05	CA	Perforated steel panel backed by 2" layer of 2 pcf OCF Type RA-23 Fiberglas	2¼	A	96 × 108	0.31	0.82	1.19	1.12	1.07	1.06	3.9	RAL
1.10	CA	Perforated steel panel backed by 4" layer of 2 pcf OCF Type R-23 Fiberglas	4¼	A	48 × 108	0.86	1.09	1.22	1.06	1.05	1.04	5	RAL
0.75	Conweb Tufflex G-37	Cellulose, nonwoven panel core	1	A	—	0.12	0.29	0.65	0.94	1.05	0.91	0.78	TC
0.60	Conweb Tufflex G-37	Cellulose, nonwoven panel core	¾	A	—	0.12	0.16	0.55	0.72	0.91	0.89	0.20	TC
0.55	Conweb Tufflex G-40	Cellulose, nonwoven panel core	⅝	A	—	0.15	0.13	0.42	0.72	0.93	0.87	0.21	TC

APPENDIX 3.5 Acoustical Panels (Also See Appendix 3.4) (Continued)

NRC	Company Trade name	Description	Thickness, inches (mm)	Mounting type	Unit size, inches	Sound absorption coefficients, Hz						Weight, lb/ft² (kg/m²)	Test lab
						125	250	500	1000	2000	4000		
1.10	EAS M-90 Panel	Perforated steel panel backed with 6 pcf mineral fiber	2½	A	—	0.36	1.01	1.23	1.14	1.02	0.78	2.2	RAL
1.15	EAS M-90 Panel	Perforated steel panel backed with 6 pcf mineral fiber	3½	A	—	0.81	1.25	1.17	1.16	1.05	0.82	3.7	RAL
0.55	Farbo Vicracoustic	Trimline panel, polyester covering	½	A	96 × 108	0.04	0.11	0.38	0.80	0.98	1.04	0.5	CK
0.65	Farbo Vicracoustic	Trimline panel, perforated vinyl wall covering	½	A	96 × 108	0.00	0.15	0.56	0.93	0.94	0.78	0.56	CK
0.95	IAC Mark III	Perforated metal ceiling panel backed with fiberglass	2	E-400	24 × 48	0.63	0.71	0.98	1.11	1.03	1.08	1.8	CK
1.00	IAC Mark V	Perforated metal ceiling panel backed with fiberglass	3	E-400	24 × 48	0.56	0.84	1.16	1.16	0.92	0.82	3.1	CK
0.95	Perdue LSS-RHRF	Fabric-covered panel, 8 pcf rockwool core	1	A	24 × 48 48 × 48	0.21	0.66	1.04	1.05	0.97	0.98	0.6	AS
0.95	Perdue RHH7FP	Fabric-covered panel, 8 pcf rockwool core	1	A	24 × 48 48 × 48	0.28	0.67	1.11	1.05	0.98	0.98	0.6	AS
0.90	Perdue RHVP	Vinyl-covered panel, 8 pcf rockwool core	1	A	24 × 48 48 × 48	0.23	0.67	1.09	1.00	0.87	0.69	0.6	AS
0.90	Perdue RHHVP	Vinyl-covered panel, 8 pcf rockwool core	1	A	24 × 48 48 × 48	0.27	0.66	1.09	1.01	0.87	0.65	0.6	AS

						125	250	500	1000	2000	4000		
1.05	Perdue LSS-RHRF	Fabric-covered panel, 6 pcf rockwool core	2	A	24 × 48 48 × 48	0.46	0.93	1.26	1.10	1.00	1.00	1.0	AS
1.00	Perdue LSS-AT	Perforated steel facing over 6 pcf rockwool core	2	A	24 × 48 48 × 48	0.38	0.83	1.18	1.05	0.95	0.91	1.5	AS
0.60	Drupa Silencio	Perforated steel panel with acoustic resonators	3	UNE 74041	90 × 90	0.05	0.15	0.45	0.90	0.90	0.75	7	IA
0.70	Peer Almute	Type A300c, porous sintered metal panel	0.1 (3mm)	E-200	24 × 48	0.44	0.81	0.87	0.52	0.69	0.80	0.9	RAL
0.65	Peer Almute	Type A300c, porous sintered metal panel	0.1 (3mm)	E-400	24 × 48	0.85	0.80	0.46	0.60	0.70	0.80	0.9	RAL
1.00	Peer Almute	Same as above but backed with 2" fiberglass	2.1	E-400	24 × 48	0.77	1.03	0.93	1.07	1.03	1.07	1.9	RAL
1.00	Peer Almute	Same as above but 2" fiberglass spaced 1/4" from porous metal panel	2.35	E-400	24 × 48	0.88	0.92	0.99	1.09	1.05	1.06	1.9	RAL
0.80	Peer Almute	Type A250c, porous sintered metal panel	0.1 (3mm)	E-400	20 × 20	0.95	0.88	0.60	0.74	0.88	1.07	0.8	CK
0.95	Peer Almute	Same as above but backed with 4" fiberglass	4.1	E-400	20 × 20	1.01	0.97	0.86	0.90	0.99	1.19	1.1	CK
0.40	Tectum panel	Silicate-treated wood fiber, organic binder	1	A	24 × 96 24 × 48	0.06	0.13	0.24	0.45	0.82	0.64	1.6	RAL
0.45	Tectum panel	Silicate-treated wood fiber, organic binder	1	D-20	24 × 96 24 × 48	0.07	0.15	0.36	0.65	0.71	0.81	1.6	RAL
0.80	Tectum panel	Silicate-treated wood fiber, organic binder	1	C-20	24 × 96 24 × 48	0.16	0.43	1.00	1.05	0.79	0.98	1.6	RAL
0.85	Tectum panel	Silicate-treated wood fiber, organic binder	1	C-40	24 × 96 24 × 48	0.32	0.70	1.09	0.93	0.76	0.94	1.6	RAL
0.55	Tectum panel	Silicate-treated wood fiber, organic binder	1½	A	24 × 96 24 × 48	0.07	0.22	0.48	0.82	0.64	0.96	2.5	RAL

APPENDIX 3.5 Acoustical Panels (Also See Appendix 3.4) (Continued)

NRC	Company Trade name	Description	Thickness, inches (mm)	Mounting type	Unit size, inches	Sound absorption coefficients, Hz						Weight, lb/ft² (kg/m²)	Test lab
						125	250	500	1000	2000	4000		
0.60	Tectum panel	Silicate-treated wood fiber, organic binder	1½	D-20	24 × 96 24 × 48	0.15	0.26	0.62	0.83	0.70	0.91	2.5	RAL
0.90	Tectum panel	Silicate-treated wood fiber, organic binder	1½	C-20	24 × 96 24 × 48	0.24	0.57	1.17	0.87	0.93	0.87	2.5	RAL
0.95	Tectum panel	Silicate-treated wood fiber, organic binder	1½	C-40	24 × 96 24 × 48	0.40	0.84	1.18	0.84	0.94	0.88	2.5	RAL
0.60	Tectum panel	Silicate-treated wood fiber, organic binder	2	A	24 × 96 24 × 48	0.15	0.26	0.62	0.94	0.64	0.92	3.3	RAL
0.70	Tectum panel	Silicate-treated wood fiber, organic binder	2	D-20	24 × 96 24 × 48	0.15	0.36	0.74	0.82	0.82	0.92	3.3	RAL
0.95	Tectum 1 panel	Silicate-treated wood fiber, organic binder	2	C-20	24 × 96 24 × 48	0.24	0.67	1.14	0.87	1.06	0.96	3.3	RAL
1.00	Tectum panel	Silicate-treated wood fiber, organic binder	2	C-40	24 × 96 24 × 48	0.42	0.89	1.19	0.85	1.08	0.94	3.3	RAL
0.80	Tectum panel	1" Tectum over 1" layer of 3 pcf fiberglass	2	C-40	24 × 48	0.16	0.43	1.00	1.05	0.79	0.98	1.9	RAL
0.90	Tectum panel	1½" Tectum over 1" layer of 3 pcf fiberglass	2½	C-40	24 × 48	0.24	0.57	1.17	0.87	0.93	0.87	1.8	RAL
0.95	Tectum panel	2" Tectum over 1" layer of 3 pcf fiberglass	3	C-40	24 × 48	0.24	0.67	1.14	0.87	1.06	0.96	2.9	RAL
0.85	Tectum panel	1" Tectum over 2½" OCF noise barrier batt	3½	C-40	24 × 48	0.32	0.70	1.09	0.93	0.76	0.94	2.8	RAL
0.95	Tectum panel	1½" Tectum over 2½" OCF noise barrier batt	4	C-40	24 × 48	0.40	0.84	1.18	0.87	0.93	0.87	3.5	RAL

1.00	Tectum panel	2" Tectum over 2¹⁄₂" OCF noise barrier batt	4¹⁄₂	C-40	24 × 48	0.42	0.89	1.19	0.85	1.08	0.94	3.4	RAL
0.90	Tectum panel	2" Tectum over 2¹⁄₂" OCF noise barrier batt	4¹⁄₂	C-20	24 × 48	0.24	0.57	1.17	0.87	0.93	0.87	3.4	RAL
0.95	Tectum panel	2" Tectum over 2¹⁄₂" OCF noise barrier batt	4¹⁄₂	C-40	24 × 48	0.40	0.84	1.18	0.84	0.94	0.88	3.4	RAL
1.00	Isover PB R	Fiberglass construction	(80)	—	0.6m × 1.25m	0.60	1.10	1.07	0.94	0.96	0.94	4	IfL
0.65	Isover Climatel S	Fiberglass construction	(25)	—	1.2m × 12m	0.14	0.25	0.56	0.81	0.88	0.90	0.63	BI
0.60	Isover PB A	Fiberglass construction	(50)	—	0.6m × 1.25m	0.59	0.75	0.63	0.60	0.39	0.26	2.5	EMPA
0.85	Soning SONIT	Acoustical panel fabricated bonded sand particles	(30)	D	30cm × 100cm	0.23	0.57	1.00	0.97	0.94	0.71	27	Vzrt

APPENDIX 3.6 Acoustical Roof Decks

NRC	Company Trade name	Description	Thickness, inches (mm)	Mounting type	Unit size, inches	Sound absorption coefficients, Hz						Weight, lb/ft² (kg/m²)	Test lab
						125	250	500	1000	2000	4000		
0.80	ASCPac Acustadek B	Steel deck, perforated webs, absorptive backing	1½	A	108 × 96	0.23	0.67	1.21	0.82	0.46	0.24	3.0	RAL
0.85	ASCPac Acustadek B	Steel deck, total perforated absorptive backing	1½	A	108 × 96	0.23	0.48	0.92	0.97	0.95	0.76	2.1	RAL
0.80	ASCPac Acustadek BF	Steel deck, pan perforated absorptive backing	1½	A	108 × 96	0.53	0.58	0.75	0.97	0.86	0.57	4.3	RAL
0.85	ASCPac Acustadek N	Steel deck, perforated webs, absorptive backing	3	A	108 × 96	0.38	0.94	1.18	0.90	0.44	0.24	3.6	RAL
0.90	ASCPac Acustadek N	Steel deck, total perforated absorptive backing	3	A	108 × 96	0.43	0.61	1.01	1.05	1.00	0.76	2.6	RAL
0.90	ASCPac Acustadek NF	Steel deck, pan perforated absorptive backing	3	A	108 × 96	0.80	0.78	1.16	0.88	0.69	0.47	4.2	RAL
0.65	Epic EP150A	Perforated steel roof deck, backed by fiberglass	1½	A	—	0.20	0.33	0.74	1.00	0.57	0.41	—	RAL
1.00	Epic ESC2SSA	Perforated steel roof deck, backed by fiberglass	2	A	—	0.96	1.02	1.02	1.08	0.95	0.79	—	RAL
0.75	Epic EPICORE-A	Perforated steel roof deck, backed by fiberglass	2	A	—	0.10	0.21	0.79	0.98	0.95	0.86	—	RAL
0.95	Epic ER2RA	Perforated steel roof deck, backed by fiberglass	2	A	—	0.26	0.60	1.18	0.98	1.00	0.91	—	RAL
0.80	Epic EP300K	Perforated steel roof deck, backed by fiberglass	3	A	—	0.44	0.89	1.06	0.73	0.47	0.25	—	RAL
0.70	Epic E450A	Perforated steel roof deck, backed by fiberglass	4½	A	—	0.37	0.57	0.91	0.70	0.52	0.49	—	RAL

	Product	Description	Thickness		Size								
1.10	Epic EP450A	Perforated steel roof deck, backed by fiberglass	$4^{1}/_{2}$	A	—	0.85	1.14	1.29	1.10	0.92	0.74	—	RAL
1.80	Epic E750A	Perforated steel roof deck, backed by fiberglass	$7^{1}/_{2}$	A	—	0.48	0.77	0.88	0.86	0.70	0.60	—	RAL
0.55	MFG Fibroplank	Type M-173, wood fibers with portland cement binder	$1^{1}/_{2}$	A	96×108	0.09	0.21	0.42	1.00	0.58	0.80	5	RAL
0.90	MFG Fibroplank	Similar to above but with $2^{1}/_{2}$" fiberglass batts in cavities between furring	$1^{1}/_{2}$	C-40	96×108	0.39	0.82	1.23	0.75	0.81	0.92	5	RAL
0.60	MFG Fibroplank	Type M-173a, wood fibers with portland cement binder	2	A	96×108	0.13	0.23	0.62	1.03	0.61	0.81	6	RAL
0.65	MFG Fibroplank	Type M-173b, wood fibers with portland cement binder	$2^{1}/_{2}$	A	96×108	0.15	0.32	0.78	0.85	0.73	0.88	7	RAL
0.70	MFG Fibroplank	Type M-173c, wood fibers with portland cement binder	3	A	96×108	0.20	0.30	0.89	0.70	0.88	0.92	8	RAL
0.55	Tectum Tectum I	Structural roof deck	$1^{1}/_{2}$	A	48×96	0.07	0.22	0.48	0.82	0.64	0.96	2.4	RAL
0.60	Tectum Tectum I	Structural roof deck	2	A	48×96	0.15	0.26	0.62	0.94	0.64	0.92	3.5	RAL
0.65	Tectum Tectum I	Structural roof deck	$2^{1}/_{2}$	A	48×96	0.20	0.31	0.72	0.84	0.77	0.90	4.5	RAL
0.80	Tectum Tectum I	Structural roof deck	3	A	48×96	0.21	0.41	1.00	0.75	1.00	0.97	5.3	RAL
0.60	Tectum Tectum II with Isyo	Structural roof deck	4	A	48×96	0.20	0.31	0.55	0.83	0.74	0.95	3.5	RAL
0.60	Tectum Tectum III	Structural roof composite	$3^{1}/_{2}$	A	48×96	0.16	0.23	0.49	0.78	0.88	0.88	4.4	RAL

APPENDIX 3.7 Sprayed-on Acoustical Materials

NRC	Company Trade name	Description	Thickness, inches (mm)	Mounting type	Sound absorption coefficients, Hz						Weight, lb/ft^2	Test lab
					125	250	500	1000	2000	4000		
0.75	ICC K13	Cellulose-base fiber, white, sprayed-on, "carpet" finish	1	A	0.19	0.60	1.05	1.11	1.03	0.98	0.29	AS
1.00	ICC K13	Cellulose-base fiber, white, sprayed-on, "carpet" finish	3	A	0.59	0.99	1.04	1.03	1.00	0.98	0.88	AS
0.65	ICC K13FC/ Dura-K	Cellulose-base fiber, white, sprayed-on, textured finish	1/2	A	0.15	0.16	0.46	0.87	1.07	1.12	0.25	AS
0.75	ICC K13FC	Cellulose-base fiber, white, sprayed-on, textured finish	3/4	E-400	0.25	0.36	0.74	0.98	0.99	0.99	0.38	AS
0.90	ICC K13FC	Cellulose-base fiber, white, sprayed-on, textured finish	1	A	0.12	0.38	0.88	1.16	1.15	1.12	0.50	AS
0.60	PI Pyrok Acoustement 40	Acoustical plaster, Portland cement-base	1	A	0.18	0.35	0.64	0.73	0.73	0.77	3.4	CK
0.5	BHS Pyrok	Spray-on, medium structure material	2	A	0.06	0.14	0.30	0.59	0.92	0.56	10	EMPA
0.81	BHS Limpet	Spray-on mineral-fiber material	2.5	A	0.05	0.30	0.75	1.00	1.07	1.05	7	EMPA

APPENDIX 3.8 Sound-Rated Masonry Blocks

NRC	Company Trade name	Description	Thickness, inches (mm)	Mounting type	Unit size, inches	Sound absorption coefficients, Hz						Weight, lb/ft² (kg/m²)	Test lab
						125	250	500	1000	2000	4000		
—	Prdfoot Soundblox	Type A-1 slotted concrete masonry block, unfilled	4	A	8 × 16	0.12	0.85	0.36	0.36	0.42	0.45	23	G&H
—	Prdfoot Soundblox	Type A-1 slotted concrete masonry block, unfilled	6	A	8 × 16	0.62	0.84	0.36	0.43	0.27	0.50	26	G&H
—	Prdfoot Soundblox	Type A-1 slotted concrete masonry block, unfilled	8	A	8 × 16	0.97	0.44	0.38	0.39	0.50	0.60	32	G&H
—	Prdfoot Soundblox	Type Q, same as above but with metal septa in cavities	8	A	8 × 16	1.07	0.97	0.61	0.37	0.56	0.55	38	G&H
—	Prdfoot Soundblox	Type R, similar to above with cavities filled with fiberglass	12	A	8 × 16	0.48	0.83	0.86	0.54	0.47	0.44	62	G&H
—	Prdfoot Soundblox	Type RSC, fiberglass filled cavities, metal septa	12	A	8 × 16	0.57	0.76	1.09	0.94	0.54	0.59	70	G&H
0.85	RPG Diffusorblox	Unpainted concrete masonry unit	12	A	8 × 16	0.98	0.90	0.93	0.77	0.80	0.77	6	RAL
0.40	RPG Diffusorblox	Painted concrete masonry unit	12	A	8 × 16	0.76	0.51	0.57	0.34	0.24	0.26	6	RAL
0.55	Stark Starkustic	Structural clay hollow tile with perforated ceramic facing; hollows filled with fiberglass pads	4	A	8 × 16	0.19	0.64	0.73	0.62	0.20		25.9	RAL
—	Tectum	Sound absorption blocks spaced 24" on centers	3	A	15½ × 15½	0.22	0.32	1.01	1.60	1.66	1.64	8.4	RAL
—	Tectum	Sound absorption blocks spaced 32" on centers	3	A	15½ × 15½	0.27	0.43	1.13	1.77	1.75	1.75	8.4	RAL

APPENDIX 3.9 Hung Panels or Baffles; Suspended (Unit) Absorbers

(The sound absorption provided by such absorbers, which are hung from the ceiling, depends on how closely they are spaced. Therefore, information on such test conditions should be obtained from the manufacturer. There is no standard method for measuring and rating the sound-absorptive characteristics of these units. These tabulated sound absorption coefficients were obtained by dividing the total absorption of each unit by the total area of each unit.)

NRC	Company Trade name	Description	Thickness, inches (mm)	Mounting type	Unit size, inches	Sound absorption coefficients, Hz						Weight, lb/ft² (kg/m²)	Test lab
						125	250	500	1000	2000	4000		
—	INC 24G baffles	Hanging panels, 1.55 pcf fiberglass in polyethylene casing 0.002" thick	1½	hung	24 × 48	0.32	0.59	1.49	1.53	1.36	0.59	0.1	RAL
—	INC 27G baffles	Hanging panels, 2.70 pcf fiberglass in polyethylene casing 0.002" thick	1½	hung	24 × 48	0.31	0.61	1.28	1.64	1.42	1.03	0.35	RAL
—	INC 27E baffles	Hanging panels, 2.70 pcf fiberglass in polyethylene casing 0.003" thick	1½	hung	24 × 48	0.32	0.62	1.27	1.48	0.86	0.46	0.39	RAL
—	Prdfoot Baffles	Fiberglass core with polyethylene cover	1½	hung	24 × 48	0.24	0.66	1.31	1.74	1.49	1.03	0.25	RAL
—	Tectum	Hanging panels of 1" Tectum, spaced 12" face to face	1	hung	24 × 48	0.20	0.16	0.30	0.48	0.60	0.82	1.6	RAL
—	Tectum	Hanging panels of 1" Tectum, spaced 24" face to face	1	hung	24 × 48	0.12	0.20	0.29	0.49	0.65	0.91	1.6	RAL
—	Tectum	Hanging panels of 1" Tectum, spaced 36" face to face	1	hung	24 × 48	0.13	0.18	0.29	0.51	0.65	0.90	1.6	RAL
—	Sonex Baffles	2-sided wedge-shaped polyurethane foam, hanging panels	3	hung	31 × 48	0.58	0.47	0.84	1.26	1.61	1.80	0.8	TCT

3.78

—	Sonex 1 Baffles	2-sided wedge-shaped melamine foam, hanging panels	3	hung	24 × 48	0.74	0.78	1.42	1.76	1.83	1.84	0.4	TCT
—	BradIns	Suspended rockwool panels enclosed in polypropylene film	(50)	hung	50cm × 120cm	0.18	0.44	0.83	1.25	1.14	0.96	3.0	LC
—	SiegK Baffel	Suspended acoustical panels	(140)	hung	60cm × 120cm	0.30	0.65	0.90	1.10	1.15	1.30	2.3	EMPA

3.79

APPENDIX 3.10   General Building Materials and Furnishings

	Sound absorption coefficients, Hz					
	125	250	500	1000	2000	4000
Brick, unglazed	0.03	0.03	0.03	0.04	0.0	0.07
Brick, unglazed, painted	0.01	0.01	0.02	0.02	0.02	0.03
Carpet:						
Woven wool loop, 1.2kg/m² (35oz/yd²), 2.4mm (³/₃₂in) pile height, no pad	0.10	0.16	0.11	0.30	0.50	0.47
Woven wool loop, 1.4kg/m² (40oz/yd²), 6.4mm (³/₄in) pile height, no pad	0.15	0.17	0.12	0.32	0.52	0.57
Woven wool loop, 2.3kg/m² (66oz/yd²), 9.5mm (³/₈in) pile height, no pad	0.17	0.18	0.21	0.50	0.63	0.83
Loop pile tufted carpet, 1.4kg/m² (40oz/yd²), 9.5mm (⁶/₁₆in) pile height:						
On hair pad, 1.4kg/m² (40oz/yd²)	0.03	0.25	0.55	0.70	0.62	0.84
On hair pad, 3.0kg/m² (86oz/yd²)	0.10	0.40	0.62	0.70	0.63	0.88
On hair and jute pad, 3.0kg/m² (86oz/yd²)	0.20	0.50	0.68	0.72	0.65	0.90
Loop pile tufted carpet, 0.7kg/m² (20oz/yd²):						
No pad	0.04	0.08	0.17	0.33	0.59	0.75
With 1.4kg/m² (40oz/yd²) hair pad	0.10	0.19	0.35	0.79	0.69	0.79
Concrete block, coarse	0.36	0.44	0.31	0.29	0.39	0.25
Concrete block, painted	0.10	0.05	0.06	0.07	0.09	0.08
Drapes: (also see Figs. 30.15–30.17):						
Light velour 338g/m² (10oz/yd²) hung straight, in contact with wall	0.03	0.04	0.11	0.17	0.24	0.35
Medium velour, 475g/m² (14oz/yd²) draped to half area	0.07	0.31	0.49	0.75	0.70	0.60
Heavy velour, 610g/m² (18oz/yd²) draped to half area	0.14	0.35	0.55	0.72	0.70	0.65
Floors:						
Concrete or terrazzo	0.01	0.01	0.015	0.02	0.02	0.02
Linoleum, asphalt, rubber, or cork tile on concrete	0.02	0.03	0.03	0.03	0.03	0.02
Wood	0.15	0.11	0.10	0.07	0.06	0.07
Wood parquet in asphalt on concrete	0.04	0.04	0.07	0.06	0.06	0.07

APPENDIX 3.10   General Building Materials and Furnishings   (*Continued*)

	Sound absorption coefficients, Hz					
	125	250	500	1000	2000	4000
Glass:						
Large panes of heavy plate glass	0.18	0.06	0.04	0.03	0.02	0.02
Ordinary window glass	0.35	0.25	0.18	0.12	0.07	0.04
Gypsum board, 1.27cm ($^1/_2$in), nailed to 5.1- by 10.2-cm (2- by 4-in) studs 41cm (16in) center-to-center	0.29	0.10	0.05	0.04	0.07	0.09
Marble or glazed tile	0.01	0.01	0.01	0.01	0.02	0.02
Mineral spray-on materials:						
1.27cm ($^1/_2$in) mineral fiber	0.05	0.15	0.45	0.70	0.80	0.80
1.9cm ($^3/_4$in) mineral fiber	0.10	0.30	0.60	0.90	0.90	0.95
2.5cm (1in) mineral fiber	0.16	0.45	0.70	0.90	0.90	0.85
1.27cm ($^1/_2$in) mineral fiber on metal lath, 2.54cm (1in) airspace)	0.25	0.50	0.80	0.90	0.90	0.85
Plaster, gypsum, or lime, smooth finish on tile or brick	0.013	0.015	0.02	0.03	0.04	0.05
Plaster, gypsum, or lime, rough finish on lath	0.14	0.10	0.06	0.05	0.04	0.03
Same, with smooth finish	0.14	0.10	0.06	0.04	0.04	0.03
Plywood paneling, 1cm ($^3/_8$in) thick	0.28	0.22	0.17	0.09	0.10	0.11
Water surface, as in a swimming pool	0.008	0.008	0.013	0.015	0.020	0.025

Sound in Enclosed Spaces

Cyril M. Harris

INTRODUCTION

When sound waves strike a surface, some of the incident sound is reflected, some is transmitted through it, and some is absorbed. This chapter describes the acoustical properties of a room when sound is reflected from surfaces within the room. Procedures are given for calculating the total amount of sound absorbed by these surfaces. Then, the total absorption is related to (1) the average noise level in the room and (2) the reverberation in the room. (*Reverberation* is the persistence of sound in a room after a source has stopped emitting sound.) Finally, descriptions are presented showing how sound level varies with distance from a noise source in a room. Such relationships depend on the location of the source as well as the acoustical characteristics of the room; reflections from the walls, ceilings, floor, and from objects within the room all affect the distribution of sound in the room.

REFLECTION OF SOUND WAVES FROM WALLS AND CEILINGS

When sound waves travel outward from a source and strike a surface (such as a wall or ceiling), their direction of travel is changed; i.e., they are *reflected*. In many problems related to noise control in buildings, it is convenient to indicate the direction of sound waves by sound rays. *Sound rays* are imaginary lines that are drawn perpendicular to the wavefronts of the sound waves to indicate their direction of travel, as illustrated in Fig. 2.4. *Upon striking a surface, the angle of reflection of the sound waves depends on the ratio of the dimensions of the reflecting surface to the wavelength of the incident*

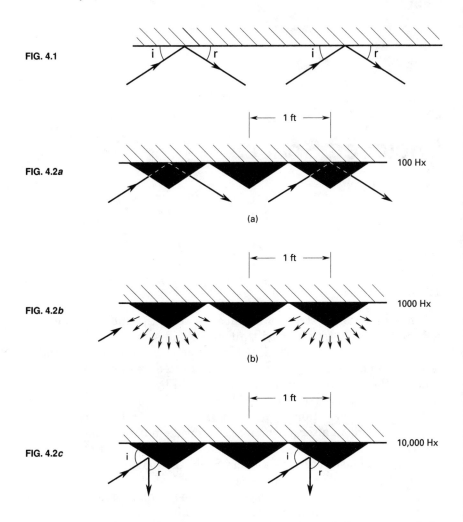

FIG. 4.1

FIG. 4.2a

100 Hx

(a)

FIG. 4.2b

1000 Hx

(b)

FIG. 4.2c

10,000 Hx

sound. (The relationship between wavelength and frequency of the sound waves was given in Fig. 2.3.)

When sound is reflected from a flat, hard surface whose dimensions are *large compared to the wavelength* of the incident sound, the angle of reflection $\angle r$ is equal to the angle of the incidence $\angle i$; this relationship, called the *law of reflection,* is illustrated in Fig. 4.1. The solid lines with arrowheads represent sound rays. It is important to emphasize that this law holds *only* when the dimensions of the reflecting surface are large compared with the wavelength of the incident sound waves.

This section considers the reflection of sound from a large, hard, flat surface on which there are *surface irregularities,* for example, the splayed surfaces as shown in solid black in Fig. 4.2. Three general cases are compared:

FIG. 4.1   Reflection of sound from a flat surface that is very large compared with the wavelength λ of the incident sound. The solid lines with arrowheads represent "sound rays" which indicate the direction of travel of the sound waves. In this case, the angle of reflection ∡r is equal to the angle of incidence ∡i.

FIG. 4.2   The reflection of sound from a large, flat surface on which there are surface irregularities in the form of solid, splayed surfaces that are identical in shape and size—each having an overall dimension of about 1 foot (0.3 m). Only the frequency (and therefore the wavelength) of the incident sound is different in each of the following examples: (a) The incident sound waves have a frequency of 100 Hz [wavelength of 11 feet (3.4 m)]. Because the dimensions of the surface irregularities are small compared with the wavelength of the incident sound, the sound waves reflect as though the entire surface were perfectly flat, so that the angle of reflection is the same as in Fig. 4.1. This is illustrated by drawing the sound rays (which are imaginary lines showing the direction of propagation of the sound waves) as though they do not "see" the solid, splayed surface. (b) The incident sound waves have a frequency of 1000 Hz [wavelength of 1.1 feet (0.34 m)]. Because the dimensions of the surface irregularities are comparable to the wavelength of the incident sound, the incident sound is scattered in all directions. (c) The incident sound waves have a frequency of 10,000 Hz [wavelength of 0.11 feet (0.034 m)]. In this case, the dimensions of each of the surface irregularities are large compared with the wavelength of the incident sound. Therefore, the law of reflection applies to each surface irregularity, i.e., the angle of reflection ∡r from each of these surfaces is the same as the angle of incidence ∡i.

a. The dimensions of the surface irregularities are small compared with the wavelength λ of the incident sound waves.

b. The dimensions of the surface irregularities are comparable in size to the wavelength λ of the incident sound waves.

c. The dimensions of the surface irregularities are large compared with the wavelength λ of the incident sound waves.

In each case, the surface irregularities are the same splayed surfaces (identical in shape and size), each having an overall dimension of about 1 foot (0.3 m). Furthermore, the angle of incidence is the same. However, in each case, the frequency of the incident sound is different so that the ratio of dimensions of the surface irregularities to the wavelength of the incident sound is different.

Surface Irregularities Small in Size Compared with the Wavelength

In Fig. 4.2a, the incident sound waves have a frequency of 100 Hz. According to Fig. 2.3, this frequency corresponds to a wavelength of 11 feet (3.4 m). Therefore, the dimensions of the splayed surfaces are small compared with the wavelength of the incident sound. In this case, the sound waves do not "see" the surface irregularities—the splayed surfaces (shown in solid black) are too small to affect the incident sound waves. Therefore, reflection from the splayed surfaces does not obey the law of reflection. Instead, the incident sound follows the law of reflection *from the large surface* just as though this entire surface were perfectly flat.

Surface Irregularities Comparable in Size with the Wavelength

In Fig. 4.2*b*, the incident sound waves have a frequency of 1000 Hz. According to Fig. 2.3, this frequency corresponds to a wavelength of 1.1 feet (0.34 m). Here, the dimensions of the splayed surfaces are about the same as the wavelength of the incident sound. Therefore, the law of reflection does not hold for reflection from the splayed surfaces. In this case, the incident sound is scattered effectively in all directions.

Surface Irregularities Large in Size Compared with the Wavelength

In Fig. 4.2*c*, the incident sound waves have a frequency of 10,000 Hz. According to Fig. 2.3, this frequency corresponds to a wavelength of 0.11 feet (0.034 m). Here, the dimension of each splayed surface is large compared with the wavelength of the incident sound. Therefore, the law of reflection holds for reflections *from the splayed surfaces,* as illustrated.

ABSORPTION OF SOUND IN A ROOM BY THE MATERIALS OF WHICH IT IS CONSTRUCTED AND BY ITS FURNISHINGS

Sound Absorption Coefficients

The absorption of sound by materials is described in detail in Chap. 3. The *sound absorption coefficient* α of a material is that fraction of randomly-incident acoustic energy which is absorbed (or otherwise not reflected) when sound waves strike its surface. A sound absorption coefficient of 0.00 indicates 0 percent absorption (i.e., perfect reflection); a coefficient of 1.00 indicates 100 percent absorption (i.e., complete absorption). The sound absorption of materials varies with frequency. Sound absorption coefficients for a number of different building materials are given in the appendixes of Chap. 3 for various frequencies.

All materials absorb some sound, but an *acoustical material* is one whose primary function is to absorb sound. The sound-absorptive properties of an acoustical material depend not only on the frequency of the incident sound waves but also on the angle of incidence. At any given frequency, unless otherwise specifically stated, the coefficients which appear in the tables of this book, in formulas, commercial literature, and texts, represent values of absorption coefficients *averaged* over all angles of incidence. Such average values are obtained from laboratory measurements.*

Unit of Sound Absorption

The unit of sound absorption is the *sabin*; one *sabin* is the equivalent of 1 square foot of a perfectly absorptive surface. One *metric sabin* is the equivalent of 1 m² of a perfectly absorptive surface. For example, a surface of 10 ft² having a sound absorption coefficient α of 0.65 provides an absorption of 6.5 sabins. A surface S of 10 m² having a sound absorption coefficient α of 0.65 provides an absorption of 6.5 metric sabins.

Total Sound Absorption in a Room A

The total sound absorption A in a room is equal to the sum of:

1. The absorption provided by all the surfaces in the room $A_{surface}$—primarily due to the walls, ceiling, and floor.
2. The absorption due to the furnishings in the room $A_{furnishings}$.
3. The absorption due to air A_{air}. Thus the total sound absorption within the room (i.e., the room absorption) is given by

$$A = A_{surface} + A_{furnishings} + A_{air} \qquad (4.1)$$

Absorption Provided by All the Surfaces in the Room $A_{surface}$. This term represents the absorption resulting primarily from the walls, ceiling, and floor surfaces. The sound absorption due to a surface (such as a ceiling) is obtained by multiplying its sound absorption coefficient by its area. The sum of the absorption provided by all of the surfaces A is then obtained by adding the individual contributions of each of the various surfaces:

$$A_{surface} = \alpha_1 S_1 + \alpha_2 S_2 + \alpha_3 S_3 + \cdots \qquad \text{sabins} \qquad (4.2)$$

---

*For example, the American Society for Testing and Materials (ASTM) defines sound absorption as: "A measure of the sound absorptive properties of a material as approximated by ASTM Method C423, Test for Sound Absorption and Sound Absorption Coefficients by the Reverberation Room Method. Ideally, the fraction of the randomly incident sound power which is absorbed or otherwise not reflected by the material."

TABLE 4.1   Calculation of Surface Absorption A$_{surface}$ at 500 Hz in an Unfurnished Room

Surface	Absorption coefficient α	Area S ft^2	Area S m^2	Absorption A_b sabins	Absorption A_b metric sabins
Floor concrete	0.02	968	90	19	1.8
Ceiling plaster	0.03	968	90	29	2.7
Walls, plaster, and glass	0.06	1356	126	82	7.6
Miscellaneous				10	0.9
Total absorption				140	13.0

A sample calculation of the surface absorption in a small, unfurnished room at 500 Hz is given in Table 4.1. For example, what is the absorption provided by the concrete floor in this room? The absorption coefficient α of concrete has a value of 0.02 at 500 Hz. Therefore, the absorption provided by the floor is 0.02 multiplied by the area of the floor, 968 square feet (90 m^2), yielding an absorption of 19 sabins (1.8 metric sabins).

Similarly, the sound absorption coefficient at 500 Hz is multiplied by the area of each of the other surfaces in the room to find its contribution to the surface absorption $A_{surface}$ (expressed in sabins). Finally, the absorption for all the various areas must be added to obtain the absorption provided by all of the surfaces in the room as illustrated in Table 4.1. Following this procedure for the example of Table 4.1, the total sound absorption in the room $A_{surface}$ is 140 sabins (13.0 metric sabins) at 500 Hz. Then, similar calculations usually are made at the following frequencies: 125, 250, 1000, 2000, and 4000 Hz.

Absorption Due to Furnishings.   Appendix 3.10 provides the sound absorption coefficients of some common building furnishings. In most places of assembly, a major contributor to this category of sound absorption is *chair absorption, A$_{chair}$.* Chair absorption is usually expressed in terms of the absorption in sabins (or metric sabins) per chair—depending on the system of units employed. Therefore, the value of A_{chair} is given by the absorption per chair times the number of chairs. Values of chair absorption are usually given at various frequencies for the: (1) occupied chair, i.e., with a person sitting in it, and (2) unoccupied chair. The sound absorption provided by a seated audience is frequently the largest contributor to the total absorption in the room.

Air Absorption.   The absorption of sound by air A_{air} usually can be disregarded because its contribution to the total absorption in most noise control problems is relatively small. However, at high frequencies (above 2000 Hz) A_{air} in very large rooms can be an important contribution to the total room absorption.

A_{air} is given by

$$A_{air} = 4mV \qquad \text{sabins} \qquad (4.3)$$

where m is the air attenuation coefficient per foot (or per meter) and V is the volume of the room in ft^3 (or m^3). The values of m are given in Fig. 4.3 as a function of relative humidity[1] for various frequencies at a temperature of 20°C. Unlike the absorption contributed by a surface (such as a ceiling), the absorption contributed by the air within a

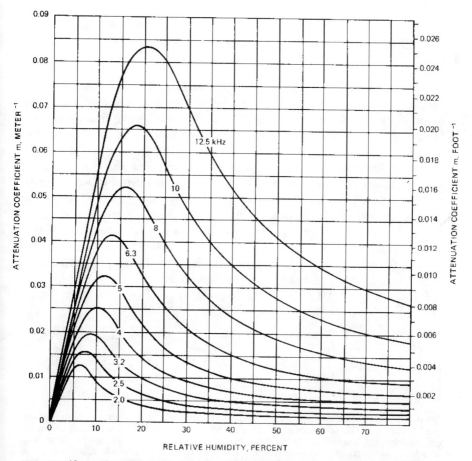

FIG. 4.3 Absorption of sound in air versus humidity at various frequencies. Values of the total attenuation coefficient m versus percent relative humidity for air at 20°C and normal atmospheric pressure for frequencies between 2000 and 12,500 Hz.[1,2] Values of m (a measure of sound absorption in air) are given in both U.S. Customary System and SI units. (*After C. M. Harris.*[1,2])

room depends on the volume of the room. Reference 2 provides more detailed information.

In calculating the total sound absorption in a room, the absorption due to air is simply added to the absorption provided by the walls, floor, ceiling, and materials and furnishings within the room. At frequencies below 2000 Hz, air absorption is usually negligible in rooms of any size.

Example:

Suppose a room has a volume of 600,000 ft³ (17,000 m³). What is the sound absorption due to air A_{air} at a frequency of 4000 Hz and a relative humidity of 40 percent? According to Fig. 4.3, for these conditions, the value of m is equal to 0.0022 per foot (0.0072 per meter). Therefore, from Eq. (4.3) the sound absorption due to air A_{air} is 5300 sabins (490 metric sabins).

MULTIPLE REFLECTIONS OF SOUND IN A ROOM

The reflection of sound waves by the boundaries of the room usually result in a complicated spatial pattern of sound within the room. For example, Fig. 4.4 depicts the progress of a sound wave in a rectangular room having hard, flat walls. The solid circles, or arcs of circles, represent the wavefronts of sound radiated by the source; the lines with the arrowheads (i.e., the sound rays) indicate the directions in which the waves travel. Figure 4.4a shows a wavefront 0.005 seconds after it has left the source S—before it strikes the walls. Figure 4.4b shows the wavefront 0.01 seconds after it has left the source. The wavefront now has traveled twice as far as in Fig. 4.4a; part of the wave has reflected from the nearest wall. Figure 4.4c shows the wavefront 0.02 seconds after it has left the source. There are reflections from the sidewalls and double reflections from both the end wall and sidewalls. Figure 4.4d shows the wavefront 0.06 seconds after it has

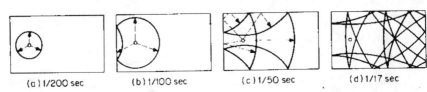

(a) 1/200 sec   (b) 1/100 sec   (c) 1/50 sec   (d) 1/17 sec

FIG. 4.4 Progress of a single sound wave in a rectangular room (shown in plan) having hard, flat walls. The solid circles, or arcs of circles, represent the wavefronts of waves radiated by the source; the dotted lines and arrows (i.e., the sound rays) indicate the directions in which the waves travel. (a) The wavefront 0.005 seconds after it has left the source and before it strikes the walls. (b) The wavefront 0.01 seconds after it has left the source; part of the wave has reflected from the nearest wall. (c) The wavefront 0.02 seconds after it has left the source; there are reflections from the walls. (d) The wavefront 0.06 seconds after it has left the source; the original wavefront has broken into a large number of segments, all traveling in different directions in the room.

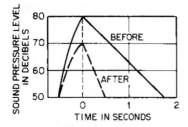

FIG. 4.5 An idealized curve showing the buildup of reflected sound in a room when a source is turned on; at time $t = 0$ seconds, the source is turned off and the sound pressure level decreases linearly. The solid curve shows conditions before the addition of acoustical material in the room; the dashed curve shows conditions after the addition of acoustical material.

left the source. Now, the reflection pattern is quite complicated. The original wavefront has broken into a large number of segments, all traveling in different directions in the room. Some segments of the original wavefront (reflections from the floor and ceiling) are not shown in this illustration.

The Effects of the Boundaries of a Room in Producing Multiple Reflections

Effects of multiple reflections are illustrated by Fig. 4.5, which shows the average level of reflected sound in a room when a source starts radiating sound; it then shows how the level of reflected sound dies away when the source is stopped at $t = 0$. The solid line illustrates the case of a room in which there is very little sound absorption. In this example, the sound level increases to a value of 80 dB after the sound source is turned on and dies away slowly after the sound is turned off. The dashed curves show the effect of increasing the sound absorption by "treating" the room with acoustical material. Because of the added absorption, the sound level only reaches a maximum value of 70 dB; then, it dies away more rapidly when the source is turned off.

Diffusion of Sound in a Room

When a noise source emits sound continuously in a room, the room is filled with reflected sound waves traveling in many different directions. The greater the uniformity of the reflected sound level in the room, the greater the "diffusion" in the room. Sound is said to be *perfectly diffuse* in a room if the level of the reflected sound is everywhere equal and if the reflected sound waves travel in all directions with equal probability. In such a room, it is difficult to determine the direction from which a sound originates unless one is very close to the source.

The principal means of providing diffusion of sound in a room are by:

1. Irregularities on the wall surfaces, for example, large splays, convex surfaces, pilasters, coffers, and surface ornamentation.
2. Objects within the room that scatter the sound, for example, freestanding columns, statues, or chairs.
3. Sound-absorptive materials that are nonuniformly distributed in the room. (This contribution to the diffusion of sound in a room is usually much less significant than the above two contributions.)

Surface irregularities and objects in a room are most effective in promoting diffusion when their dimensions are roughly equal to the wavelength of the incident sound. For this reason, to obtain excellent diffusion over a range of frequencies requires that surface irregularities or objects be of many different sizes. Sound is more diffuse in a furnished room than it is in an empty room.

In a room having very good diffusion, the sound level tends to decrease relatively uniformly with increasing distance from a sound source. In contrast, in a room having poor diffusion, in moving away from the source, the decrease in sound level is much more irregular, often being marked by a significant maxima and minima.

The diffusion of sound in a room will be very poor:

1. If the walls and ceiling are flat, unbroken surfaces
2. If one of the room dimensions is many times one of the other dimensions (say, 5 times one of the other dimensions) as is sometimes the case in a very large office having a low ceiling height
3. If the shape of the room is unusual (such as a cruciform church or an auditorium having a very large balcony overhang)
4. If the room is connected by an opening (i.e., "coupled") to another room having quite different acoustical characteristics
5. If the source of sound in the room includes one or more strong discrete frequency components (i.e., pure tones)

Noise Reduction Provided by the Addition of Sound-Absorptive Material

The addition of acoustical material to a room provides the following significant benefits:

1. It reduces the average noise level in the room.
2. It increases the rate at which the reflected sound dies out after the source is turned off, i.e., it reduces the persistence of sound in the room, thereby reducing its potential for annoyance.

3. It tends to localize noise to the region of its origin; a distant source is attenuated relatively more than a source nearby, so that the noise reduction of unexpected, distant sources (which are particularly annoying) is especially beneficial.

Reduction in Noise Level

The addition of acoustical materials can be extremely effective in reducing the average noise level in a room. This reduction is given by

$$\text{level reduction} = 10 \log_{10} \left(\frac{A_{\text{after}}}{A_{\text{before}}} \right) \quad \text{dB} \tag{4.4}$$

where A_{before} is the total sound absorption in sabins before addition of the acoustical material, i.e., before "acoustical treatment," and A_{after} is that after treatment. This relationship, which applies in a room having reasonably good diffusion, is shown graphically in Fig. 4.6.

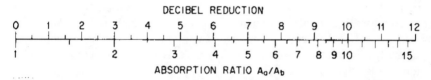

FIG. 4.6 Reduction in the level of reflected sound in a regularly proportioned room in which diffuse conditions prevail, due to an increase in the total sound absorption in the room from A_{before} to A_{after}.

If a room contains very little sound absorption, the ratio of the sound absorption after acoustic treatment A_{after} to the sound absorption before treatment A_{before} can have a value of at least 4:1. For this ratio, according to Fig. 4.6, the additional sound absorption will result in a 6-dB decrease in level of the reflected sound in the room—a very substantial reduction. In contrast, if a room contains considerable sound absorption before treatment, it is usually impractical to increase the ratio of $A_{\text{after}}/A_{\text{before}}$ by more than 2:1. According to Fig. 4.6, this ratio will result in a decrease in noise level of only 3 dB. This illustrates that *the addition of the same amount of sound absorption is more effective in decreasing the average noise level in a room containing little sound absorption in it than it is in a room already containing considerable sound absorption.*

Example: Consider the unfurnished room of Table 4.1 which has the following dimensions: 19.7 ft × 49.2 ft × 9.8 ft (6 m × 15 m × 3 m). The total absorption before treatment A_{before} due to the walls, ceiling, and floor is 140 sabins (13.0 metric sabins). If the plaster ceiling [which has an area of 968 square feet (90 m²) and a sound absorption coefficient of 0.03] is now covered with an acoustical material having an absorption coefficient of 0.70, the net *increase* in sound absorption is 968 ft^2 (0.70 − 0.03) = 649 sabins (60.3 metric sabins). Therefore, the total sound absorption after treatment A_{after} is 140 + 649 = 789 sabins (73.3 metric sabins).

How much noise reduction in the room is achieved by the installation of acoustical material on the ceiling? According to Eq. (4.4), the reduction in level of the reflected sound in the room is

$$\text{level reduction} = 10 \log_{10} \frac{A_{after}}{A_{before}} \quad \text{dB} = 10 \log_{10} \frac{789}{140} = 7.5 \text{ dB}$$

This same value is obtained if the ratio of absorption is expressed in SI units, i.e., the level reduction = $10 \log_{10} (73.3/13.0) = 7.5$ dB.

Quantity of Sound Absorption Required for Noise Control Purposes

What Ratio of A_{after} to A_{before} Is Required?   To produce a noticeable reduction in noise level in a room, the ratio of (a) the total absorption in the room after acoustical material has been added to the room to (b) the total absorption in the room before acoustical material has been added to the room, i.e., A_{after}/A_{before}, should be at least 3:1. In general, a smaller ratio will not be perceived by the ear as a reduction, under average conditions.

Rule of thumb to determine how much additional acoustical material is required.   In the absence of quantitative information required for the calculation procedure given below, the following rule of thumb is useful for estimating the surface area of a room that should be covered by acoustical material for noise reduction purposes:

Apply a material having a noise reduction coefficient (NRC) of at least 0.6 over the entire ceiling; the higher the ceiling, the higher must be the value of the NRC to provide satisfactory results.

As noted below, in a room where the ceiling height is not small compared to the other dimensions, treatment of only the ceiling may not yield satisfactory results.

Rooms with High Ceilings.   In a rectangular room having a high ceiling and smooth, reflective walls, the application of acoustical material only on the ceiling generally does not yield satisfactory results for noise reduction purposes—no matter how absorptive the ceiling treatment is. This is because sustained reflections by sound waves bounce back and forth between the walls—grazing the ceiling treatment. Acoustical materials are not especially effective in absorbing sound waves that graze the surface. Thus, in a room having a very high ceiling, the perceived noise reduction provided only by a ceiling treatment usually is disappointingly low. In such a room, some sound absorptive material should be applied on the side walls.

Procedure for Calculating the Required Absorption in a Room

The amount of sound absorption that is required in a room, for noise control purposes, may be calculated as follows:

1. First, calculate the total absorption in the room before treatment A_{before}.
2. Determine the existing or expected noise level in the room.
3. Determine the acceptable noise level in the room from Table 7.12.
4. To obtain the required noise reduction in decibels, subtract the acceptable sound level (Step 3) from the existing (or expected) sound level (Step 2).
5. Using the required noise reduction determined from Step 4, determine the ratio of A_{after}/A_{before} from Eq. (4.4).
6. Using the value of A_{before} from Step 1, and A_{after}/A_{before} (from Step 5), determine the required amount of absorption after treatment A_{after}.
7. Subtract A_{before} (Step 1) from A_{after} (Step 6) to obtain the required additional sound absorption, in sabins, to achieve acceptable conditions.

Procedure for Calculating the Reduction in A-Weighted Sound Level Resulting from the Addition of Acoustical Material in a Room

Step 1. Measure or estimate the sound level in each octave band (i.e., determine the octave-band levels) of the reflected sound before the application of the acoustical material.

Step 2. To the octave-band levels determined in Step 1, add the adjustment for A-weighting given in boldface in Table 2.2. This will provide the A-weighted octave-band levels before treatment.

Step 3. Calculate the A-weighted sound level before treatment. This may be done by combining the A-weighted octave-band levels determined in Step 2.

Step 4. From Eq. (4.4), for each octave band of Step 2, calculate the reduction in level resulting from the application of acoustical material using the values of the sound absorption coefficient for the center frequency of each octave band.

Step 5. For each octave-band level determined in Step 3, subtract the corresponding reductions calculated in Step 4. This will provide the A-weighted octave-band levels after treatment.

Step 6. Combine the A-weighted octave-band levels of Step 5 (using Fig. 2.21) to obtain the A-weighted sound levels after treatment.

Step 7. The difference between the sound levels of Step 3 and Step 6 represents the reduction in A-weighted sound level resulting from the installation of acoustical material.

TABLE 4.2 Sample Calculation of Noise Reduction in a Room by Acoustical Treatment

Octave-band center frequency, Hz	Octave-band level before treatment, dB	Adjustment for A-weighting, dB	A-weighted octave-band level before treatment, dB	Reduction in octave-band level caused by treatment, dB	A-weighted octave-band level after treatment, dB
125	83	−16.1	66.9	−2.6	64.3
250	81	−8.6	72.4	−5.8	66.6
500	79	−3.2	75.8	−8.7	67.1
1000	77	0	77.0	−8.9	68.1
2000	75	1.2	76.2	−8.5	67.7
4000	72	1.0	73.0	−7.9	65.1
A-weighted sound level before treatment:	82.3 dB(A)		A-weighted sound level after treatment:	74.4 dB(A)	

Example: Suppose the noise in a room before treatment has the octave-band levels shown in Table 4.2. This octave-band spectrum corresponds to an A-weighted sound level of 82.3 dB(A). In this example, the sound absorption coefficients of the walls, ceiling, and floor before treatment are 0.05 at all frequencies. The room then is treated by covering 40 percent of its surface area with acoustical material 1 inch (2.5 cm) thick having the following sound absorption coefficients:

Frequency, Hz	125	250	500	1000	2000	4000
Absorption coefficient	0.15	0.40	0.85	0.90	0.80	0.70

The calculated values of reduction in each octave band are shown in Table 4.2. Combining these octave-band levels by the use of Fig. 2.21 yields a calculated reduction in A-weighted sound level of 82.3 − 74.4 = 7.9 dB(A). (In this example, contributions to the A-weighted sound level in octave bands other than those considered here are assumed to be negligible.)

REVERBERATION

Suppose a source emits sound in a room. The sound which travels from the source to a listener by a direct air path, without any reflections, is called the *direct sound.* It is the first sound to reach the listener because it travels from the source directly to the listener by the shortest possible path. It is then followed by reflections from the walls, ceiling, and floor, and from objects within the room. In general, these reflected waves arrive in such rapid succession that they are not heard as distinct repetitions of the original sound. This is because the ear is unable to resolve two sounds (i.e., hear them as two distinct sounds) if they are spaced closer in time than about 0.06 second. As a result, the series of reflections are heard as a prolongation of sound from the source, after it has stopped. The prolongation of sound after the source has stopped is called *reverberation*.

Reverberation Time

The *reverberation time* of a room is the time required for the sound level in the room to decrease 60 dB after the source is stopped. Reverberation time T_{60} is given, approximately, by

$$T_{60} = 0.049 \frac{V}{A} \qquad \text{seconds} \qquad (4.5a)$$

where V is the volume in cubic feet and A is the absorption in sabins. Since the absorption in a room varies with frequency, the reverberation time also is different at different frequencies.

In SI units, the corresponding equation is

$$T_{60} = 0.161 \frac{V}{A} \qquad \text{seconds} \qquad (4.5b)$$

where V is the volume of the room in cubic meters and A is the total sound absorption in the room in metric sabins.

Figure 4.7 shows a record of the decay of sound in a room in which there is good diffusion. As a result of good diffusion of sound in the room, the sound level decreases at nearly a constant rate. (The

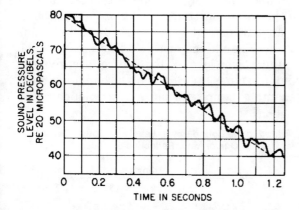

FIG. 4.7 A high-speed recording showing how the sound pressure level decays with time in a room having good sound diffusion.

greater the diffusion of sound in the room, the smoother will be the decay rate.) In this example, note that the sound level decays 30 dB in 0.9 second. Therefore, according to the above definition, the reverberation time of the room (i.e., the time to decay 60 dB) is 1.8 seconds.

Example: Calculate the reverberation time of the room considered in Table 4.1 which has a volume of 8700 cubic feet (246 m³) and a total sound absorption of 140 sabins (13 metric sabins). From Eq. (4.5a), the reverberation time T_{60} = 0.049 × 8700/140 = 3.0 seconds. In SI units, Eq. (4.5b) t_{60} = 0.161 × 246/13 = 3.0 s.

Decay Rate

The decay rate of sound in a room is the average rate at which the *reverberant* (reflected) *sound level* decreases after the source stops emitting sound; it is given by

$$\text{decay rate} = \frac{60}{T_{60}} \quad \text{decibels per second} \tag{4.6}$$

For example, the room whose decay characteristics are shown in Fig. 4.7 has a reverberation time of 1.8 seconds. Therefore, according to Eq. (4.6), the decay rate of sound in the room is 33.3 dB/second.

The Effect of a Nearby Reflective Surface on the Effective Power Output of a Noise Source

If a noise source is within 3 feet (1 m) of a reflective surface such as a wall or the ceiling, the source effectively radiates a greater amount of sound than it would if the same source were not close to the reflective surface. Therefore, an adjustment must be made to take this increase into consideration. The values of this adjustment, which must be added to the sound power level of the source, are given in Table 4.3. These approximate values are commonly used in engineering computations. For example, suppose a noise source (such as an

TABLE 4.3   Adjustment to be Added to the Sound Power Level of a Sound Source When It Is Located within 3 feet (1 m) of One or More Reflective Surfaces

Number of reflective surfaces	Adjustment to be added, dB
1 (e.g., on a ceiling or floor)	3
2 (e.g., at an intersection of a ceiling and wall)	6
3 (e.g., at a corner of a room)	9

HVAC air outlet) produces a sound power level of 100 dB re 1 pico-watt when it is far from any reflective surface. If this same air outlet is now set into a ceiling, an adjustment of 3 dB must be added to the rated sound power level of the source, so that its effective sound power level is 103 dB; if it is set into a ceiling at the intersection with a wall, an adjustment of 6 dB must be added, so that its effective sound power level is 106 dB; if it is set into a corner of the room, an adjustment of 9 dB must be added, so that its effective sound power level is 109 dB.

SOUND LEVEL VERSUS DISTANCE FROM A SOURCE IN A ROOM IN WHICH THERE IS GOOD DIFFUSION

Figure 4.8 provides an example of how the sound level decreases with increasing distance from a source in a room in which there is good diffusion. Three curves are shown:

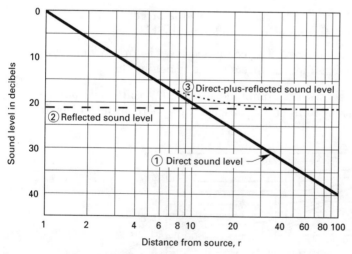

FIG. 4.8 Sound level versus distance from a source in a room in which diffuse conditions prevail. Near the source, the *direct sound level* L_d Curve 1 shows the level of the direct sound L_d; this value depends on the sound power of the source and decreases 6 dB for each doubling of distance from the source. Curve 2 shows the level of the *reflected sound level* L_r; this value is independent of the distance from the source—depending primarily on the sound power of the source and the total amount of absorption A in the room. Curve 3 shows the *direct-plus-reflected sound level* L_p, obtained by combining the levels of Curves 2 and 3 according to Fig. 2.21.

Curve 1: Level of the direct sound L_d. *Direct sound* is the sound that travels directly from the source to the point of observation—no reflection of sound is involved; for this reason, the direct sound is not affected by the characteristics of a room. The sound level of the direct sound (L_d) is the same in a room as it is in a "free field" far from any reflecting surface; as indicated in Eq. (2.9), it decreases 6 dB for each doubling of distance from the source as indicated by the solid line.

Curve 2: Level of the reflected sound L_r. In a room in which the sound is perfectly diffuse, the reflected sound is approximately equal everywhere in the room (except close to the walls), so that it is independent of distance from the source, as indicated by the horizontal dashed line in Fig. 4.8. The level of the reflected sound depends only on the sound power level of the source L_W and the total sound absorption A in the room, as indicated by Eq. (4.9), below.

Curve 3: The combined direct-plus-reflected sound level L_p. Curves 1 and 2 may be combined by the use of Fig. 2.21. An example of their combined level is shown as Curve 3 in Fig. 4.8.

The above curves illustrate that:

1. *Near the Source:* The combined level is largely determined by the direct sound; the reflected sound is negligible.

2. *Far from the Source:* The combined level is largely determined by the reflected sound; the direct sound is negligible.

Figure 4.9 shows the combined direct-plus-reflected sound L_p for various values of total sound absorption in a room in which there is

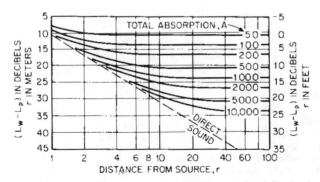

FIG. 4.9 Graph for converting the sound power level L_W (re 1 picowatt) to total sound pressure level L_W in a room. ($L_W - L_p$) is plotted as a function of distance from the sound source. Use ordinate on the right if the distance r is in feet; use ordinate on the left if the distance r is in meters.

good diffusion. In an ordinary room, these values, though approximate at best, provide engineers with useful guidance. The value of L_p is the sound level that would be measured by a sound-level meter. Since the value of L_p depends not only on the total sound absorption A in the room but also on the value of the sound power level of the source L_W (which is usually constant in any given problem), it is convenient to plot the quantity $(L_W - L_p)$ as a function of distance r from the source. For example, what is the sound level 6 feet from a source having a sound power level L_W of 100 dB, in a room having a total sound absorption A of 500 sabins (that is, 46 metric sabins)? According to Fig. 4.9, for this value of A, $(L_W - L_p) = 10$ dB. Therefore, the combined direct-plus-reflected sound level L_p at this distance is equal to 90 dB. This same value is obtained if the corresponding calculations are made in SI units.

Effects of Adding Sound Absorption in a Room

Figure 4.9 illustrates the effect of adding sound absorption in a room. At distances far from the source, the decrease in sound level that results from the addition of acoustical material in the room is the same as that given by Eq. (4.4). For example, if the total room absorption A is increased from 50 to 200 sabins, the reduction in total sound level at *large* distances from the source is 6 dB. Close to the source, the corresponding reduction in sound level is much less. As a general rule, the greater the total absorption in a room, the greater is the distance from the source at which a given increase in absorption is fully effective in reducing the combined direct-plus-reflected sound level L_p.

These curves are based on the assumption that sound in the room is reasonably diffuse. Although this is usually not the case, for engineering purposes, these curves often provide useful estimates.

Numerical Procedure for Calculating L_p. Consider a noise source of sound power level L_W in a room in which there is good diffusion. (If the sound in the room is *not* diffuse, then apply the methods presented in the last section of this chapter.) At any distance r from the source, the sound level L_p can be calculated as follows:

Step 1. Adjust the sound power level of the source L_W if the source is close to a reflective surface, according to Table 4.3.

Step 2. Determine the Direct Sound Level L_d. The direct sound level is given by Eq. (2.9), i.e.,

$$L_d = L_W - 20 \log_{10} r - 0.6 \quad \text{dB} \qquad (4.7a)$$

where r is the distance from the source in feet; L_W is the sound power level of the source.

In SI units:

$$L_d = L_W - 20 \log_{10} r - 10.9 \quad \text{dB} \qquad (4.7b)$$

where r is the distance from the source in meters and L_W is the sound power level of the source.

Step 3. Determine the reflected sound level L_r. The *reflected sound* at any point in a room is the sum of reflections from all boundaries of the room—it does *not* include the sound which travels to the point directly from the source. In general, if the sound in a room is diffuse, the level of the reflected sound is fairly uniform throughout the room. Under these conditions, at a distance r from the source, the reflected sound level (i.e., the *reflected sound* level[†] L_r) in a room is given by

$$L_r = L_W - \log_{10} A + 16.3 \quad \text{dB} \qquad (4.8a)$$

where L_r represents the sound power level of the source, and A is the total absorption in sabins.

In SI units:

$$L_r = L_W - 10 \log_{10} A + 6.0 \quad \text{dB}$$

Step 4. Obtain L_p by combining L_d and L_r according to Fig. 2.21.

SOUND LEVEL VERSUS DISTANCE FROM A SOURCE IN A ROOM IN WHICH THERE IS POOR DIFFUSION

In rooms such as offices and homes, the diffusion of sound is usually poor. In such rooms, the decrease in sound level with increasing distance from the sound source does not follow the smooth curves of Fig. 4.9. For example, Fig. 4.10 shows the sound level versus distance from a source in an office having smooth, hard walls and little furniture—conditions resulting in poor sound diffusion. Note that for a band of noise, the curve of sound level versus distance from the source is reasonably smooth. When the source contains discrete frequency components, the sound level in the room varies markedly, often in distinct patterns. At some points in the room there are maxima; in others there are minima, as illustrated in Fig. 4.10 for a 1000-Hz source.

This section shows how to calculate the sound level at any distance from a sound source in a room in which sound diffusion is

---

†Sometimes referred to as the *reverberant sound level,* but the term *reverberant sound* implies sound that is decaying; in contrast, *reflected sound,* for example, may be decaying or steady-state.

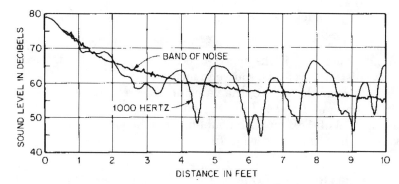

FIG. 4.10 Example of how sound pressure level varies with distance from a sound source in a typical office for two different sound sources: (*a*) A 1000-Hz pure tone; (*b*) an octave band of white noise having a center frequency of 850 Hz. Note that the shape of these curves is significantly different from the curves of Fig. 4.8. This is because of the lack of diffuse conditions in the office. (*V. O. Knudsen and C. M. Harris.*[3])

poor. This method of calculation applies to any normally furnished room provided:

- There is some scattering of sound in the room.

- The absorption is primarily concentrated on one surface, such as a sound-absorptive ceiling or a carpeted floor.

- The proportions of the room are reasonably regular, i.e., no dimension is more than 5 times another.

- The ceiling is between 8 and 12 feet (2.5 and 3.5 m) high.

- There are no very strong discrete frequency components in the spectrum of the noise source.[4]

Under the above conditions, the sound pressure level L_p at a distance r feet (5 feet above the floor) from the source is given by

$$L_p = L_W - 5 \log_{10} V - 3 \log_{10} f - 10 \log_{10} r + 25 \quad \text{dB} \quad (4.9a)$$

where L_W is the sound power of the sound source; for example, if the source is an air terminal device (e.g., and air outlet in an air-conditioning system, such as any of those shown in Fig. 7.20), L_W represents the sound power level of the source, flush with a ceiling, measured in accordance with ARI Standard 885[6]; V is the volume of the room in cubic feet; and f is the octave-band center frequency in hertz. This equation applies anywhere in the room except at positions very close to the source and is usually accurate within 2 dB.

The corresponding equation in the SI units is

$$L_p = L_W - 5 \log_{10} V - 3 \log_{10} f - 10 \log_{10} r + 12 \qquad \text{dB} \quad (4.9b)$$

where L_W has the same significance as above; V is the volume of the room in cubic meters; f is the octave-band center frequency in hertz; and r is the distance from the source in meters.

Notice that near the source, the value of $(L_W - L_p)$ decreases 3 dB for each doubling of distance from the source. This is in contrast to a decrease in level of 6 dB for each doubling of distance from the source in a room in which there is good diffusion.

Multiple Sources in a Large Office

In many office buildings, air-supply outlets are located flush with the ceiling of the air-conditioned space. Typically, they form a distributed array of noise sources in the ceiling. Their geometric pattern depends on (1) the floor area served by each air-supply outlet, (2) the ceiling height, and (3) the air-load requirements. In the interior zones of the building where the air-load requirements are essentially uniform, the air delivery per air outlet is usually the same throughout the space; thus, the noise sources tend to have nominally equal sound power levels. One method of calculating the sound pressure level in a room due to such a distributed array of noise sources is to determine the contribution of each source at some chosen reference point in the room using Eq. (4.9) and then combining these individual contributions by means of Fig. 2.21 to determine the sound pressure level at the reference point. However, when there are a large number of diffusers, this method is cumbersome.

For this special case of multiple sources on a ceiling, the average sound pressure level in the room L_p in a horizontal plane 5 feet (1.5 m) above the floor can be calculated by the following formula:

$$L_p = L_W - 5 \log X - 28 \log_{10} h + 1.3 \log_{10} N - 3 \log_{10} f + C \quad (4.10)$$

where L_W = sound power level of single air outlet in the array [i.e., combined sound power of (1) the sound propagated down the duct to the diffuser and (2) the sound generated at the outlet], in dB re 1 picowatt

X = ratio of floor area served by each outlet to the square of the ceiling height (for example, $X = 1$ if area served = h^2)

h = ceiling height, ft (m)

N = number of diffusers in room (N must be at least 4)

f = octave-band center frequency, Hz

C = proportionality constant, which equals 31 U.S. Customary units or 17 SI units

This equation usually provides results accurate within 1 to 2 dB for 4 or more air diffusers.

Extended Floor and Ceiling

Equations (4.9) and (4.10) do not apply in a large room whose length and/or width are more than about 5 times the ceiling height. For such conditions, Fig. 4.11 provides guidance. These results, based on experimental data, show the sound power level minus the total sound level $(L_W - L_p)$ as a function of distance from the source for three values of absorption coefficient of the ceiling: 0.2, 0.50, and 1.00. Here the ceiling height of 10 feet (3 m) is small compared with the other dimensions of the room. When the absorption coefficient equals 0.02 (a highly reflective ceiling), the sound level decreases roughly 3 dB for each doubling of the distance from the source. However, when the absorption coefficient equals 0.50, the decrease in sound level with an increase in distance is much more rapid. When the absorption coefficient equals 1.00, multiple reflections do not exist. Instead, the

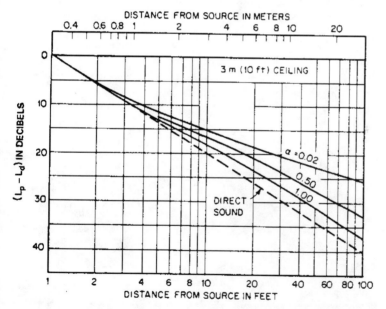

FIG. 4.11 Graph showing the sound power level minus the total sound pressure level, i.e. $(L_W - L_p)$ in a room in which one dimension is small compared with the other dimensions. In such a room, diffuse conditions do not prevail. If the ceiling has a sound absorption coefficient equal to 1.00, the value of $(L_W - L_p)$ approaches the value of the sound pressure level of the direct sound. (*Calculated from data compiled by H. J. Sabine.*)

reflected sound level is due to a single reflection from the floor; at considerable distance from the source, the reflected sound level decreases approximately 6 dB for each doubling of distance from the source.

REFERENCES

1. C. M. Harris, "Absorption of Sound in Air vs. Humidity and Temperature," *Journal of Acoustical Society of America,* vol. 41, no. 155, 1967.
2. C. M. Harris, "Absorption of Sound in Air vs. Humidity and Temperature," NASA contractor report NASA CR-647, Clearinghouse for Federal Scientific and Technical Information, Springfield, VA 22151, January 1967.
3. V. O. Knudsen and C. M. Harris, *Acoustical Designing in Architecture,* Chap. 8, Acoustical Society of America, New York, 1978.
4. T. J. Schultz, "Relationship between Sound Power Level and Sound Pressure Level in Dwellings and Offices," *ASHRAE Transactions,* vol. 91, no. 1A, 1983, pp. 124–153.
5. P. M. Morse, *Vibration and Sound,* Chap. 8, Acoustical Society of America, New York, NY 10017, 1980.
6. *Procedure for Estimating Occupied Space Sound Levels in the Application of Air Terminals and Air Outlets,* Standard 885–90, Air-Conditioning and Refrigeration Institute, 1501 Nelson Boulevard, Arlington, VA 22209.

5

Airborne Sound Insulation

A. C. C. Warnock

J. D. Quirt

INTRODUCTION

This chapter considers the insulation provided by various partition elements (walls, floors, windows, and doors) against *airborne sound,* i.e., sound that reaches the partition elements by propagating from the source through the air. Chapter 6 considers insulation against *structureborne sound,* i.e., sound that starts as vibration or impacts in the building structure itself. Chapter 10 discusses the control of noise in multifamily dwellings and office buildings, incorporating considerations from Chaps. 5 and 6.

When sound waves strike a partition, the varying sound pressures cause the partition to vibrate, as illustrated in Fig. 1.2. A fraction of the vibrational energy carried by the sound waves is transferred to the partition whose vibration sets air on the other side in motion, thereby generating sound in the adjacent space. In complex partitions consisting, for example, of layers of material and cavities, some of the energy of the sound waves dissipates within the partition, reducing the sound energy radiated on the second side. If the partition has holes or cracks (leaks) through it, or if it is porous, the sound waves also may reach the other side of the partition by way of these leaks or through the pores.

In the appendix of this chapter, the airborne sound insulation characteristics of commonly used materials and constructions are tabulated. These data are presented as follows:

Appendix 5.1   Gypsum Board and Stud Partitions

5.1a   Single layer of gypsum board; no cavities

5.1b   Gypsum board with wood studs

5.1c   Gypsum board attached to resilient channels on wood studs

5.1d   Gypsum board on double wood studs

5.1e   Gypsum board on staggered wood studs

5.1f   Gypsum board on steel studs

5.1g   Gypsum board attached to resilient channels on steel studs

Appendix 5.2   Masonry Walls

5.2a   4-inch (90-mm) concrete block walls

5.2b   6-inch (140-mm) concrete block walls

5.2c   8-inch (190-mm) concrete block walls

5.2d   12-inch (290-mm) concrete block walls

5.2e   Cavity concrete block walls

Appendix 5.3   Floor/Ceiling Constructions

5.3a   Concrete floor/ceilings

5.3b   Concrete floating floor concrete floor/ceilings

5.3c   Wood joist (or truss) floors

5.3d   Wood joist (or truss) floors with concrete topping

5.3e   Wood joist floors with concrete floating topping

Appendix 5.4   Windows

5.4a   Single panes of glass

5.4b   Single panes, laminated glass

5.4c   Double glazing

5.4d   Double glazing, laminated glass

Appendix 5.5   Doors

5.5a   Solid-core wood doors

5.5b   Hollow-core steel doors

5.5c   Hollow-core steel door and solid-core wood door in same frame

5.5d   Hollow-core steel door and solid-core wood door in separate frames

The presentation of material in this chapter follows the above sequence after a discussion of the ratings of partitions and general characteristics of constructions for airborne sound insulation. It concludes with a consideration of partitions made up of a combination of these elements. Guidance is provided for the selection of appropriate constructions for the control of airborne sounds.

SOUND INSULATION RATINGS

Sound Transmission Loss

The sound *transmission loss* (TL) of a partition is a measure of the airborne sound insulation it provides. Expressed in decibels (dB), it is a measure of the ratio of the energy striking the partition relative to the energy which is transmitted through it.[1,3] (The corresponding term used in many countries outside North America is *sound reduction index*.[2]) If a partition is completely "acoustically transparent," it has a sound transmission loss of 0 dB. The greater the sound insulation provided by a partition, the higher its sound transmission loss.

The sound transmission loss of a partition varies with frequency, usually increasing as the frequency increases, as illustrated in Fig. 5.1 for three types of partitions. Note that in Curve (a), the sound insulation of the masonry wall increases more or less steadily with increasing frequency. Curves (b) and (c), for the masonry wall with gypsum board attached to it, exhibit a dip in the curve at low frequencies, but then the insulation increases relative to the bare wall. The relatively poor insulation of partitions at low frequencies explains why one hears the bass sounds from a neighbor's hi-fi but not the higher-frequency sounds that carry the melody.

Sound Transmission Class

Although sound insulation varies with frequency and is very different for different types of partitions, it is convenient to compare the effectiveness of two partitions using a method of rating sound insulation that can be represented by a single number. In North America, the most commonly used single-number rating of sound insulation is called the *sound transmission class*[5] (STC). An STC rating of zero (0) indicates that a partition provides no airborne sound insulation. The higher the STC rating, the better the sound insulation provided by a partition. Figure 5.2 shows the STC ratings for a number of common types of wall constructions.

In many countries other than in North America, the single-number rating system[5] (somewhat similar to the *sound transmission class*)

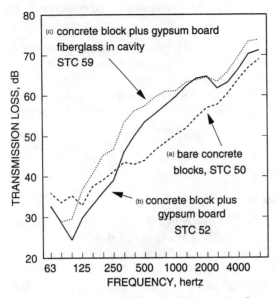

FIG. 5.1 Measured values of sound transmission loss versus frequency for (a) an 8-inch (190-mm) hollow concrete block wall. (b) Same construction as (a) but with gypsum board attached to one side using 2-inch (50-mm), light-weight steel furring; note the dip in the cure near 100 Hz. (c) Same construction as (b) but with fiberglass batts in the cavity between the gypsum board and the concrete block. In general, the STC (sound transmission class) ratings are a measure of the overall sound insulation of wall constructions.

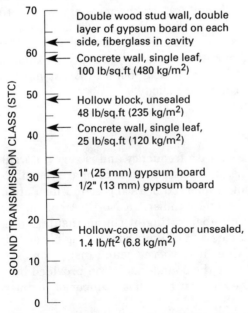

FIG. 5.2 Sound transmission class (STC) ratings of a number of common wall constructions.

used to express the overall sound insulation value of a partition is called the *weighted sound reduction index* R_w.*

GENERAL CHARACTERISTICS OF CONSTRUCTIONS FOR AIRBORNE SOUND INSULATION

This section presents a general discussion of the main physical factors affecting airborne sound insulation provided by single-leaf partitions and two-leaf partitions (i.e., cavity walls). Additional details concerning such gypsum board and masonry partitions are given in sections which follow. Recommended STC ratings for party walls and floors are given in Tables 10.1 and 10.2.

Single-Leaf Partitions

A *single-leaf partition* is a partition that has both exposed faces rigidly connected at all points, so they move as one. This category includes all types of solid homogeneous panels (such as gypsum board and plywood) and concrete block, brick, and poured concrete. (A panel of sandwich construction, such as a honeycomb panel, may act as a single leaf provided that it has a rigid core.) The sound insulation rating of a single-leaf partition depends mainly on its mass per unit area; to a lesser extent it is affected by its material properties, such as stiffness. In U.S. Customary units, the mass per unit area of a wall is expressed in pounds per square foot; in SI units, it is expressed in kilograms per square meter (kg/m^2).

The sound insulation of a single-leaf partition increases with increasing mass because the heavier the partition, the less it vibrates in response to sound waves and therefore the less sound it radiates on the side opposite the sound source. The increase in mass can be achieved either by an increase in the partition's thickness or density. For example, according to the data given in App. 5.2, the sound transmission class (STC) of a single-leaf partition of poured concrete 3 inches (75 mm) thick which has a weight of 35 pounds per square foot ($175 \ kg/m^2$) is about 47. The data show that each time the mass per unit area is doubled, the STC rating increases by about 5. Therefore, increasing the thickness of this wall to 6 inches (150 mm) will increase the STC rating to about 52; increasing its thickness to 12 inches (300 mm) will increase the STC rating to about 57.

---

*Values of weighted sound reduction index are determined according to ISO Standard 717,[5] from measured values[2] of the *sound reduction index*. Sound reduction index is equivalent to the *sound transmission loss*.

Two-Leaf Partitions (Cavity Walls)

A two-leaf partition is composed of two single-leaf partitions with an airspace between them.

As described below, the sound insulation provided by a two-leaf partition depends on:

- The mass per unit area of the component leafs
- The depth of the airspace between the two leafs
- The mechanical connection between the two leafs
- The amount of sound-absorptive material in the airspace

Mass per Unit Area of Component Leafs. In general, the heavier the component leafs, the higher the sound insulation provided by a two-leaf partition. As seen above, it is inefficient to improve the sound insulation of a *heavy* single-leaf partition merely by increasing its mass per unit area (either by increasing the thickness of the partition or by increasing its density). For example, consider a solid single-leaf partition having a sound transmission class (STC) rating of 35. Doubling its mass per unit area will improve its STC rating approximately 5 to a rating of 40. In contrast, if two such single-layer partitions (each having an STC rating of 35) form a two-leaf partition in which the two leafs are not "mechanically coupled," in theory, the resulting STC rating could be as high as 2 times 35, i.e., 70. Such theoretical values are not usually achieved in practice. Nevertheless, *a two-leaf partition usually provides substantially higher sound insulation than a single-leaf partition of equivalent mass.*

Depth of the Airspace between the Two Leafs. In general, the larger the airspace between the two leafs in a cavity wall, the higher the sound insulation. The airspace may also be the cause of a dip in the sound insulation at low frequencies, shown in Fig. 5.1. The larger the airspace or the heavier the materials, the lower the frequency at which the dip occurs. The resulting dip may reduce the sound transmission class rating below that for a single layer of the material with the same total thickness.

Mechanical Connection between the Two Leafs. Rigid mechanical connections between the two leafs, permit sound to travel efficiently from one leaf to the other through such connections, thereby "bridging" the space between the leafs and reducing the sound insulation of the construction. Therefore, where mechanical connections are required by code, they should be sufficiently resilient to avoid a reduction in sound insulation. In constructions where the two leafs are rigidly connected by structural supports, the addition of sound-absorptive material within the cavity will provide only small improvements to the sound insulation.

Sound-Absorptive Material in Airspace between Leafs. As illustrated in Fig. 5.1, the addition of sound-absorptive material in the cavity between a double-leaf partition improves its sound insulation. The following considerations affect this improvement in sound insulation:

- Porous, fibrous materials (such as fiberglass) can provide significant improvement.

- The higher the resistance to airflow of the porous material which is placed in the cavity, the greater the improvement in sound insulation. (Increasing density of fibrous material tends to correlate with increasing airflow resistance.)

- Closed-cell foam insulation, such as foamed polystyrene, are poor absorbers of sound and therefore will not improve the sound insulation.

- The airspace between leafs should be at least three-quarters filled with sound-absorptive material. A greater fraction provides little additional increase in sound insulation. In any case, the fibrous material should not be so densely compressed that it forms a solid bridge between leafs; a solid bridge between the leafs can reduce the sound insulation provided by the partition.

- The position or arrangement of the sound-absorptive material inside the cavity usually has little effect provided the whole area of the partition is covered. For example, in the staggered stud construction shown in Fig. 5.3, it does not matter whether the material is against one face or zigzags between the studs. On the other hand, if all of the sound-absorptive material in a wall is stuffed into the bottom one-third or so, the sound insulation will be lower than it would be if the material were distributed over the whole surface.

To achieve the improvement in sound insulation resulting from the addition of sound-absorptive material to the cavity between leafs in two-leaf construction, the two leafs must be well isolated from each other. Additional layers of gypsum board are effective only if they significantly change the weight of the layer to which they are attached.

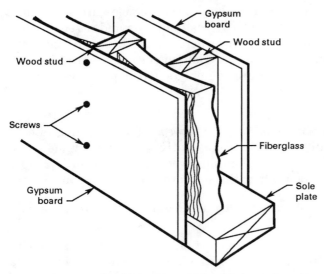

FIG. 5.3 A staggered-stud partition with sound-absorptive material in the cavity.

SOUND LEAKS

A *sound leak* is the passage of sound through a crack or hole in a construction, such as a partition, which may significantly reduce the effectiveness of the sound insulation which it provides. Examples of sound leaks and methods of avoiding them are given throughout this chapter for various types of constructions. This section shows how to determine the magnitude of the reduction in sound insulation that is a result of a sound leak.

Figure 5.4 shows the effects on the sound transmission class (STC) rating of a wall as a result of leaks which represent various fractions of the total wall area. For example, suppose the area of the leak has an area equal to 0.0001 times the wall area, and suppose the wall has a sound transmission class (STC) rating of 60. According to Fig. 5.4, the leak reduces the effective sound insulation of the wall to an STC rating of only 40. This graph shows that unless the area of the leak relative to that of the wall is *very* low, the STC rating is determined largely by the fractional area of the leak. *The higher the acoustical insulation that is sought, the more important it is to eliminate all sound leaks by the use of nonhardening caulking to seal all holes and cracks.*

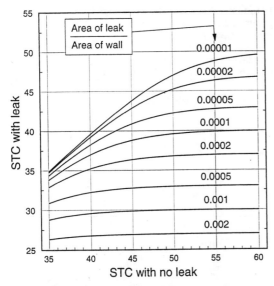

FIG. 5.4 The effects on the sound transmission class (STC) rating of wall leaks which represent various fractions of the total wall area.

GYPSUM BOARD PARTITIONS

Single-Leaf Partitions

Table 5.1 gives the sound transmission class (STC) rating of stud walls with gypsum board ¹/₂ inch (12.7 mm) thick which is fire-rated and which has a weight of about 1.6 lb/ft² (7.8 kg/m²). The STC rating for gypsum board of different thickness or weight on otherwise similar constructions can be estimated from values in Table 5.1 as follows: Increase or decrease the rating by 1 for each 12 percent increase or decrease in weight. If the increase in thickness is obtained by cementing two layers of gypsum board together, the joints of the two layers either should be staggered, or the joints between the first layer of boards should be run vertically and the joints of the second layer should be run horizontally in order to minimize the possibility of cracks through the two layers.

Two-Leaf Partitions with Wood or Metal Studs

As indicated in the previous section, "General Characteristics of Constructions for Airborne Sound Insulation" (see the subsection on

TABLE 5.1   Approximate Sound Transmission Class (STC) Ratings for Stud Walls with ¹/₂-inch (12.7-mm) Thick Gypsum Board on Both Surfaces. (Absorptive Batts Should Fill at least 75 percent of Cavity.)

Structure	One layer gypsum board on each side of stud, STC	Two layers gypsum board on each side of stud, STC
Wood 2 × 4 (38 × 89 mm) studs, 24 inches on center with empty cavities	33	43
With absorptive batts	36	46
2¹/₂-inch (65-mm), 24-gauge steel studs with empty cavities	36	45
With absorptive batts	44	52
3⁵/₈-inch (90-mm), 24-gauge steel studs with empty cavities	39	50
With absorptive batts	47	56
Wood 2 × 4 (38 × 89 mm) studs, 24 inches on center, with resilient steel channels on one side and empty cavities	40	52
With absorptive batts	48	56
Staggered 2 × 4 (38 × 89 mm) wood studs on 2 × 6 (140 mm) plate with empty cavities	41	52
With absorptive batts	48	55
6-inch (150-mm) load-bearing steel studs with resilient metal channels on one side and empty cavities	45	56
With absorptive batts	56	61
2 rows 2 × 4 (38 × 89 mm) wood studs separated 1 inch (25 mm), and empty cavities	46	57
With absorptive batts	57	63

two-leaf partitions), a properly built two-leaf construction provides much better sound insulation than a single-leaf partition having the same mass per unit area of partition.

In general, the sound insulation provided by a two-leaf gypsum partition depends on factors such as the following:

- *The Mass per Unit Area of the Gypsum Board:*   The more massive, the better the sound insulation.

- *Type of Gypsum Board,* e.g., fire-rated vs. standard.

- *The Presence (or Absence) of Sound-Absorptive Material in the Airspace between the Two Leafs, as well as the Characteristics (e.g., Type and Thickness) of Such Material.*

- *The Type of Mechanical Attachment between the Two Leafs,* for example, the stiffness of steel studs and/or the stiffness of the resilient channels to which the gypsum board is attached. Screws which are too long may short-circuit resilient metal channels where they are used to mount gypsum board as illustrated in Fig. 5.5. As a result, the sound insulation that the wall provides may be reduced by several decibels. Usually, the greater the number of screws shorting the construction, the lower the sound insulation.

- *The Stud and Screw Spacing:*   Generally, the closer the studs, the poorer the sound insulation at low frequencies. For example, for a simple wood stud wall, reducing inter-stud spacing from 24 to 16 inches (600 to 400 mm) may reduce the STC rating by as much as 10. Smaller spacing between the screws attaching the gypsum board to the studs slightly exaggerates this effect. The effect of stud spacing is reduced for steel stud, or double-stud constructions, but stud spacings less than 24 inches (600 mm) tend to decrease the sound insulation at low frequencies.

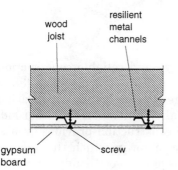

FIG. 5.5 A gypsum panel attached to a resilient metal channel by metal screws. Because the screws are too long, the sound isolation is "shorted," thereby reducing the sound insulation that would otherwise be achieved.

Examples of Various Types of Gypsum Board Constructions

Figure 5.6 shows various type of two-leaf gypsum board constructions with their corresponding sound transmission class (STC) ratings. In Fig. 5.6a, a separate row of light-weight steel studs with a $3\frac{1}{2}$-inch

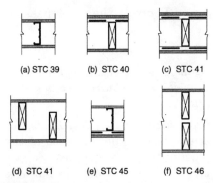

(a) STC 39   (b) STC 40   (c) STC 41

(d) STC 41   (e) STC 45   (f) STC 46

FIG. 5.6 Section views of various types of two-leaf gypsum board constructions with their corresponding sound transmission class ratings with ¹/₂-inch (12.7-mm) gypsum board and no sound-absorptive material in the cavity (see Table 5.1). (*a*) Gypsum board directly screwed to each side of light-weight steel studs providing a 3¹/₂-inch (90-mm) airspace between gypsum boards. (*b*) Gypsum board attached to one side of 3¹/₂-inch (90-mm) wood studs by means of resilient metal channels on one side; gypsum boards on the opposite side are screwed directly to the wood studs. (*c*) Gypsum board is attached to resilient metal channels on both sides of the same studs used in (*b*). (*d*) Gypsum board is attached to "staggered wood studs." (*e*) Gypsum boards are attached on one side to load-bearing steel studs, with resilient metal channels on one side and screwed directly to the studs on the other side. (*f*) Gypsum board screwed directly to double wood studs, with a space between the studs.

(90-mm) airspace gives a highly effective and reliable construction; wood studs yield similar results. In Fig. 5.6*b*, 1¹/₂- × 3¹/₂-inch (38- × 89-mm) wood studs are used; on one side gypsum boards are attached to the studs by means of resilient metal channels; on the other side gypsum boards are screwed on. Such a construction provides greater sound insulation than a similar construction in which the gypsum boards are screwed directly to *both* sides of the wood studs. Thus, the use of resilient metal channels as a method of attachment greatly reduces the transmission of acoustic energy between the gypsum board and the stud. In Fig. 5.6*c*, the STC rating is increased to an even greater value by attaching the gypsum board by means of resilient metal channels on *both* sides of the studs. However, to achieve the benefit to the fullest extent, the periphery of the gypsum board should not make contact with the adjacent wall; a small gap should be left between them; then this gap should be filled with nonhardening caulking.

Staggered studs, shown in Fig. 5.6d (and Fig. 5.3), usually provide a significant improvement over the use of single studs shown in Fig. 5.6a—especially if a sound-absorptive material is placed between the studs; however, there is some transfer of sound energy through the soleplates at the top and bottom of the wall which limits the sound insulation. Figure 5.6e represents a construction composed of load-bearing steel studs with resilient metal channels on one side. In Fig. 5.6e, non-load-bearing steel studs are fabricated of 26-gauge (0.7-mm-thick) sheet steel; these studs are flexible enough to transmit negligible vibration between layers of gypsum board attached to both sides. In Fig. 5.6f, double wood studs are employed which increase the spacing between leafs; this increased spacing provides significant improvement in sound insulation.

As indicated in Fig. 5.1, stud and gypsum board walls exhibit a strong dip in the sound insulation at low frequencies. The larger the airspace or the heavier the gypsum board, the lower the frequency at which the dip occurs. (See the section on two-leaf partitions.) The effect of this dip can be to reduce the sound insulation *below* that which would be obtained for a wall formed from solid material of the same total weight as the panels used to form the double wall.

Tabular Values of Two-Leaf Gypsum Walls   (Appendix 5.1)

The sound transmission class (STC) ratings given in this appendix depend significantly on construction details and the quality of construction. Better or worse ratings may occur. For example, in Fig. 5.7a, a section view of a gypsum wall attached to a soleplate (which runs along the floor and to which the studs are attached) rests firmly on the surface of the flooring; the soleplate is caulked on both sides with a nonhardening caulking compound. In contrast, in Fig. 5.7b, the soleplate does not make firm contact with the flooring because of debris under it; furthermore, the resulting crack along the floor has not been caulked. This permits sound to leak under the soleplate as indicated by the arrow. As a result of this construction defect, the rating tabulated in Appendix 5.1 for this construction will not be achieved. Such a crack must be caulked on both sides of the partition.

In Fig. 5.8, gypsum board is resiliently attached to the studs and is *not* permitted to make contact with the flooring. If there is direct contact, the sound insulation will be reduced, and the rating for this construction given in Appendix 5.1 will not be achieved. Note that the

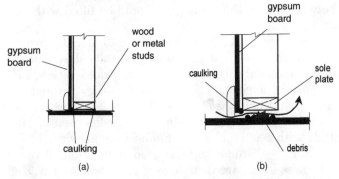

FIG. 5.7 A section view of a gypsum board wall; studs are attached to a soleplate which runs along the floor. (*a*) The soleplate rests firmly on the surface of the flooring; there is a nonhardening caulking compound on both sides. (*b*) The soleplate does not make firm contact with the flooring because of debris under it, and the crack along the floor is caulked, thereby permitting sound to leak under the base of the partition as indicated by the arrow. A similar situation occurs along the crack between the ceiling and partition, so this crack must also be caulked on both sides of the partition.

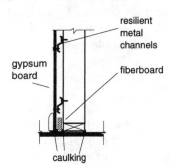

FIG. 5.8 Vertical section of resiliently-held gypsum board that is *not* permitted to make contact with the flooring. The space between the gypsum board and flooring is filled with a nonhardening caulking.

baseboard attached to the gypsum board should not contact the flooring; otherwise it will bridge the sound isolation between the gypsum board and floor (this crack should be caulked).

Another situation that gives rise to poorer sound insulation than expected on the basis of the values shown in Appendix 5.1 is illustrated in the horizontal section of Fig. 5.9*a*. It is usually economical to install electrical or telephone outlet boxes so that an outlet box on one side of a wall is "back-to-back" with a similar outlet box on the opposite side of the wall. Because outlet boxes are fabricated of lightweight metal and usually contain holes, they can be a serious source of sound leaks because they permit sound to enter one box and exit from the box on the other side of the wall. Such a situation can be improved by back-plastering the boxes, or by off-setting the boxes as

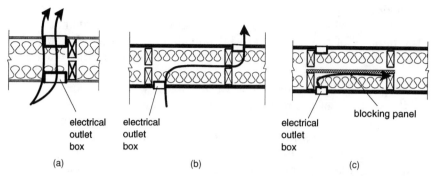

electrical
outlet
box

electrical
outlet
box

electrical
outlet
box

blocking panel

(a)   (b)   (c)

FIG. 5.9 Horizontal section of a gypsum board wall in which there are electrical outlets or telephone outlets set in the wall. (*a*) The outlets are "back to back" so that sound enters one box and exits the other side through the other outlet. (*b*) The outlets are offset, which provides some improvement as a result of the sound-absorptive material in the cavity. (*c*) A "blocking panel" is inserted before the gypsum board is attached to the studs.

shown in Fig. 5.9*b* to increase the leakage path. Another technique is to insert a "blocking panel," as shown in Fig. 5.9*c*, before gypsum board is attached to the studs.

MASONRY WALLS (CONCRETE BLOCK, POURED CONCRETE, BRICK)

Solid and hollow-core concrete blocks are manufactured in a variety of thicknesses, core sizes, aggregates, and densities. Their physical properties may vary significantly from one manufacturer to another. Representative values of sound transmission class (STC) for walls constructed of these materials are given in Table 5.2, and in

TABLE 5.2   Sound Transmission Class (STC) Ratings for 50 percent Solid, Normal, and Light-weight Block Walls Sealed on at least One Side [Typical Block Dimensions Are $7^5/_8 \times 15^5/_8$ inch (190×390 mm).]

Block thickness		Light-weight block			Normal-weight block		
		Weight/unit area			Weight/unit area		
inches	(mm)	lb/ft²	(kg/m²)	STC	lb/ft²	(kg/m²)	STC
4	(90)	17	(80)	43	25	(120)	44
6	(150)	25	(120)	44	37	(180)	46
8	(200)	33	(160)	45	42	(200)	48
10	(250)	37	(180)	47	52	(250)	49
12	(300)	45	(220)	48	62	(300)	51

Appendix 5.2—*provided* that their surfaces are properly sealed. The sound insulation provided by a hollow-core block depends not only on the density of the block material but also on whether the surface of the hollow cores are sealed in the process of removing the block from its "form." The more porous the block, the more sound will leak through the block structure and the greater will be the improvement if the surfaces of the block are sealed (for example, by concrete paint, epoxy paint, or plaster). Sealing the surface of a very porous block typically provides an increase in sound transmission class (STC) rating of about 8, although the increase may be as much as 30. Attaching a layer of gypsum board directly to a porous block's surface is not an effective means of sealing the blocks.

Single-Leaf Masonry Walls

In the thicknesses commonly used in buildings, well-sealed concrete block provides approximately the same sound insulation as a solid concrete wall or brick wall of the same weight per unit area—provided all cracks, openings and voids are properly sealed.

Masonry block walls sometimes develop cracks along the mortar joints or in the blocks themselves. This leads to sound leakage of the type illustrated in Fig. 5.10. This is especially true after a building "settles." A poured concrete wall, although massive and apparently solid, may permit sound to leak through the wall if there are cracks or voids in the construction, as illustrated in Fig. 5.11.

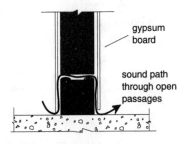

gypsum
board

sound path
through open
passages

FIG. 5.10 Sound leakage through a concrete block wall. Even if properly constructed, such cracks may occur as a large building settles—even before occupancy.

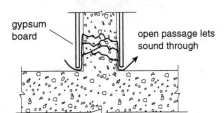

gypsum
board

open passage lets
sound through

FIG. 5.11 Sound leakage through cracks in a poured concrete wall.

Before finishing a masonry wall with gypsum board, it is essential to ensure that the wall is free of imperfections by sealing any cracks with mortar.

Two-Leaf Masonry Walls

As indicated in an earlier general discussion on two-leaf walls, two-leaf masonry walls can, in principle, provide very high sound insulation because they comprise two independent heavy layers separated by an airspace. The increased insulation usually is limited by the practical difficulties of constructing two masonry leafs that are structurally isolated. Depending on the height of a block wall, metal ties are required for structural reasons and/or to meet the applicable code. These ties between leafs permit sound energy to travel along them, from one leaf to the other. The detrimental effects of mechanical ties can be minimized by the use of special ties with interlocking hooks or resilient couplings.

There is transmission of energy along the floor and ceiling, along walls abutting the periphery of the cavity wall, and through other parts of the structure. Physical breaks in the floor, ceiling, and abutting walls are needed to reduce transmission along these flanking paths.[†1] For example, if a block wall is of limited height, some building codes permit concrete block to be laid on a layer of homogenized baked cork [usually about 3/4 inch (20 mm) thick] with caulking along the cork layer. Similarly, the block wall should be isolated from the slab above.

During construction, workmen sometimes use the airspace between leafs as a convenient place to dump rubble and debris, thereby bridging the gap and reducing the sound insulation. Such construction defects, usually concealed and impossible to correct after the wall is complete, may be obviated by specifying that the airspace between leafs must be filled with a light, porous material such as fiberglass board.

Improving the Sound Insulation of an Existing Masonry Wall by Attaching a Gypsum Board to Its Surface

A common method of improving the sound insulation of an existing masonry wall is to add a layer of gypsum board on one or both sides of the wall. Before gypsum board is added to a porous wall, it is essential to seal the block wall by concrete paint, epoxy paint, or a skim

---

†A *flanking path* is a path for sound transmission other than the common partition between the two spaces.

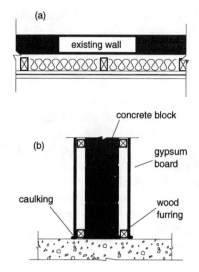

FIG. 5.12 Improving the sound insulation of an existing wall by attaching wood battens to the existing wall; sound-absorptive material is placed between the battens; then, gypsum board is screwed to the wood battens: (*a*) horizontal section, (*b*) vertical section.

coat of plaster on the masonry surfaces to prevent the transmission of sound through the pores.

Figure 5.12 shows a common method of improving the sound insulation of an existing masonry wall. Wood battens are attached to the existing wall; sound-absorptive material is placed between the battens; and, the gypsum board is screwed to the wood battens. Another method is illustrated in Fig. 5.13 where resilient metal channels are used to attach the gypsum board to the wood battens. Once the resiliently-attached gypsum board is in place, no nails, no screws, nor any other mechanical devices may be driven through the gypsum

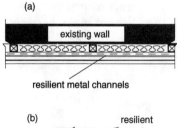

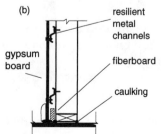

FIG. 5.13 Resilient metal channel is used to attach the gypsum board to the wood battens: (*a*) horizontal section, (*b*) vertical section.

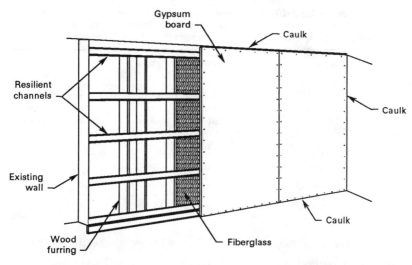

FIG. 5.14 Gypsum board resiliently-mounted on an existing masonry wall to increase the sound insulation of the wall; note that the gap at the periphery of the gypsum board must be caulked.

board into the wall. Otherwise, the additional benefits of the added gypsum board may be largely negated.

Figure 5.14, which shows a similar construction, emphasizes that the periphery of the resiliently-mounted gypsum board must not make contact with the floor, ceiling, or adjacent walls. The gap between the gypsum board and these surfaces must be carefully caulked with a nonhardening caulking compound. Otherwise, the benefits of such a construction will be minimal.

The improvement in sound transmission class (STC) rating which results from the attachment of a variety of added gypsum board finishes to an existing concrete wall is given in Table 5.3. The STC ratings for the complete wall system can be calculated by adding the improvements given in Table 5.3 to the STC rating of the concrete block from Table 5.2.

A layer of resiliently-attached gypsum board can provide an improvement in sound insulation of 10 dB or more. The distance between the added layer and the existing wall should not be less than about 1 inch (25 mm); otherwise, the sound insulation at low frequencies may be decreased instead of being improved. If two layers of gypsum board are used, it is better to stagger the joints between the two layers.

While gypsum board attached to an existing wall may increase the sound transmission class (STC) for the combination, they also may reduce the sound insulation at low frequencies (see Fig. 5.1). In criti-

TABLE 5.3   Increase in Sound Transmission Class (STC) Ratings When ⅝-inch (16-mm) Gypsum Board Is Attached to a Concrete Block Wall, with and without Fiberglass Batts Filling the Cavity between Gypsum Board and Concrete Block

Gypsum board attached	Without fiberglass in cavity		With fiberglass in cavity	
	Gypsum board on one side of blocks	Gypsum board on both sides of blocks	Gypsum board on one side of blocks	Gypsum board on both sides of blocks
Directly on concrete block	+0	−1		
On ½-inch (13-mm) resilient channels	+2	−1	+4	−1
On 1½-inch (40-mm) wood furring	+3	+4	+5	+9
On 2-inch (50-mm) resilient furring	+2	+2	+9	+14
On 2½-inch (65-mm) steel studs	+8	+7	+10	+22
On 3-inch (75-mm) resilient furring	+7		+11	

cal situations where good low-frequency sound insulation must be provided, it may be necessary to examine the characteristics of sound transmission loss as a function of frequency.

FLOOR/CEILING CONSTRUCTIONS‡

Figure 5.15 and Appendix 5.3 give approximate sound transmission class (STC) ratings for typical floor/ceiling constructions. To obtain high STC ratings, it is necessary to avoid rigid structural connections between the floor and the ceiling layers, including the periphery of the structure.

Resilient channels are commonly used to attach the gypsum board to the bottom of the floor joists, as illustrated in the joist floor constructions shown in Figs. 5.16 and 6.9. This method of attachment provides much better sound insulation than attachment of the gypsum boards directly to the studs. A slight gap should be left around the gypsum board construction at the walls; this gap should then be filled with a nonhardening caulking.

Figure 5.17 shows a floor/ceiling construction which uses separate joists to support the ceiling structure. Separate joists may result in a significant improvement in sound insulation. Such a construction will be even better if the ceiling is supported by resilient metal channels.

---

‡Also see "Floor/Ceiling Assemblies" in Chap. 6.

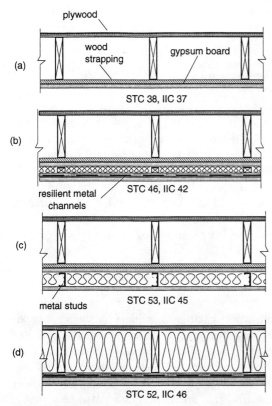

FIG. 5.15 Sound transmission class (STC) ratings of typical floor/ceiling constructions. The impact insulation class (IIC) rating for such constructions is described in Chap. 6.

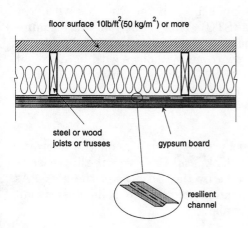

FIG. 5.16 The resilient method of attachment of gypsum board to floor joists, with fiberglass between the joists, provides much greater sound insulation than screwing the gypsum board directly to the joists. A detail is shown of the resilient metal channel.

FIG. 5.17 A floor/ceiling construction which uses separate joists to support the ceiling structure.

In this case a gap should be left between the gypsum board ceiling and the walls; this gap must be filled with nonhardening caulking.

The airborne sound insulation ratings for some typical floor/ceiling constructions are given in the next chapter in Table 6.1. This table also includes impact insulation class (IIC) ratings for the same constructions (IIC ratings are described in Chap. 6). Tables 10.1 and 10.2 give recommended STC and IIC ratings for floor/ceiling constructions. In addition, airborne sound insulation data for many types of constructions are given in Appendix 5.3.

WINDOWS

Typical values of sound insulation ratings provided by various types of window constructions are given in Fig. 5.18 and in Table 5.4. For high sound insulation, the purchase of commercially available windows that have been rated by a recognized testing laboratory is certain to provide better performance for a given cost than individually designed units. To obtain a sound transmission class rating above 45, it is necessary to select acoustical windows with specially designed frames, and glass mounting is recommended. Ratings for specific products are given in manufacturers' literature and publications such as *Sweet's Catalog.*

Transmission of sound through a hollow window-frame can significantly reduce the sound insulation, especially for windows with very high sound transmission class (STC). This reduction can be minimized by drilling one or more holes in the hollow frame and pumping a mastic material to fill the hollow frame. Windows with light-weight metal frames tend to have lower STC values than those listed in Table 5.4. Light-weight frames should be avoided.

Single Glazing (Unlaminated)

The sound insulation provided by single glazing, on the average, increases with increasing glass thickness. However, the increase is limited in the mid-frequency range by the stiffness of the glass. As indicated in Fig. 5.12, a single, unlaminated layer of solid glass usually does not provide an STC rating above 35.

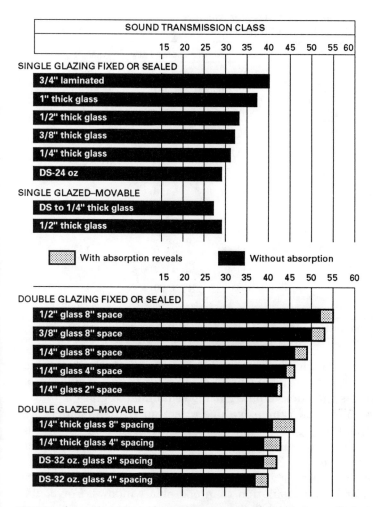

FIG. 5.18 Approximate sound insulation ratings of various types of windows. Actual values may vary by as much 5 dB or more depending on the seal of the window and the type of window frame. Also see Table 5.4.

Laminated Glass. Laminated glass is two or more layers of glass bonded together by thin plastic interlayers. It can provide higher values of sound transmission class than solid glass of equal thickness. This is because the sound insulation versus thickness of single sheets of glass exhibits a dip at a frequency determined by the stiffness of the glass. The improvement in sound insulation is primarily due to damping by the plastic interlayers which reduce the magnitude of the dip.

TABLE 5.4   Sound Transmission Class for Windows having Effective
Weather-stripping but No Sound-Absorption around Their Perimeter Surfaces

STC for sealed window	STC for operable window	Single-glazed glass thickness, inches (mm)	Double-glazed, airspace between glass, inches (mm)		
			Both $^1/_8$-inch (3-mm) glass	Both $^1/_4$-inch (6-mm) glass	$^1/_4$-inch (6-mm) and laminated $^9/_{32}$-inch (7-mm) glass
30	27	$^1/_8$ (3), $^5/_{32}$ (4)	$^1/_4$ (6)		
32	29	$^1/_4$ (6)	$^3/_8$ (10)		
34	31	$^1/_4$ (6)L*	$^3/_4$ (20)	$^5/_{16}$ (8)	
36	32	$^1/_2$ (12)	$1^1/_4$ (30)	$^1/_2$ (13)	
38	34	$^1/_2$ (12)L†*	2 (50)	$^3/_4$ (20)	$^3/_8$ (10)
40	36	$^3/_4$ (20)L†*	$2^3/_4$ (70)	$1^1/_4$ (30)	$^5/_8$ (16)
42	37		4 (100)	2 (50)	1 (25)
44	39		6 (150)	$3^1/_4$ (80)	$1^1/_2$ (40)
46	41			$4^3/_4$ (120)	$2^7/_8$ (60)
48	43				4 (100)

*L denotes laminated glass, for example, $^1/_4$ (6)L is $^1/_4$-inch (6-mm) thick laminated glass.

Double Glazing.   Double glazing is two panes of glass with an airspace between them. Double glazing provides greater sound insulation at high frequencies than does single glazing or laminated glass.

Table 5.4 compares typical values of sound transmission class (STC) for sealed windows (Column 1) with corresponding values for operable windows (Column 2), and for single-glazed windows of different thicknesses (Column 3). These STC values increase with increasing thickness of glass; for glass of a given thickness, sealed windows provide greater sound insulation than operable windows. For double glazing, Columns 4, 5, and 6 show the spacing between panes (for three types of glass, respectively) that yield the STC values shown in Columns 1 and 2. The overall improvement provided by double glazing depends primarily on the separation of the layers and glass thickness. For each doubling of the airspace, there is an increase in STC rating of about 3. There is some advantage in using two panes of laminated glass, especially for glass thicker than $^1/_4$ inch (6 mm).

DOORS AND FOLDING PARTITIONS

The sound insulation provided by a door depends not only on mass per unit area and on the type of door but also on installation details (including the door frame and gaskets around the perimeter).

TABLE 5.5   Sound Insulation of Conventional Doors

Door type	Mass per unit area		STC (not sealed)	STC (good seals)
	lb/ft²	kg/m²		
Hollow-core wood	1.4	7	16	20
Solid-core wood	4.1	20	20	28
Hollow-core steel (18 ga.)	5.1	25	20	30
Two hollow-core doors, 4-inch (100-mm) space	1.4	7 each	22	26
Two doors, solid-core wood or hollow steel 2³/₄-inch (70-mm) space	4.1	20 each	28	40
Two doors, solid-core wood or hollow steel 2³/₄-inch (70-mm) space with absorption	4.1	20 each	40	44
Two doors, solid-core wood or hollow steel 9-inch (230-mm) space with absorption	4.1	20 each	42	50

Typical values of sound insulation, in terms of sound transmission class (STC), for conventional types of interior doors are listed in Table 5.5. The first column in the table gives STC values for doors with typical gaps between the edges and the frame [approximately 0.25 inch (6 mm) thick total for top and bottom and 0.1 inch (3 mm) total for the sides]. If the gap is larger, the STC is even lower. Unless the leakage of sound through cracks around the door is reduced, the effective STC rating will not greatly exceed 20, regardless of improvements to the door panels. *The door frame must be fitted into the wall in such a way as to avoid cracks or openings that provide a sound leakage path.*

Rubber or neoprene gaskets compressed between the door and frame can be quite effective if properly adjusted. For example, see the gasket in Fig. 5.19a which can be adjusted along the length of the door. A gasket should be tight enough to require strong effort to insert a stiff plastic card between the gasket and the door, and it should be "light tight." Magnetic seals (like those used for refrigerator doors) work well with metal doors.

Figure 5.19 illustrates a problem in obtaining good sound insulation with a door. In Fig. 5.19a, the door frame has been fully grouted. In contrast, in Fig. 5.19b, the frame has not been grouted. The resulting airspace permits sound to travel along a path shown by the heavy arrow—through the hollow door frame and out the opposite side since the frame itself provides relatively little sound insulation. This is called *flanking transmission* of sound and is responsible, in many cases, for the disappointment architects experience when they have

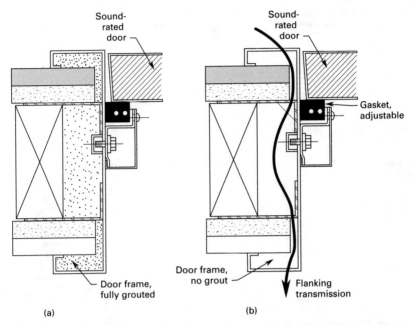

FIG. 5.19 (*a*) A gasketed door which is set in a door frame that is fully grouted. (*b*) Same as (*a*), but here the grouting in the door frame has been omitted, permitting sound to bypass, i.e., "flank" the door, as illustrated by the heavy arrow. Such flanking transmission significantly lowers the sound insulation provided by the door.

specified doors of high sound insulation rating, only to experience poor results because of the lack of grouting in the door frames.

Providing a Seal at the Door Bottom

An *automatic door bottom,* sometimes called an *automatic threshold closer* or *drop seal,* may be used to close the gap at the door bottom and control sound leakage under a door. Such closing mechanisms are of two types: (1) those having the drop mechanism in the center of the door such as the one shown in Fig. 5.20, and (2) those having the drop mechanism attached to the exterior surface of the door. For an automatic door bottom to be effective, it must close against a flat, hard floor or sill surface. The seal must be carefully adjusted to press firmly against this surface (over the full width of the door) when the door closes. Periodic maintenance is required. The use of a rubber scraper along the bottom edge of the door to obtain a seal usually provides poor results and causes carpet wear.

Some commercially available noise-rated doors use a special type of hinge that lowers the door as it closes, thereby pressing a gasket

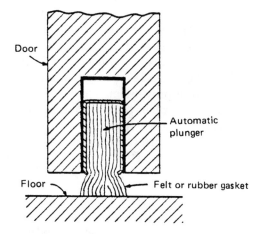

Door

Automatic
plunger

Floor

Felt or rubber gasket

FIG. 5.20 An automatic door bottom containing a movable plunger which is pushed down against the threshold when the door is closed.

along the bottom edge of the door against the floor and effecting a good seal. As with an automatic door bottom, the gasket must press firmly against a flat, hard floor or sill surface to provide an effective seal across the full width of the door.

"Noise-Rated" Doors

Commercial doors are available that provide sound transmission class (STC) ratings from 35 to over 50. Such doors are normally laboratory tested in accord with the relevant standard.[6] The sound insulation values for specific products are given in manufacturers' literature and publications such as *Sweet's Catalog*. Because test methods have evolved significantly, product ratings more than 10 years old are questionable.

Installation of noise-rated doors is of critical importance in achieving such high insulation. The rated performance will not be achieved in field installations unless the door frame is fitted into the wall to avoid cracks or hollows that could transmit sound, the gaskets are properly adjusted, and flanking transmission is avoided. The avoidance of flanking transmission generally requires that door frames be fully grouted, as illustrated in Fig. 5.19a. Manufacturers' recommendations for installation should be followed rigorously. Periodic readjustment or replacement of the seals is required to maintain the sound insulation provided by such doors.

Improving Existing Single Doors

The noise insulation of an existing single door, which is not noiserated, can often be increased by improving perimeter seals. Good seals at the perimeter (discussed above) are essential to achieve sound transmission class (STC) ratings above 20. An automatic door bottom can be attached to the face of a door to seal the gap at the bottom of the door. For a light-weight hollow-core wood door, bonding a heavy layer on the door surface (for example, a layer of gypsum board or sheet steel) can provide an additional improvement.

The use of two doors with an airspace between them sometimes is a less expensive and acoustically more effective alternative in situations where such a combination does not interfere unacceptably with access and meets code requirements. Typical STC ratings are shown in Table 5.5.

Ordinary Exterior Doors

The framing of exterior doors commonly includes a sill and weather-stripping with plastic or spring metal seals along all four edges. Although the weather-stripping usually is not specifically designed as an acoustical seal, it reduces leakage of sound around the door. Data for ordinary exterior doors are given in Table 5.6. Because of variability in typical seals, actual performance of specific doors may be significantly poorer. The addition of a light-weight storm door (usually having a two-section single-glazed window) increases the sound transmission class (STC) by about 7 for a typical exterior door. With good seals, the increase in STC rating can exceed 10.

Folding Doors, Accordion Doors, and Operable Partitions

A *folding door,* also called a *multifolding door,* is a door usually composed of a number of hinged panels hung on a ceiling track; when the

TABLE 5.6 Sound Transmission Class of Ordinary Exterior Doors with Weather-Stripping [All Doors 1³/₄ inch (45 mm) Thick. Exterior Doors Which Are Noise-Rated Typically Provide Very Much Higher Sound Insulation.]

Type of door	Weight		Sound transmission class (STC)
	lb/ft²	(kg/m²)	
Hollow-core wood	1.5	7	20
Hollow-core wood [30 percent of area glazed, with ¹/₈-inch (3-mm) glass]	1.5	7	19
Solid-core wood	3.6	17	26
Steel-faced door, rigid polyurethane core	3.2	16	26
Fiberglass-reinforced plastic door, rigid polyurethane core	2.4	12	24

door is open, the panels stack against each other and are housed in a relatively small space. A door of this type is sometimes called an *accordion door*; however, this term usually connotes a door which is fabric faced (e.g., of heavy plastic) and hung from an overhead track, folding back like the bellows of an accordion. They behave essentially in the same way as ordinary swinging doors except that they may provide an additional path for sound to leak from one side of the door to the other by cracks between the door and ceiling, between the door and the floor, and the joints between segments.

An *operable partition* is a partition composed of a number of large panels which are hung from a ceiling track, permitting the panels to be moved easily from their closed position (in which the panels form a partition) to an open position (in which the panels are stacked against each other); the panels also may be supported by a floor track. A partition of this type is usually used to subdivide a large space. Panels extend from floor to ceiling and are typically 4 ft (1200 mm) wide. The mechanism for operating the partition must also activate the sealing systems. Commercially available partitions of this type are available with sound transmission class (STC) ratings between 20 and 50 when properly installed. Sealing an operable partition is difficult because floors and ceilings are rarely flat and parallel over the distances involved. Thus, the seals at the top and bottom of the partition must accommodate such variations, with reasonable forces applied to the task of opening and closing the partition. Mechanical performance and durability are major considerations. In partitions that have floor tracks, the tracks may become filled with debris, making the partitions difficult to operate. Sound leaks must be prevented where the supporting frame meets the ceiling and side walls.

Flanking transmission along floors, walls, and ceilings abutting the operable partition can significantly reduce its sound insulation (see Fig. 5.19b for an illustration of flanking). To avoid flanking, do not install a folding floor or operable partition:

- Below a continuous suspended ceiling or open ceiling plenum
- Below ventilation ducts bypassing the partition
- Above or below light-weight, unbroken floor layers
- Abutting wall surfaces that bypass the partition

Installation. It is desirable to have the manufacturer or contractor of a folding door or operable partition guarantee its performance as installed. Therefore, obtain an agreement from the contractor that the field conditions are satisfactory *before* starting installation of a folding door or operable partition because the sound insulation provided by such partitions depends critically on their installation details. If the door or partition does not appear to provide the sound insulation that was expected, it may be necessary, to verify by testing[3] that the quoted sound insulation rating has been achieved. A clause in the agreement that holds the contractor responsible for the costs of testing and making the necessary adjustments, should the door or partition fail the test, often is helpful in ensuring that the contractor does a satisfactory job. Where a test is not feasible, it may be adequate to compare proposed installation details with the standard test report (which should describe all details of the installation) and to perform a visual check of the installation. Illuminating one side of the partition and inspecting for visible light from a darkened room on the other side can identify major cracks. Whatever process is used to establish satisfactory initial performance, continuing adjustment and maintenance are essential to maintain good sound insulation.

MULTI-ELEMENT PARTITIONS

A multi-element partition is a partition comprising two or more components having different sound insulation properties, for example, a wall containing a door or window. In such a case, the effective value

TABLE 5.7 Adjustments for Determining Component Sound Transmission Class from Fractional Area and Number of Components in Partition

Fractional area	Number of components		
	2	3	4
0.0315	−12	−10	−9
0.04	−11	−9	−8
0.05	−10	−8	−7
0.063	−9	−7	−6
0.08	−8	−6	−5
0.1	−7	−5	−4
0.125	−6	−4	−3
0.16	−5	−3	−2
0.2	−4	−2	−1
0.25	−3	−1	0
0.315	−2	−0	1
0.4	−1	1	2
0.5	0	2	3
0.63	1	3	4
0.8	2	4	5
1.0	3	5	6

of airborne sound insulation of the multi-element partition is determined by the areas and sound transmission properties of the individual components. Components having low values of sound insulation, such as windows and doors, reduce the overall sound insulation. By selecting the areas and sound transmission class (STC) ratings of the individual components, the STC rating for the multi-element partition can meet the design criterion. The simplest way to ensure that the composite structure has the required STC rating is to require that all components have this rating. This is usually uneconomical.

The overall STC rating is determined mainly by sound transmission through weaker components, so there are limits to what can be achieved by increasing the sound insulation of one component relative to the others. Instead, the following procedure is recommended to determine the STC value of each component so that the multi-element partition has a specified STC rating:

Step 1. Suppose A represents the total area of the multi-element partition and suppose that each component has an area designated as A_1, A_2, etc. First, determine the fractional area of each component, i.e., A_1/A, A_2/A.

Step 2. For each value of fractional area from Step 1, find the corresponding adjustment in a column to the right in Table 5.7. This adjustment will depend on the number of components in the composite partition.

Step 3. Indicate the required STC rating of the multi-element partition.

Step 4. Determine the STC value of the component by adding the adjustment of Step 2 to the specified value of the STC value for the composite partition.

Example: Two components, a wall and a door, are to be combined so that the required STC rating of the multi-element partition is 50. In this example, there are two components: (1) a door which will occupy $1/4$ of the total wall area (including the door), and (2) a wall that will occupy the remaining area. What should be the STC ratings of the wall and the door to yield the required rating of STC 50?

Step 1. The fractional area of the door A_1/A is 0.25; the fractional area of the wall is 0.75.

Step 2. From Table 5.7, the correction term for a fractional area of 0.25 of the door is −3. The table does not tabulate a fractional area of 0.75, so this value is rounded off to the next higher value in the table, i.e., to 0.8 for which the correction term is +2.

Step 3. The required rating is STC 50.

Step 4. The STC for the wall is 50 + 2 = 52. The STC for the door is 50 − 3 = 47.

REFERENCES§

1. ASTM E90, "Standard Test Method for Laboratory Measurement of Airborne Sound Transmission Loss of Building Partitions."
2. ISO 140/III, "Laboratory Measurements of Airborne Sound Insulation of Building Elements."
3. ASTM E336, "Standard Test Method for Measurement of Airborne Sound Insulation in Buildings."
4. ASTM E413, "Classification for Rating Sound Insulation."
5. ISO 717/1, "Rating of Sound Insulation in Buildings and of Building Elements—Part 1: Airborne Sound Insulation in Buildings and of Interior Building Elements."
6. ASTM E1408, "Standard Test Method for Laboratory Measurement of the Sound Transmission Loss of Door Panels and Door Systems."
7. ASTM E557, "Standard Practice for Architectural Application and Installation of Operable Partitions."

§ASTM standards are available from American Society for Testing and Materials, 1916 Race Street, Philadelphia, PA 19103-1187. ISO documents are available from the International Organization for Standardization, CH-1211 Geneva 20, Switzerland.

Appendix

5

Tables of Sound Insulation Ratings

A. C. C. Warnock

J. D. Quirt

LIST OF TABLES IN THIS CHAPTER APPENDIX

Appendix 5.3   Floor/Ceiling Constructions

5.3a   Concrete floor/ceilings

5.3b   Concrete floating floor on concrete floor/ceilings

5.3c   Wood joist (or truss) floors

5.3d   Wood joist (or truss) floors with concrete topping

5.3e   Wood joist floors with concrete floating topping

Appendix 5.4   Windows

5.4a   Single panes of glass

5.4b   Single panes, laminated glass

5.4c   Double glazing

5.4d   Double glazing, laminated glass

Appendix 5.5   Doors

5.5a   Solid-core wood doors

5.5b   Hollow-core steel doors

5.5c   Hollow-core steel door and solid-core wood door in same frame

5.5d   Hollow-core steel door and solid-core wood door in separate frames

ABBREVIATIONS USED IN THIS APPENDIX

STC (Sound Transmission Class).   A single-number rating used to compare the sound insulation properties of walls, floors, ceilings, windows, or doors. The higher this value, the better the sound insulation. For example, see Fig. 5.2.

R_w (Weighted Sound Reduction Index).   **A single-number rating system (somewhat similar to *Sound Transmission Class*)** used in many countries, other than North America, to express the overall sound insulation value of a partition. See footnote, page 5.5.

TL (Transmission Loss).   A measure of the airborne sound insulation, expressed in decibels (abbreviated *dB*), provided by a partition. Transmission loss varies with frequency, generally increasing with frequency as illustrated in Fig. 5.1. The higher this number, the better the sound insulation.

Test Lab. In these tables, the following symbols were used to represent the laboratories where the sound insulation measurements were made:

CKAL	Cedar Knolls Acoustical Laboratory
G&H	Geiger & Hamme
NBS	National Bureau of Standards
NGC	National Gypsum Company
NRCC	National Research Council Canada
OC	Owens Corning Corp.
RAL	Riverbank Acoustical Laboratory
USG	U.S. Gypsum Company

APPENDIX 5.1   Gypsum Board and Stud Partitions

5.1*a*   Single Layer of Gypsum Board; No Cavities

Description	STC	R_w	TL (Transmission Loss), dB						
			Frequency, Hz						
			63	80	100	**125**	160	200	**250**
$^3/_8$"(10mm) gypsum board	**26**					**12**	15	17	**17**
$^1/_2$"(13mm) gypsum board	**28**					**15**	17	19	**20**
2 layers of $^1/_2$"(13mm) gypsum board	**31**					**19**	24	25	**26**
$^5/_8$"(16mm) gypsum board, 1"(25mm) tongue and groove gypsum board, $^5/_8$"(16mm) gypsum board, laminated with adhesive	**36**					**27**	29	29	**31**

5.1*b*   Gypsum Board with Wood Studs

Description	STC	R_w	TL (Transmission Loss), dB						
			Frequency, Hz						
			63	80	100	**125**	160	200	**250**
$^1/_2$"(13mm) gypsum board, 2×4"(40×90mm) studs 24"(600mm) oc	**27**					**13**	17	19	**20**
$^1/_2$"(13mm) gypsum board, 2×4"(40×90mm) wood studs, $^1/_2$"(13mm) gypsum board; studs 16"(400mm) oc	**33**					**12**	16	21	**23**
2 layers of $^1/_2$"(13mm) gypsum board, 2×4"(40×90mm) wood studs, $^1/_2$"(13mm) gypsum board; studs 16"(400mm) oc	**37**					**16**	17	25	**26**
2 layers of $^1/_2$"(13mm) gypsum board, 2×4"(40×90mm) wood studs, 2 layers of $^1/_2$"(13mm) gypsum board; studs 24"(600mm) oc	**39**					**20**	22	29	**27**

APPENDIX 5.1 Gypsum Board and Stud Partitions (Continued)

TL (Transmission Loss), dB												
Frequency, Hz												
315	400	**500**	630	800	**1000**	1250	1600	**2000**	2500	3150	**4000**	Test lab
19	20	**23**	24	26	**28**	30	32	**33**	31	25	**23**	NRCC
21	23	**25**	26	27	**29**	31	32	**32**	29	25	**27**	NRCC
26	29	**30**	30	31	**32**	29	28	**29**	31	35	**37**	NRCC
32	33	**35**	35	35	**35**	36	35	**37**	39	41	**43**	NGC

TL (Transmission Loss), dB												
Frequency, Hz												
315	400	**500**	630	800	**1000**	1250	1600	**2000**	2500	3150	**4000**	Test lab
22	22	**25**	26	28	**30**	32	33	**33**	28	26	**28**	NRCC
26	28	**32**	35	38	**41**	43	45	**44**	37	36	**39**	NRCC
29	31	**36**	37	40	**42**	42	43	**45**	44	44	**48**	NRCC
32	37	**39**	41	43	**43**	40	39	**42**	47	51	**55**	NRCC

APPENDIX 5.1 Gypsum Board and Stud Partitions (Continued)

5.1*c* Gypsum Board Attached to Resilient Channels on Wood Studs

			TL (Transmission Loss), dB						
			Frequency, Hz						
Description	STC	R_w	**63**	80	100	**125**	160	200	**250**
5/8"(16mm) gypsum board, 2 × 4"(40 × 90mm) wood studs, 1/2"(13mm) resilient channels, 5/8"(16mm) gypsum board; studs 16"(400mm) oc	**38**					**16**	19	26	**26**
5/8"(16mm) gypsum board, resilient channels, 2 × 4"(40 × 90mm) wood studs, resilient channels, 5/8"(16mm) gypsum board; studs 16"(400mm) oc	**38**					**18**	22	27	**27**
2 layers of 5/8"(16mm) gypsum board, 2 × 4"(40 × 90mm) wood studs, resilient channels, 5/8"(16mm) gypsum board; studs 16"(400mm) oc	**43**					**27**	28	34	**33**
2 layers of 1/2"(13mm) gypsum board, 3 5/8"(40 × 90mm) wood studs, resilient channels, 2 layers of /2"(13mm) gypsum board	**49**	52				**26**	30	33	**39**
2 layers of 1/2"(13mm) gypsum board, 3 5/8"(40 × 90mm) wood studs, resilient channels, 2 layers of 1/2"(13mm) gypsum board; studs 16"(400mm) oc	**52**	55				**38**	31	38	**45**
2 layers of 1/2"(13mm) gypsum board, 2 × 4"(40 × 90mm) wood studs, 3"(75mm) mineral fiber batts, resilient channels, 2 layers of 1/2"(13mm) gypsum board; studs 16"(400mm) oc	**59**	61				**35**	41	47	**53**

APPENDIX 5.1   Gypsum Board and Stud Partitions (Continued)

					TL (Transmission Loss), dB							
					Frequency, Hz							
315	400	**500**	630	800	**1000**	1250	1600	**2000**	2500	3150	**4000**	Test lab
32	33	**37**	40	44	**45**	47	46	**40**	40	44	**48**	NRCC
32	34	**37**	40	45	**50**	55	53	**41**	37	42	**51**	NRCC
34	37	**40**	42	44	**45**	46	49	**49**	49	53	**54**	NRCC
42	47	**49**	52	55	**57**	60	61	**61**	58	53	**56**	RAL
49	53	**52**	54	56	**57**	58	59	**53**	55	58	**62**	USG
56	57	**59**	60	61	**63**	64	65	**65**	64	59	**61**	RAL

APPENDIX 5.1 **Gypsum Board and Stud Partitions (Continued)**

5.1*d* Gypsum Board on Double Wood Studs

Description	STC	R_w	TL (Transmission Loss), dB						
			Frequency, Hz						
			63	80	100	**125**	160	200	**250**
$\frac{1}{2}$"(13mm) gypsum board, $\frac{1}{4}$"(6mm) gypsum board, $1\frac{5}{8}$"(40mm) fiberglass batts, 2×4"(40×90mm) wood studs, 1"(25mm) air, $3\frac{5}{8}$" (40×90mm) wood studs, $\frac{1}{4}$"(6mm) gypsum board, $\frac{1}{2}$"(13mm) gypsum board; studs 16"(405mm) oc on separate plates spaced 1"(25mm) apart	52					28	31	40	37
$\frac{3}{8}$"(9mm) gypsum board, 3"(75mm) fiberglass batts, $3\frac{5}{8}$"(40×90mm) wood studs, 1"(25mm) air, 2×4" (40×90mm) wood studs, 6"(150mm) fiberglass batts, $\frac{3}{8}$"(9mm) gypsum board; double row of 2×4"(40×90mm) studs 16"(405mm) oc on separate plates, spaced 1"(25mm) apart	55					31	34	41	44
$\frac{5}{8}$"(16mm) gypsum board, 2×4"(40×90mm) wood studs, 3"(75mm) fiberglass batts, 1"(25mm) air, $\frac{1}{2}$"(13mm) wood fiberboard, $3\frac{5}{8}$" (40×90mm) wood studs, $\frac{5}{8}$"(16mm) gypsum board; studs 16"(405mm) oc on separate plates spaced 1"(2.5mm) apart	58					36	40	41	47
2 layers of $\frac{1}{2}$"(13mm) gypsum board, 2×4"(40×90mm) wood studs on separate plates spaced 1"(25mm) apart, 1.5"(40mm) fiberglass batts, 1"(25mm) air, 2 layers of $\frac{1}{2}$"(13mm) gypsum board	62					41	45	51	52

APPENDIX 5.1   Gypsum Board and Stud Partitions (Continued)

| | | | | | TL (Transmission Loss), dB | | | | | | | |
| | | | | | Frequency, Hz | | | | | | | |
315	400	**500**	630	800	**1000**	1250	1600	**2000**	2500	3150	**4000**	Test lab
43	51	**53**	57	62	**65**	66	66	**68**	67	68	**71**	G&H
49	53	**55**	57	57	**62**	64	66	**67**	66	64	**65**	OC
50	56	**59**	61	63	**63**	64	65	**62**	62	65	**68**	OC
57	60	**61**	61	64	**65**	65	66	**65**	62	63	**64**	OC

APPENDIX 5.1   Gypsum Board and Stud Partitions (Continued)

5.1e   Gypsum Board on Staggered Wood Studs

| | | | TL (Transmission Loss), dB | | | | | | |
| | | | Frequency, Hz | | | | | | |
Description	STC	R_w	63	80	100	125	160	200	250
$5/8$"(16mm) gypsum board, staggered wood studs [24"(600mm) oc on 2×6" wood plates], $5\,5/8$"(140mm) space, $5/8$"(16mm) gypsum board	39					27	27	27	25
$5/8$"(16mm) gypsum board, $5\,1/2$"(140mm) studs staggered 8" (200mm) oc on 2×6"(40 $\times$ 140mm) plates, $5/8$"(16mm) gypsum board	43					29	30	33	36
$5/8$"(16mm) gypsum board, $5\,1/2$" (140mm) staggered wood studs, 2"(50mm) mineral fiber batts, $5/8$"(16mm) gypsum board	45	47				25	31	35	37
2 layers of $5/8$"(16mm) gypsum board, $5\,1/2$"(140mm) staggered wood studs, 2 layers of $5/8$"(16mm) gypsum board	47	49				30	33	35	40
$1/4$"(6mm) gypsum board, $3/8$"(9mm) gypsum board, $3\,5/8$"(40 $\times$ 90mm) fiberglass batts, 2×4"(40 $\times$ 90mm) wood studs spaced 16"(405mm) oc and staggered 8"(200mm) oc, $3/8$"(9mm) gypsum board, $1/4$"(6mm) gypsum board	55					33	41	46	46

APPENDIX 5.1   Gypsum Board and Stud Partitions (Continued)

					TL (Transmission Loss), dB							
					Frequency, Hz							
315	400	**500**	630	800	**1000**	1250	1600	**2000**	2500	3150	**4000**	Test lab
31	37	**37**	39	43	**46**	46	42	**38**	38	44	**49**	NRCC
39	43	**44**	44	46	**46**	50	50	**43**	39	45	**51**	OC
41	40	**40**	43	46	**46**	51	51	**47**	47	51	**54**	RAL
40	42	**44**	46	49	**51**	52	52	**48**	48	53	**57**	RAL
47	49	**54**	54	54	**56**	59	60	**61**	62	63	**63**	OC

APPENDIX 5.1   Gypsum Board and Stud Partitions (Continued)

<table>
<tr><td colspan="3"></td><td colspan="7">TL (Transmission Loss), dB</td></tr>
<tr><td colspan="3"></td><td colspan="7">Frequency, Hz</td></tr>
<tr><td colspan="3">5.1f   Gypsum Board on Steel Studs</td><td></td><td></td><td></td><td></td><td></td><td></td><td></td></tr>
<tr><td>Description</td><td>STC</td><td>R_w</td><td>**63**</td><td>80</td><td>100</td><td>**125**</td><td>160</td><td>200</td><td>**250**</td></tr>
<tr><td>1/2"(13mm) gypsum board, 2 1/2"(65mm) steel studs, 1/2"(13mm) gypsum board</td><td>**34**</td><td>34</td><td></td><td></td><td>14</td><td>**13**</td><td>21</td><td>22</td><td>**21**</td></tr>
<tr><td>5/8"(16mm) gypsum board, staggered steel studs, 2 1/2"space, 5/8"(16mm) gypsum board</td><td>**38**</td><td></td><td></td><td></td><td></td><td>**15**</td><td>20</td><td>25</td><td>**26**</td></tr>
<tr><td>2 layers of 1/2"(13mm) gypsum board, 2 1/2"(65mm) steel studs, 1/2"(13mm) gypsum board</td><td>**39**</td><td>38</td><td></td><td></td><td>16</td><td>**18**</td><td>26</td><td>25</td><td>**25**</td></tr>
<tr><td>1/2"(13mm) gypsum board, 2 1/2"(65mm) steel studs 24"(610mm) oc, 2"(50mm) fiberglass batts, 1/2" (13mm) gypsum board</td><td>**45**</td><td></td><td></td><td></td><td></td><td>**21**</td><td>29</td><td>32</td><td>**35**</td></tr>
<tr><td>1/2"(13mm) gypsum board, 3 5/8" (40 × 90mm) steel studs 24"(610mm) oc, 2 layers of 1/2"(13mm) gypsum board</td><td>**45**</td><td></td><td></td><td></td><td></td><td>**29**</td><td>31</td><td>35</td><td>**35**</td></tr>
<tr><td>2 layers of 1/2"(13mm) gypsum board, 2 1/2"(65mm) steel studs, 2 layers of 1/2"(13mm) gypsum board</td><td>**45**</td><td>44</td><td></td><td></td><td>20</td><td>**23**</td><td>32</td><td>33</td><td>**30**</td></tr>
<tr><td>2 layers of 1/2"(13mm) gypsum board, 2 1/2"(65mm) steel studs, 2 layers of 1/2"(13mm) gypsum board</td><td>**50**</td><td></td><td></td><td></td><td></td><td>**32**</td><td>36</td><td>36</td><td>**40**</td></tr>
<tr><td>2 layers of 1/2"(13mm) gypsum board, 2 1/2"(65mm) steel studs, 5/8"(40mm) mineral fiber batts, 2 layers of 1/2"(13mm) gypsum board</td><td>**53**</td><td>53</td><td></td><td></td><td></td><td>**26**</td><td>35</td><td>37</td><td>**43**</td></tr>
<tr><td>2 layers of 1/2"(13mm) gypsum board, 3 5/8"(40 × 90mm) steel studs 24" (600mm) oc, 5/8"(40mm) mineral fiber batts, 2 layers of 1/2"(13mm) gypsum board</td><td>**55**</td><td>56</td><td></td><td></td><td>31</td><td>**34**</td><td>36</td><td>46</td><td>**47**</td></tr>
<tr><td>2 layers of 5/8"(16mm) gypsum board, 3 5/8"(40 × 90mm) steel studs, 2" (50mm) mineral fiber batts, 2 layers of 5/8"(16mm) gypsum board</td><td>**56**</td><td>57</td><td></td><td></td><td></td><td>**39**</td><td>39</td><td>44</td><td>**49**</td></tr>
</table>

APPENDIX 5.1   Gypsum Board and Stud Partitions (Continued)

					TL (Transmission Loss), dB							
					Frequency, Hz							
315	400	**500**	630	800	**1000**	1250	1600	**2000**	2500	3150	**4000**	Test lab
24	31	**33**	36	39	**43**	43	45	**44**	36	35	**39**	OC
30	34	**39**	40	42	**44**	45	46	**40**	42	48	**49**	NRCC
29	36	**39**	41	44	**47**	48	49	**49**	40	40	**44**	OC
40	45	**48**	51	53	**55**	57	58	**56**	49	42	**43**	RAL
35	42	**48**	47	49	**51**	53	56	**53**	44	41	**46**	OC
35	42	**45**	45	48	**49**	50	52	**52**	45	47	**52**	OC
39	47	**52**	52	53	**55**	57	58	**58**	49	49	**54**	OC
47	51	**54**	55	57	**56**	56	59	**58**	58	56	**58**	USG
51	55	**56**	56	60	**61**	60	63	**59**	52	54	**57**	USG
49	54	**57**	57	59	**61**	63	63	**60**	62	53	**57**	USG

APPENDIX 5.1   Gypsum Board and Stud Partitions (Continued)

5.1g   Gypsum Board Attached to Resilient Channels on Steel Studs

Description	STC	R_w	63	80	100	125	160	200	250
			\multicolumn{7}{c}{TL (Transmission Loss), dB}						
1/2"(13mm) gypsum board, resilient channels, 3⅝"(40 × 90mm) steel studs, 3"(75mm) mineral fiber batts, 1/2"(13mm) gypsum board	50	51	14	12	17	26	32	38	43
2 layers of 1/2"(13mm) gypsum board, resilient channels, 3⅝"(40 × 90mm) steel studs, 3"(75mm) mineral fiber batts, 1/2"(13mm) gypsum board	55	57	17	19	25	33	37	44	48
1/2"(13mm) gypsum board, resilient channels, 6"(150mm) steel studs, 4.9"(125mm) mineral fiber batts, 1/2"(13mm) gypsum board	56	57	16	21	25	32	38	44	48
2 layers of 1/2"(13mm) gypsum board, resilient channels, 3⅝"(40 × 90mm) steel studs, 3"(75mm) mineral fiber batts, 2 layers of 1/2"(13mm) gypsum board	60	61	20	27	33	38	42	48	53
2 layers of 1/2"(13mm) gypsum board, resilient channels, 6"(150mm) steel studs, 4.9"(125mm) mineral fiber batts, 1/2"(13mm) gypsum board	60	62	17	27	32	38	43	49	52
2 layers of 1/2"(13mm) gypsum board, resilient channels, 6"(150mm) steel studs, 4.9"(125mm) mineral fiber batts, 2 layers of 1/2"(13mm) gypsum board	63	64	25	33	38	43	46	51	54

APPENDIX 5.1   Gypsum Board and Stud Partitions (Continued)

| | | | | | TL (Transmission Loss), dB | | | | | | | |
| | | | | | Frequency, Hz | | | | | | | |
315	400	**500**	630	800	**1000**	1250	1600	**2000**	2500	3150	**4000**	Test lab
46	51	**53**	53	52	**52**	54	55	**55**	53	48	**52**	RAL
49	54	**56**	56	56	**56**	59	61	**61**	58	54	**58**	RAL
51	57	**60**	60	61	**62**	62	62	**63**	58	53	**56**	RAL
54	59	**61**	61	60	**60**	62	64	**65**	62	59	**63**	RAL
55	59	**62**	63	63	**63**	64	65	**67**	62	58	**62**	RAL
56	60	**63**	64	65	**65**	66	68	**69**	63	61	**66**	RAL

APPENDIX 5.2   Masonry Walls

5.2a   4-inch (90-mm) Concrete Block Walls

| | | | TL (Transmission Loss), dB | | | | | | |
| | | | Frequency, Hz | | | | | | |
Description	STC	R_w	63	80	100	125	160	200	250
Very porous, wood fiber aggregate 4"-concrete blocks [20lb/ft²(98kg/m²)]; no finish on either side	14	14	10	8	7	8	6	7	9
4"-concrete block [30lb/ft²(147kg/m²)]	37	37	29	27	27	30	29	30	30
4"(90mm) concrete block [30lb/ft² (147kg/m²)]	44	44	32	31	30	32	32	35	37
Paint, 4"(90mm) solid concrete block [39lb/ft²(191kg/m²)], 1/2"(13mm) gypsum board	46					32	35	32	34
1/2"(13mm) gypsum board, paint, 4"(90mm) solid concrete block [39lb/ft²(191kg/m²)], 1/2"(13mm) gypsum board	47					31	32	30	33
1/2"(13mm) gypsum board, 4"(90mm) solid concrete block [39lb/ft² (191kg/m²)], paint, 1"(25mm) fiberglass batts, resilient channels, 1/2"(13mm) gypsum board	52					28	35	36	40

5.2b   6-inch (140-mm) Concrete Block Walls

| | | | TL (Transmission Loss), dB | | | | | | |
| | | | Frequency, Hz | | | | | | |
Description	STC	R_w	63	80	100	125	160	200	250
6"(140mm) concrete block [41lb/ft²(202kg/m²)]	45					30	31	32	34
1/2"(13mm) gypsum board, 6"(140mm) concrete block [41lb/ft²(202kg/m²)]	46					29	33	32	34
1/2"(13mm) gypsum board, 3/4" (19mm) wood furring, 6"(140mm) concrete block [41lb/ft²(202kg/m²)], 3/4"(19mm) wood furring,1/2"(13mm) gypsum board	47					26	26	31	33
6"(140mm) 75%-solid, concrete block [49lb/ft²(240kg/m²)]	47	47	35	33	34	37	38	36	34
Paint, 6"(140mm) 75%-solid concrete block [49lb/ft²(240kg/m²)]	48	48	37	35	36	38	39	36	34

APPENDIX 5.2   Masonry Walls (Continued)

| | | | | | TL (Transmission Loss), dB | | | | | | | |
| | | | | | Frequency, Hz | | | | | | | |
315	400	**500**	630	800	**1000**	1250	1600	**2000**	2500	3150	**4000**	Test lab
10	10	**10**	11	11	**13**	15	16	**17**	19	21	**24**	NRCC
32	34	**37**	37	36	**35**	36	35	**38**	39	40	**41**	NRCC
38	39	**39**	41	42	**44**	45	47	**49**	50	52	**55**	NRCC
36	38	**42**	45	48	**50**	53	55	**56**	57	56	**57**	NRCC
38	41	**45**	50	54	**56**	58	61	**62**	62	60	**61**	NRCC
46	48	**52**	54	58	**59**	59	62	**62**	62	60	**62**	NRCC

| | | | | | TL (Transmission Loss), dB | | | | | | | |
| | | | | | Frequency, Hz | | | | | | | |
315	400	**500**	630	800	**1000**	1250	1600	**2000**	2500	3150	**4000**	Test lab
38	39	**41**	44	46	**48**	49	52	**56**	56	54	**55**	NRCC
37	38	**41**	45	49	**53**	55	57	**63**	61	59	**62**	NRCC
40	44	**50**	56	60	**62**	63	64	**67**	64	62	**64**	NRCC
38	40	**42**	45	48	**51**	54	55	**57**	61	63	**64**	NRCC
38	40	**43**	46	49	**52**	54	55	**58**	62	64	**65**	NRCC

APPENDIX 5.2   Masonry Walls (Continued)

5.2*b*   6-inch (140-mm) Concrete Block Walls (*Continued*)

Description	STC	R_w	63	80	100	125	160	200	250
			TL (Transmission Loss), dB						
$1/2$"(13mm) gypsum board, $3/4$"(19mm) wood furring, 6"(140mm) concrete block [41lb/ft²(202kg/m²)]	49					31	30	33	35
6"(140mm) concrete block [41lb/ft²(202kg/m²)], $3/4$"(19mm) wood furring, 1"(25mm) fiberglass batts, $1/2$"(13mm) gypsum board	50					28	31	36	37
6"(140mm) 100%-solid concrete block [62lb/ft²(301kg/m²)]	50	50	38	32	35	38	36	35	37
$1/2$"(13mm) plaster, 6"(140mm) concrete block [41lb/ft²(202kg/m²)], $1/2$"(13mm) plaster	51					36	35	39	41
6"(140mm) 75%-solid, concrete block [49lb/ft²(240kg/m²)], $1 1/2$"(38mm) wood furring, $1 1/2$"(38mm) fiberglass batts, $1/2$"(13mm) gypsum board	55	55	32	28	31	38	45	45	42
$1/2$"(13mm) gypsum board, resilient channels, 6"(140mm) concrete block [38lb/ft²(185kg/m²)], resilient channels, $1/2$"(13mm) gypsum board	57	47	27	19	20	38	50	51	48
$1/2$"(13mm) gypsum board, $1/2$"(13mm) fiberglass batts, resilient channels, 6"(140mm) concrete block [38lb/ft² (185kg/m²)], resilient channels, $1/2$" (13mm) fiberglass batts, $1/2$"(13mm) gypsum board	58	54	28	24	27	34	39	48	53
Paint, 6"(140mm) 100%-solid, concrete block [62lb/ft²(301kg/m²)], $1 1/2$"(38mm) fiberglass batts, $1 1/2$" (38mm) wood furring, $1/2$"(13mm) gypsum board	58	55	34	30	28	38	44	44	44
$5/8$"(16mm) gypsum board, $2 1/2$" (65mm) steel studs, $2 1/2$"(65mm) fiberglass batts, 6"(140mm) 75%-solid, concrete block [49lb/ft²(240kg/m²)]	61	61	33	36	39	44	46	47	48
$1/2$"(13mm) gypsum board, $1 5/8$" (40mm) steel studs, $1 5/8$"(40mm) fiberglass batts, 6"(140mm) block [38lb/ft²(185kg/m²)], $1 5/8$"(40mm) fiberglass batts, $1 5/8$"(40mm) steel studs, $1/2$"(13mm) gypsum board	64	59	23	25	32	40	51	56	57

APPENDIX 5.2   Masonry Walls (Continued)

					TL (Transmission Loss), dB							
					Frequency, Hz							
315	400	**500**	630	800	**1000**	1250	1600	**2000**	2500	3150	**4000**	Test lab
41	43	**48**	52	55	**57**	58	61	**64**	63	60	**62**	NRCC
44	45	**49**	52	54	**56**	56	60	**63**	61	58	**61**	NRCC
41	45	**46**	49	53	**55**	57	60	**62**	64	66	**69**	NRCC
42	44	**48**	50	52	**54**	55	57	**60**	62	60	**60**	NRCC
45	49	**51**	53	57	**60**	63	64	**66**	66	64	**67**	NRCC
46	48	**56**	64	69	**73**	77	77	**76**	76	73	**74**	NRCC
60	62	**65**	68	72	**75**	77	77	**78**	77	74	**78**	NRCC
48	52	**54**	58	60	**63**	65	67	**68**	69	67	**69**	NRCC
52	56	**58**	60	63	**65**	66	66	**67**	69	73	**76**	NRCC
61	61	**62**	63	66	**69**	76	79	**78**	73	72	**75**	NRCC

APPENDIX 5.2   Masonry Walls (Continued)

5.2c   8-inch (190-mm) Concrete Block Walls

Description	STC	R_w	TL (Transmission Loss), dB						
			Frequency, Hz						
			63	80	100	125	160	200	250
8"(190mm) concrete block [48lb/ft^2(236kg/m^2)], $^5/_8$"(16mm) gypsum board	50	50	36	33	31	35	34	36	35
8"(190mm) concrete block [48lb/ft^2(236kg/m^2)], resilient channels, $^5/_8$"(16mm) gypsum board	51	51	36	32	33	31	34	35	38
Paint, 8"(190mm) block [51lb/ft^2(249kg/m^2)]	53					37	39	45	46
Paint, 8"(190mm) block [51lb/ft^2(249kg/m^2)], $^5/_8$"(16mm) gypsum board	54					38	38	41	42
$^5/_8$"(16mm) gypsum board, $1^1/_2$" (38mm) wood studs, 8"(190mm) concrete block [48lb/ft^2(236kg/m^2)], $1^1/_2$"(38mm) wood studs, $^5/_8$"(16mm) gypsum board	54	48	33	25	21	30	35	44	46
8"(190mm) concrete block [48lb/ft^2(236kg/m^2)], $1^1/_2$"(38mm) wood studs, $1^1/_2$"(38mm) fiberglass batts, $^5/_8$"(16mm) gypsum board	55	55	32	29	29	37	42	49	48
$^5/_8$"(16mm) gypsum board, 3"(75mm) Z channels, 8"(190mm) concrete block [48lb/ft^2(236kg/m^2)]	57	56	30	27	30	34	38	40	44
$^5/_8$"(16mm) gypsum board, 3"(75mm) Z channels, 8"(190mm) concrete block [48lb/ft^2(236kg/m^2)], paint	58	57	30	29	30	34	38	41	46
$^1/_2$"(13mm) gypsum board, resilient channels, $1^1/_2$"(38mm) wood furring, $1^1/_2$"(38mm) mineral fiber batts, 8" (190mm) concrete block	58	57			33	35	39	43	47
Paint, 8"(190mm) block [51lb/ft^2(249kg/m^2)], resilient channels, $^5/_8$"(16mm) gypsum board	59					40	42	46	48
$^5/_8$"(16mm) gypsum board, 3"(75mm) Z channels, 8"(190mm) concrete block [48lb/ft^2(236kg/m^2)], $2^1/_2$"(65mm) steel studs, $^5/_8$"(16mm) gypsum board	59	55	25	23	28	35	41	48	55

APPENDIX 5.2   Masonry Walls (Continued)

					TL (Transmission Loss), dB							
					Frequency, Hz							
315	400	**500**	630	800	**1000**	1250	1600	**2000**	2500	3150	**4000**	Test lab
41	43	**46**	50	53	**55**	56	57	**58**	56	59	**62**	NRCC
43	47	**51**	54	58	**61**	63	64	**65**	64	66	**69**	NRCC
44	44	**46**	50	52	**54**	56	58	**59**	59	60	**60**	NRCC
44	47	**50**	54	57	**59**	62	65	**62**	63	65	**68**	NRCC
45	52	**54**	59	62	**62**	63	64	**64**	58	61	**66**	NRCC
47	49	**50**	52	55	**57**	60	62	**61**	58	61	**66**	NRCC
51	54	**56**	58	61	**62**	64	65	**63**	60	64	**69**	NRCC
52	56	**58**	60	62	**62**	64	65	**65**	62	65	**70**	NRCC
50	55	**56**	59	60	**60**	62	62	**62**	62	62	**64**	RAL
51	56	**57**	57	62	**65**	67	69	**68**	67	68	**71**	NRCC
62	70	**73**	75	76	**76**	74	73	**69**	68	72	**77**	NRCC

APPENDIX 5.2   Masonry Walls (Continued)

5.2c   8-inch (190-mm) Concrete Block Walls (*Continued*)

Description	STC	R_w	\multicolumn{7}{c}{TL (Transmission Loss), dB — Frequency, Hz}

Description	STC	R_w	63	80	100	**125**	160	200	**250**
$^5/_8$"(16mm) gypsum board, 2"(50mm) fiberglass batts, 2"(50mm) Z channels, 8"(190mm) concrete block [48lb/ft^2(236kg/m^2)]	**59**	57	**33**	29	30	**37**	41	45	**47**
8"(190mm) concrete block, 1"(25mm) air, $1^5/_8$"(40mm) steel studs, $1^5/_8$" (40mm) mineral fiber batts, $^1/_2$"(13mm) gypsum board	**59**	59			36	**39**	42	45	**50**
$^5/_8$"(16mm) gypsum board, 8"-concrete block [48lb/ft^2(236kg/m^2)], $2^1/_2$"(65mm) steel studs, $2^1/_2$"(65mm) fiberglass batts, $^5/_8$"(16mm) gypsum board	**61**	60	**31**	33	33	**40**	40	46	**48**
$^5/_8$"(16mm) gypsum board, 3"(75mm) Z channels, 3"(75mm) fiberglass batts, 8"-concrete block [48lb/ft^2(236kg/m^2)]	**61**	60	**29**	31	35	**42**	44	48	**49**
$^5/_8$"(16mm) gypsum board, 3"(75mm) Z channels, 3"(75mm) fiberglass batts, 8"-concrete block [48lb/ft^2(236kg/m^2)], $^5/_8$"(16mm) gypsum board	**62**	61	**29**	31	36	**42**	44	47	**49**
$^1/_2$"(13mm) gypsum board, $2^1/_2$"(65mm) fiberglass batts, $2^1/_2$"(65mm) steel studs, $^1/_8$"(3mm) plaster, $7^1/_2$"(190mm) lightweight concrete block [38lb/ft^2(183kg/m^2)]	**65**	61	**29**	33	34	**41**	45	49	**53**
$^5/_8$"(16mm) gypsum board, $2^1/_2$"(65mm) steel studs, 8"(190mm) concrete block [48lb/ft^2(236kg/m^2)], $2^1/_2$"(65mm) steel studs, $2^1/_2$"(65mm) fiberglass batts, $^5/_8$"(16mm) gypsum board	**65**	59	**27**	28	32	**41**	47	55	**60**
$^5/_8$"(16mm) gypsum board, 3"(75mm) Z channels, 8"(190mm) concrete block [48lb/ft^2(236kg/m^2)], $2^1/_2$"(65mm) steel studs, $2^1/_2$"(65mm) fiberglass batts, $^5/_8$"(16mm) gypsum board	**68**	62	**26**	27	35	**44**	48	55	**62**
$^5/_8$"(16mm) gypsum board, $2^1/_2$"(65mm) fiberglass batts, $2^1/_2$"(65mm) steel studs, 8"(190mm) concrete block [48lb/ft^2(236kg/m^2)], $2^1/_2$"(65mm) steel studs, $2^1/_2$"(65mm) fiberglass batts, $^5/_8$"(16mm) gypsum board	**72**	67	**27**	31	40	**49**	54	62	**67**

APPENDIX 5.2   Masonry Walls (Continued)

					TL (Transmission Loss), dB							
					Frequency, Hz							
315	400	**500**	630	800	**1000**	1250	1600	**2000**	2500	3150	**4000**	Test lab
53	56	**57**	60	61	**61**	63	64	**65**	63	66	**70**	NRCC
54	57	**58**	59	59	**60**	62	64	**64**	62	62	**63**	RAL
54	58	**60**	62	64	**64**	64	65	**65**	64	69	**72**	NRCC
56	58	**59**	60	62	**62**	64	65	**65**	62	66	**71**	NRCC
56	61	**64**	65	65	**64**	67	69	**67**	62	66	**71**	NRCC
60	63	**65**	66	67	**69**	72	74	**75**	73	71	**74**	NRCC
69	73	**74**	74	75	**73**	72	72	**73**	71	75	**78**	NRCC
70	72	**74**	76	77	**76**	74	73	**71**	69	74	**78**	NRCC
73	73	**75**	74	76	**74**	73	73	**73**	72	77	80	NRCC

APPENDIX 5.2   Masonry Walls (Continued)

5.2d   12-inch (290-mm) Concrete Block Walls

			TL (Transmission Loss), dB						
			Frequency, Hz						
Description	STC	R_w	63	80	100	125	160	200	250
12"(290mm) concrete block [63lb/ft^2(306kg/m^2)]	49					31	37	39	40
$^1\!/_2$"(13mm) gypsum board, resilient channels, paint, 12"(290mm) concrete block [53lb/ft^2(250kg/m^2)], paint	49					30	32	34	36
12"(290mm) concrete block [63lb/ft^2(306kg/m^2)], paint	50					33	38	40	41
$^1\!/_2$"(13mm) plaster, 12"(290mm) concrete block [63lb/ft^2(306kg/m^2)], paint	52					36	36	42	42
$^1\!/_2$"(13mm) gypsum board, resilient channels, 12"(290mm) concrete block [53lb/ft^2(250kg/m^2)], paint	57					37	37	41	46

5.2e   Cavity Concrete Block Walls

			TL (Transmission Loss), dB						
			Frequency, Hz						
Description	STC	R_w	63	80	100	125	160	200	250
4"(90mm) concrete block [30lb/ft^2(147kg/m^2)], 1"(25mm) air, 2$^1\!/_2$"(65mm) fiberglass batts, 4"(90mm) concrete block [30lb/ft^2(147kg/m^2)], $^5\!/_8$"(16mm) gypsum board	62	62	37	42	46	49	53	52	54
4"(90mm) concrete block [30lb/ft^2(147kg/m^2)], 3"(75mm) air, 2"(50mm) styrofoam, 4"(90mm) concrete block [30lb/ft^2(147kg/m^2)], $^5\!/_8$"(16mm) gypsum board	66	66	39	42	46	48	47	51	54
4"(90mm) concrete block [30lb/ft^2(147kg/m^2)], 3"(75mm) air, 2"(50mm) styrofoam, 4"(90mm) concrete block [30lb/ft^2(147kg/m^2)], $^5\!/_8$"(16mm) gypsum board	69	68	40	44	48	50	51	53	57
4"(90mm) concrete block [30lb/ft^2(147kg/m^2)], 4.9"(125mm) air, 4"(90mm) concrete block [30lb/ft^2 (147kg/m^2)], $^5\!/_8$"(16mm) gypsum board	69	70	40	45	51	52	52	54	57
4"(90mm) concrete block [30lb/ft^2(147kg/m^2)], 2.4"(60mm) air, 2$^1\!/_2$"(65mm) rigid fiberglass panels, 4"(90mm) concrete block [30lb/ft^2 (147kg/m^2)], $^5\!/_8$"(16mm) gypsum board	77	77	41	48	52	57	59	62	65

APPENDIX 5.2   Masonry Walls (Continued)

315	400	**500**	630	800	**1000**	1250	1600	**2000**	2500	3150	**4000**	Test lab
					TL (Transmission Loss), dB							
					Frequency, Hz							
43	43	**44**	46	49	**51**	53	56	**57**	60	59	**61**	NRCC
40	42	**46**	50	55	**59**	62	65	**66**	65	64	**63**	NRCC
43	43	**45**	46	50	**51**	53	56	**57**	60	59	**61**	NRCC
45	46	**47**	48	52	**54**	56	58	**58**	62	62	**63**	NRCC
49	52	**55**	59	62	**66**	69	72	**72**	69	68	**70**	NRCC

315	400	**500**	630	800	**1000**	1250	1600	**2000**	2500	3150	**4000**	Test lab
					TL (Transmission Loss), dB							
					Frequency, Hz							
52	53	**57**	62	64	**66**	67	68	**71**	75	79	**81**	NRCC
57	59	**66**	71	74	**77**	80	79	**81**	82	85	**83**	NRCC
60	61	**69**	74	74	**78**	78	77	**81**	83	86	**82**	NRCC
60	62	**70**	76	75	**78**	77	78	**83**	84	85	**82**	NRCC
71	72	**76**	81	79	**82**	82	83	**86**	86	87	**83**	NRCC

APPENDIX 5.3   Floor/Ceiling Constructions

5.3a   Concrete Floor/Ceilings

Description	STC	R_w	63	80	100	125	160	200	250
					TL (Transmission Loss), dB				
						Frequency, Hz			
6"(150mm) hollow-core concrete panel [45lb/ft^2(220kg/m^2)]	48					33	35	33	37
4"(100mm) concrete panel [54lb/ft^2(263kg/m^2)]	49					48	45	43	42
66-oz carpet on 50-oz hair pad; 8"(200mm) hollow-core concrete panels [57lb/ft^2(278kg/m^2)]	50					34	33	39	39
1^1/$_2$"(38mm) lightweight concrete: 8"(200mm) hollow-core concrete panels [57lb/ft^2(278kg/m^2)]	52					37	35	38	40
2"(50mm) concrete T [14"(355mm)] deep, [48lb/ft^2(234kg/m^2)]; 2"(50mm) concrete topping [27lb/ft^2(132kg/m^2)]	54					39	40	42	45
6"(150mm) concrete panel [75lb/ft^2(366kg/m^2)]	55					38	41	41	43
8"(200mm) concrete slab [95lb/ft^2(464kg/m^2)]	58					44	44	45	48

5.3b   Concrete Floating Floor on Concrete Floor/Ceilings

Description	STC	R_w	63	80	100	125	160	200	250
					TL (Transmission Loss), dB				
						Frequency, Hz			
1^5/$_8$"(40mm) concrete on 0.8"(21mm) very soft rubber pads; 6"(150mm) concrete	61	60	40	38	41	41	42	43	51
1^5/$_8$"(40mm) concrete on 1"(25mm) rigid fiberglass; 6"(150mm) concrete	62	62	38	49	48	47	43	45	51

5.3c   Wood Joist (or Truss) Floors

Description	STC	R_w	63	80	100	125	160	200	250
					TL (Transmission Loss), dB				
						Frequency, Hz			
^{5}/$_8$"(16mm) plywood on 2 × 10" (40 × 240mm) wood joists	24	24	12	11	15	10	11	13	16
^{5}/$_8$"(16mm) plywood on 2 × 10" (40 × 240mm) wood joists, ^{1}/$_2$" (13mm) gypsum board	32	32	18	19	18	13	11	21	26
^{5}/$_8$"(16mm) plywood, 2 × 10" (40 × 240mm) wood joists, 3^5/$_8$" (90mm) fiberglass batts, ^{1}/$_2$"(13mm)	33	33	19	19	18	13	12	25	33

APPENDIX 5.3   Floor/Ceiling Constructions (Continued)

| | | | | | TL (Transmission Loss), dB | | | | | | | |
| | | | | | Frequency, Hz | | | | | | | |
315	400	**500**	630	800	**1000**	1250	1600	**2000**	2500	3150	**4000**	Test lab
37	41	**43**	45	49	**51**	53	56	**57**	58	60	**60**	CKAL
39	40	**45**	46	50	**56**	53	53	**57**	62	66	**67**	NBS
39	44	**46**	48	51	**53**	55	57	**59**	63	65	**64**	CKAL
42	46	**47**	51	53	**55**	57	60	**62**	63	66	**68**	CKAL
49	47	**50**	52	51	**52**	55	58	**60**	62	65	**68**	RAL
45	48	**52**	54	57	**59**	62	65	**67**	69	71	**72**	RAL
51	53	**55**	56	56	**58**	60	62	**63**	65	66	**67**	RAL

| | | | | | TL (Transmission Loss), dB | | | | | | | |
| | | | | | Frequency, Hz | | | | | | | |
315	400	**500**	630	800	**1000**	1250	1600	**2000**	2500	3150	**4000**	Test lab
53	57	**58**	61	65	**67**	70	73	**75**	78	79	**82**	NRCC
54	57	**58**	60	64	**67**	70	70	**73**	77	79	**81**	NRCC

| | | | | | TL (Transmission Loss), dB | | | | | | | |
| | | | | | Frequency, Hz | | | | | | | |
315	400	**500**	630	800	**1000**	1250	1600	**2000**	2500	3150	**4000**	Test lab
20	23	**22**	24	25	**25**	26	25	**24**	24	25	**27**	NRCC
27	27	**34**	37	38	**41**	42	44	**45**	44	42	**46**	NRCC
31	29	**35**	39	40	**43**	44	46	**47**	47	45	**48**	NRCC

APPENDIX 5.3   Floor/Ceiling Constructions (Continued)

5.3c   Wood Joist (or Truss) Floors (*Continued*)

Description	STC	R_w	63	80	100	125	160	200	250
			TL (Transmission Loss), dB — Frequency, Hz						
$^5/_8$"(16mm) plywood on 2 × 10" (40 × 240mm) wood joists, $^5/_8$"(16mm), wood furring, $3^5/_8$"(90mm) fiberglass batts, 2 layers of $^1/_2$"(13mm) gypsum board	37	37	22	21	20	13	17	29	35
$^5/_8$"(16mm) plywood on 2 × 10" (40 × 240mm) wood joists, resilient channels, $^1/_2$"(13mm) gypsum board	41	41	17	14	24	21	20	26	28
Carpet and underpad on $^5/_8$"(16mm) plywood, 2 × 10"(40 × 240mm) wood joists, resilient channels, $^1/_2$"(13mm) gypsum board	42	42	18	16	27	24	23	30	30
$^5/_8$"(16mm) plywood on 2 × 10" (40 × 240mm) wood joists, resilient channels, 2 layers of $^1/_2$"(13mm) gypsum board	44	44	25	20	30	28	25	31	32
Carpet and underpad on $^5/_8$"(16mm) plywood on 2 × 10"(40 × 240mm) wood joists, resilient channels, 2 layers of $^1/_2$"(13mm) gypsum board	47	47	23	22	33	30	28	35	35
$^5/_8$"(16mm) plywood on 2 × 10" (40 × 240mm) wood joists; $3^5/_8$" (90mm) fiberglass batts, resilient channels, $^1/_2$"(13mm) gypsum board	47	47	17	19	27	23	26	30	35
$^5/_8$"(16mm) plywood on 2 × 10" (40 × 240mm) wood joists; $3^5/_8$"(90mm) fiberglass batts, resilient channels, 2 layers of $^1/_2$"(13mm) gypsum board	50	50	26	23	33	32	29	36	43
$^5/_8$"(16mm) plywood on 2 × 10" (40 × 240mm) wood joists, 7.1" (180mm) fiberglass batts, resilient channels, 2 layers of $^5/_8$"(16mm) gypsum board	52	52	25	26	35	36	37	37	42
Carpet on $^5/_8$"(16mm) plywood, 2 × 10"(40 × 240mm) wood joists, $3^5/_8$"(90mm) fiberglass batts, resilient channels, 2 layers of $^5/_8$"(16mm) gypsum board	54	54	27	30	36	33	40	40	44
Carpet on $^5/_8$"(16mm) plywood, 2 × 10"(40 × 240mm) wood joists, 7.1"(180mm) fiberglass batts, resilient channels, 2 layers of $^5/_8$"(16mm) gypsum board	54	54	26	30	36	35	40	41	45

APPENDIX 5.3   Floor/Ceiling Constructions (Continued)

| | | | | | TL (Transmission Loss), dB | | | | | | | |
| | | | | | Frequency, Hz | | | | | | | |
315	400	**500**	630	800	**1000**	1250	1600	**2000**	2500	3150	**4000**	Test lab
36	38	**42**	46	48	**51**	52	54	**55**	56	56	**61**	NRCC
36	37	**38**	42	43	**44**	46	47	**49**	47	45	**49**	NRCC
34	37	**38**	43	46	**50**	55	58	**60**	61	62	**68**	NRCC
37	39	**39**	43	44	**47**	50	51	**51**	50	48	**54**	NRCC
39	41	**42**	46	48	**53**	57	61	**65**	67	69	**75**	NRCC
43	48	**50**	52	57	**57**	60	58	**57**	55	52	**56**	NRCC
49	53	**53**	58	59	**61**	63	64	**64**	62	59	**63**	NRCC
44	47	**50**	49	53	**56**	56	57	**56**	53	56	**60**	NRCC
47	49	**52**	52	54	**57**	58	59	**58**	56	60	**65**	NRCC
47	49	**52**	52	55	**57**	58	59	**58**	57	61	**66**	NRCC

APPENDIX 5.3 Floor/Ceiling Constructions (Continued)

5.3c Wood Joist (or Truss) Floors (*Continued*)

			TL (Transmission Loss), dB						
			Frequency, Hz						
Description	STC	R_w	**63**	80	100	**125**	160	200	**250**
Carpet on ⅝"(16mm) plywood, 15.7"(400mm) wood trusses, 7.1"(180mm) fiberglass batts, resilient channels, ⅝"(16mm) gypsum board	**55**	55	**28**	32	37	**39**	40	41	**43**
Carpet on ⅝"(16mm) plywood, 12"(300mm) wood trusses; 3 layers of 3"(75mm) fiberglass batts, resilient channels, ⅝"(16mm) gypsum board)	**57**	57	**23**	28	33	**34**	43	44	**46**
Carpet on ⅝"(16mm) plywood, 2 × 10"(40 × 240mm) wood joists, 10.6"(270mm) fiberglass batts, resilient channels, 2 layers of ⅝"(16mm) gypsum board	**58**	58	**27**	30	38	**40**	42	45	**48**
2 layers of ⅝"(16mm) plywood on 2 × 10 (40 × 240mm) wood joists; 10.6"(270mm) fiberglass batts, resilient channels, 2 layers of ⅝" (16mm) gypsum board	**58**	57	**30**	36	36	**38**	45	45	**47**
Carpet, ½"(12mm) felt, ⅝"(16mm) plywood, 2 × 10"(40 × 240mm) wood joists, 10.6"(270mm) fiberglass batts, resilient channels, 2 layers of ⅝" (16mm) gypsum board	**59**	59	**27**	33	39	**40**	43	44	**48**
Carpet on ⅝"(16mm) plywood, 0.7" (19mm) wood fiberboard, 2 × 10" (40 × 240mm) wood joists; 8"(200mm) fiberglass batts, 3.1"(80mm) air, 5.5" (140mm) wood joists, 6"(152mm) fiberglass batts, resilient channels, ⅝"(16mm) gypsum board; double joist construction with 80-mm air space and 13-mm ethafoam spacer	**59**	59	**37**	43	42	**41**	43	45	**48**
⅝"(16mm) plywood on ½"(12mm) wood fiberboard, ⅝"(16mm) plywood, 2 × 10"(40 × 240mm) wood joists; 10.6" (270mm) fiberglass batts, resilient channels, 2 layers of ⅝"(16mm) gypsum board	**61**	61	**32**	38	41	**42**	46	46	**47**
⅝"(16mm) plywood on 0.5"(12mm) wood fiberboard, 2 × 10"(40 × 240mm) wood joists; 10.6"(270mm) fiberglass batts, resilient channels, 2 layers of ⅝" (16mm) gypsum board; fiberboard glued to the plywood	**62**	62	**28**	37	42	**43**	47	47	**51**

APPENDIX 5.3   Floor/Ceiling Constructions (Continued)

| | | | | | TL (Transmission Loss), dB | | | | | | | |
| | | | | | Frequency, Hz | | | | | | | |
315	400	**500**	630	800	**1000**	1250	1600	**2000**	2500	3150	**4000**	Test lab
46	50	**51**	55	58	**59**	61	61	**59**	58	62	**67**	NRCC
48	52	**55**	57	60	**62**	65	65	**63**	63	68	**72**	NRCC
52	54	**56**	56	58	**59**	61	62	**61**	60	62	**66**	NRCC
51	53	**53**	55	59	**60**	62	63	**63**	61	63	**66**	NRCC
52	53	**55**	57	60	**62**	65	67	**67**	65	65	**67**	NRCC
50	54	**56**	60	64	**68**	71	73	**71**	71	75	**79**	NRCC
52	56	**58**	60	63	**65**	67	68	**68**	68	67	**69**	NRCC
55	57	**59**	60	63	**65**	67	68	**68**	66	66	**67**	NRCC

APPENDIX 5.3   Floor/Ceiling Constructions (Continued)

5.3d   Wood Joist (or Truss) Floors with Concrete Topping

| | | | TL (Transmission Loss), dB | | | | | | |
| | | | Frequency, Hz | | | | | | |
Description	STC	R_w	63	80	100	125	160	200	250
$1^5/_8$"(40mm) lightweight concrete over 3-mil-polyvinyl film, $1/_4$"(6mm) wood particle board glued to $5/_8$" (16mm) plywood subfloor on 2×10" $(40 \times 240$mm) joists	46					26	30	35	36
$1^5/_8$"(40mm) lightweight concrete $[12$lb/ft$^2(59$kg/m$^2)]$ over 3-mil polyvinyl film; $1/_4$"(6mm) wood particle board,$5/_8$" (16mm) plywood, 2×10"$(40 \times 240$mm) wood joists	52					36	38	34	38
$1^5/_8$"(40mm) lightweight concrete $[12$lb/ft$^2(59$kg/m$^2)]$ over 3-mil polyvinyl film; $1/_4$"(6mm) wood particle board,$5/_8$" (16mm) plywood, 2×10"$(40 \times 240$mm) wood joists; 3"(75mm) fiberglass batts, resilient channels, $1/_2$"(13mm) gypsum board	53					40	40	37	41
Carpet on 0.7"(19mm) concrete, $1/_8$"(3mm) foam rubber, $5/_8$"(16mm) plywood on 2×10"$(40 \times 240$mm) wood joists; $10^1/_2$"(270mm) fiberglass batts, resilient channels, 2 layers of $5/_8$"(16mm) gypsum board	62	62	38	44	48	48	49	49	52
Carpet on 0.7"(19mm) concrete, $5/_8$"(16mm) plywood on 2×10" $(40 \times 240$mm) wood joists; 10.6" (270mm) fiberglass batts, resilient channels, 2 layers of $5/_8$"(16mm) gypsum board	62	62	36	44	46	45	49	48	52

5.3e   Wood Joist Floors With Concrete Floating Topping

| | | | TL (Transmission Loss), dB | | | | | | |
| | | | Frequency, Hz | | | | | | |
Description	STC	R_w	63	80	100	125	160	200	250
0.7"(19mm) concrete on $1/_8$"(3mm) foam rubber, $5/_8$"(16mm) plywood on 2×10"$(40 \times 240$mm) wood joists; 10.6"(270mm) fiberglass batts, resilient channels, 2 layers of $5/_8$"(16mm) gypsum board	62	62	38	43	45	45	50	50	51
$1^5/_8$"(40mm) concrete on 75-mm square (21-mm thick) soft neoprene pads, $5/_8$"(16mm) plywood on 2×10" $(40 \times 240$mm) wood joists; $3^5/_8$"(90mm) fiberglass batts, resilient channels, $5/_8$"(16mm) gypsum board	58	58	38	43	46	48	45	45	47

APPENDIX 5.3   Floor/Ceiling Constructions (Continued)

315	400	**500**	630	800	**1000**	1250	1600	**2000**	2500	3150	**4000**	Test lab

<table>
<tr><td colspan="12" align="center">TL (Transmission Loss), dB</td><td></td></tr>
<tr><td colspan="12" align="center">Frequency, Hz</td><td></td></tr>
<tr><td>315</td><td>400</td><td>500</td><td>630</td><td>800</td><td>1000</td><td>1250</td><td>1600</td><td>2000</td><td>2500</td><td>3150</td><td>4000</td><td>Test lab</td></tr>
<tr><td>41</td><td>43</td><td>46</td><td>43</td><td>43</td><td>47</td><td>52</td><td>55</td><td>57</td><td>57</td><td>57</td><td>60</td><td>OCF</td></tr>
<tr><td>41</td><td>44</td><td>51</td><td>53</td><td>54</td><td>57</td><td>61</td><td>63</td><td>64</td><td>63</td><td>60</td><td>62</td><td>OCF</td></tr>
<tr><td>45</td><td>49</td><td>51</td><td>51</td><td>52</td><td>54</td><td>59</td><td>61</td><td>63</td><td>62</td><td>60</td><td>63</td><td>OCF</td></tr>
<tr><td>54</td><td>56</td><td>58</td><td>60</td><td>62</td><td>65</td><td>67</td><td>67</td><td>67</td><td>66</td><td>67</td><td>69</td><td>NRCC</td></tr>
<tr><td>54</td><td>56</td><td>58</td><td>60</td><td>62</td><td>64</td><td>66</td><td>67</td><td>67</td><td>65</td><td>65</td><td>67</td><td>NRCC</td></tr>
<tr><td colspan="12" align="center">TL (Transmission Loss), dB</td><td></td></tr>
<tr><td colspan="12" align="center">Frequency, Hz</td><td></td></tr>
<tr><td>315</td><td>400</td><td>500</td><td>630</td><td>800</td><td>1000</td><td>1250</td><td>1600</td><td>2000</td><td>2500</td><td>3150</td><td>4000</td><td>Test lab</td></tr>
<tr><td>55</td><td>57</td><td>58</td><td>59</td><td>62</td><td>64</td><td>65</td><td>66</td><td>67</td><td>67</td><td>67</td><td>69</td><td>NRCC</td></tr>
<tr><td>48</td><td>52</td><td>53</td><td>54</td><td>60</td><td>63</td><td>66</td><td>68</td><td>67</td><td>64</td><td>65</td><td>67</td><td>NRCC</td></tr>
</table>

APPENDIX 5.4   Windows

5.4a   Single Panes of Glass

Description	STC	R_w	TL (Transmission Loss), dB Frequency, Hz						
			63	80	100	**125**	160	200	**250**
$^1/_8$"(3mm) glass	**29**	30		21	16	**21**	21	21	**21**
$^1/_4$"(6mm) glass	**31**	31			23	**25**	25	24	**28**
$^1/_2$"(13mm) glass	**36**	36			26	**30**	26	30	**33**

5.4b   Single Panes, Laminated Glass

Description	STC	R_w	TL (Transmission Loss), dB Frequency, Hz						
			63	80	100	**125**	160	200	**250**
$^1/_8$"(3mm) glass, 0.030"(0.75mm) plastic, $^1/_8$"(3mm) glass	**35**	35			25	**26**	28	27	**29**
$^1/_4$"(6mm) glass, 0.030"(0.75mm) plastic, $^1/_4$"(6mm) glass	**38**	38			25	**29**	28	30	**33**
$^1/_2$"(13mm) glass, 0.060"(1.5mm) plastic, $^1/_4$"(6mm) glass	**41**	41			29	**30**	29	32	**35**

5.4c   Double Glazing

Description	STC	R_w	TL (Transmission Loss), dB Frequency, Hz						
			63	80	100	**125**	160	200	**250**
$^1/_8$"(3mm) glass, $^1/_4$"(6mm) air, $^1/_8$"(3mm) glass; sealed in metal frame	**28**	28		26	22	**24**	24	24	**24**
$^1/_8$"(3mm) glass, $^1/_2$"(13mm) air, $^1/_8$"(3mm) glass	**31**	31		25	21	**24**	20	23	**19**
$^1/_8$"(3mm) glass, 1"(25mm) air, $^1/_8$"(3mm) glass	**35**	35		22	23	**25**	23	21	**20**
$^1/_8$"(3mm) glass, $^1/_2$"(13mm) air, $^1/_4$"(6mm) glass	**37**	37		25	27	**29**	20	23	**25**
$^1/_8$"(3mm) glass, 2"(50mm) air, $^1/_8$"(3mm) glass	**38**	39		18	17	**18**	27	24	**26**
$^1/_8$"(3mm) glass, 1"(25mm) air, $^1/_4$"(6mm) glass	**39**	39		24	24	**24**	24	26	**26**
$^1/_8$"(3mm) glass, 3"(75mm) air, $^1/_8$"(3mm) glass	**41**	42		16	21	**25**	32	27	**28**
$^1/_8$"(3mm) glass, 2"(50mm) air, $^1/_4$"(6mm) glass	**42**	42		21	18	**26**	30	29	**32**
$^1/_8$"(3mm) glass, 4"(100mm) air, $^1/_8$"(3mm) glass	**42**	43		11	19	**25**	29	29	**31**

APPENDIX 5.4   Windows (Continued)

					TL (Transmission Loss), dB							
					Frequency, Hz							
315	400	**500**	630	800	**1000**	1250	1600	**2000**	2500	3150	**4000**	Test lab
25	24	**28**	29	30	**31**	31	33	**34**	34	32	**25**	NRCC
26	29	**31**	33	34	**34**	35	34	**30**	27	32	**37**	RAL
33	34	**36**	37	35	**32**	32	36	**40**	43	46	**50**	RAL

					TL (Transmission Loss), dB							
					Frequency, Hz							
315	400	**500**	630	800	**1000**	1250	1600	**2000**	2500	3150	**4000**	Test lab
29	30	**32**	34	35	**35**	36	36	**35**	35	38	**43**	RAL
33	34	**36**	37	37	**37**	36	37	**41**	45	48	**51**	RAL
35	37	**38**	38	38	**37**	41	44	**48**	50	53	**56**	RAL

					TL (Transmission Loss), dB							
					Frequency, Hz							
315	400	**500**	630	800	**1000**	1250	1600	**2000**	2500	3150	**4000**	Test lab
24	19	**24**	28	31	**34**	36	38	**39**	40	40	**32**	NRCC
19	24	**29**	34	37	**40**	42	43	**45**	46	44	**35**	NRCC
26	28	**34**	37	40	**41**	43	45	**46**	46	43	**35**	NRCC
26	29	**33**	37	40	**42**	43	44	**42**	41	42	**41**	NRCC
31	32	**38**	39	43	**43**	44	47	**48**	48	45	**35**	NRCC
30	31	**37**	39	42	**42**	43	43	**42**	43	46	**46**	NRCC
33	37	**40**	41	44	**44**	46	49	**50**	50	47	**38**	NRCC
34	36	**40**	42	45	**45**	45	45	**45**	45	48	**48**	NRCC
35	38	**41**	42	44	**45**	46	48	**49**	50	49	**39**	NRCC

APPENDIX 5.4   Windows   (Continued)

5.4c Double Glazing (*Continued*)									
			TL (Transmission Loss), dB						
			Frequency, Hz						
Description	STC	R_w	63	80	100	125	160	200	250
1/8"(3mm) glass, 3"(75mm) air, 1/4"(6mm) glass	44	44		17	23	25	35	33	36
1/8"(3mm) glass, 4"(100mm) air, 1/8" (3mm) glass; sound absorptive reveals	44	43		12	21	26	30	27	32
1/8"(3mm) glass, 6"(150mm) air, 1/8"(3mm) glass	44	45		14	25	28	34	30	34
1/8"(3mm) glass, 6"(150mm) air, 1/8"(3mm) glass; double sash	44	45		14	23	27	34	30	34
1/8"(3mm) glass, 4"(100mm) air, 1/4"(6mm) glass	45	44		16	22	29	32	32	35
1/8"(3mm) glass, 4"(100mm) air, 1/4" (6mm) glass; sound absorptive reveals	46	45		14	23	28	34	34	34
1/8"(3mm) glass, 6"(150mm) air, 1/4"(6mm) glass	47	47		19	23	28	36	35	39
1/8"(3mm) glass, 6"(150mm) air, 1/4"(6mm) glass; double sash	47	47		19	24	27	36	35	39
1/4"(6mm) glass, 1/2"(13mm) air, 1/4"(6mm) glass	36	36		28	28	29	19	19	27
1/4"(6mm) glass, 1"(25mm) air, 1/4"(6mm) glass	39	39		24	23	24	26	31	32
1/4"(6mm) glass, 2"(50mm) air, 1/4"(6mm) glass	42	42		23	18	29	33	34	34
1/4"(6mm) glass, 3"(75mm) air, 1/4"(6mm) glass	45	44		20	21	28	37	38	38
1/4"(6mm) glass, 4"(100mm) air, 1/4" (6mm) glass; sound absorptive reveals	46	46		19	22	28	37	37	35
1/4"(6mm) glass, 6"(150mm) air, 1/4"(6mm) glass	46	46		20	23	24	38	41	40
1/4"(6mm) glass, 6"(150mm) air, 1/4"(6mm) glass; double sash	47	46		20	23	23	38	40	40
1/2"(13mm) glass, 0.060"(1.5mm) plastic, 1/4"(6mm) glass, 4"(100mm) air, 1/4"(6mm) glass, 0.030"(0.75mm) plastic, 1/4"(6mm) glass; unsealed, operable	50	50			31	42	33	40	42

APPENDIX 5.4   Windows (Continued)

					TL (Transmission Loss), dB							
					Frequency, Hz							
315	400	**500**	630	800	**1000**	1250	1600	**2000**	2500	3150	**4000**	Test lab
35	39	**40**	43	46	**46**	47	48	**48**	48	50	**48**	NRCC
35	38	**42**	43	46	**47**	49	51	**52**	53	54	**47**	NRCC
34	41	**43**	44	47	**47**	49	51	**53**	53	50	**40**	NRCC
35	41	**44**	43	46	**47**	49	51	**52**	53	50	**40**	NRCC
35	39	**44**	44	45	**46**	48	47	**47**	48	49	**50**	NRCC
36	39	**44**	45	47	**47**	49	49	**50**	51	53	**53**	NRCC
38	42	**44**	46	49	**49**	50	51	**50**	50	52	**50**	NRCC
40	42	**45**	47	48	**49**	50	51	**51**	51	53	**51**	NRCC
31	31	**36**	38	41	**43**	43	41	**36**	34	38	**42**	NRCC
33	34	**37**	40	43	**43**	43	40	**37**	38	43	**47**	NRCC
34	37	**40**	43	45	**45**	45	43	**40**	42	47	**49**	NRCC
36	41	**41**	45	47	**47**	48	47	**43**	44	48	**48**	NRCC
37	40	**45**	47	47	**47**	49	49	**48**	48	50	**54**	NRCC
39	43	**45**	47	48	**49**	50	49	**45**	44	50	**54**	NRCC
40	43	**46**	48	49	**49**	50	49	**46**	45	51	**54**	NRCC
43	46	**50**	50	50	**49**	50	52	**55**	60	62	**64**	RAL

APPENDIX 5.4   Windows (Continued)

5.4d   Double Glazing, Laminated Glass

Description	STC	R_w	TL (Transmission Loss), dB Frequency, Hz						
			63	80	100	125	160	200	250
$^1/_4$"(6mm) laminated glass, $^1/_2$" (13mm) air, 0.2"(5mm) glass; unsealed, operable	42	42			22	27	27	28	31
$^1/_4$"(6mm) laminated glass, 2" (50mm) air, 0.2"(5mm) glass; unsealed, operable	45	45			24	25	34	33	34
$^1/_4$"(6mm) laminated glass, 4" (100mm) air, 0.2"(5mm) glass; unsealed, operable	48	48			26	36	34	37	37
$^1/_2$"(13mm) laminated glass, 1" (25mm) air, $^1/_4$"(6mm) laminated glass; unsealed, operable	46	46			21	28	33	37	38
$^1/_2$"(13mm) laminated glass, 2" (50mm) air, 0.4"(9mm) glass; unsealed, operable	46	46			34	37	33	38	40
$^1/_2$"(13mm) laminated glass, 4" (100mm) air, 0.2"(5mm) glass; unsealed, operable	49	49			30	37	33	38	37
$^1/_2$"(13mm) laminated glass, 4" (100mm) air, $^1/_2$"(13mm) laminated glass; unsealed, operable	50	50			31	39	35	39	41
$^1/_2$"(13mm) laminated glass, 4" (100mm) air, $^1/_4$"(6mm) laminated glass; unsealed, operable	51	51			34	38	34	40	41

APPENDIX 5.4   Windows (Continued)

					TL (Transmission Loss), dB							
					Frequency, Hz							
315	400	**500**	630	800	**1000**	1250	1600	**2000**	2500	3150	**4000**	Test lab
35	38	**41**	42	43	**44**	45	47	**47**	45	50	**58**	RAL
40	41	**44**	44	46	**47**	47	48	**48**	46	50	**55**	RAL
43	44	**48**	49	51	**51**	50	51	**50**	47	51	**58**	RAL
42	43	**46**	44	44	**44**	45	49	**53**	57	59	**62**	RAL
42	44	**48**	47	46	**45**	42	46	**51**	55	59	**61**	RAL
42	45	**49**	50	51	**50**	48	50	**53**	53	57	**61**	RAL
43	46	**51**	52	52	**49**	48	50	**54**	59	61	**63**	RAL
45	47	**51**	52	53	**53**	51	52	**55**	58	60	**62**	RAL

APPENDIX 5.5   Doors

5.5a   Solid-Core Wood Doors

Description	STC	R_w	\multicolumn{7}{c}{TL (Transmission Loss), dB — Frequency, Hz}

Description	STC	R_w	63	80	100	125	160	200	250
Solid-core wood door [4.9lb/ft² (24kg/m²)]; no seals around perimeter	**22**		**16**	19	16	**19**	20	21	**22**
Solid-core wood door [4.9lb/ft² (24kg/m²)]; foam tape seals around perimeter	**26**		**18**	20	19	**22**	24	25	**25**
Solid-core wood door [4.9lb/ft² (24kg/m²)]; magnetic seals around perimeter	**30**		**20**	23	22	**25**	26	27	**29**

5.5b   Hollow-Core Steel Doors

Description	STC	R_w	63	80	100	125	160	200	250
Hollow-core steel door, 18 ga. steel faces [5.4lb/ft²(26kg/m²)]; no seals around perimeter	**17**		**12**	14	11	**13**	14	14	**15**
Hollow-core steel door, 18 ga. steel faces [5.4lb/ft²(26kg/m²)]; foam tape seals around perimeter	**28**		**21**	23	21	**21**	24	24	**25**
Hollow-core steel door, 18 ga. steel faces [5.4lb/ft²(26kg/m²)]; magnetic seals around perimeter	**32**		**21**	23	22	**24**	24	27	**28**

APPENDIX 5.5   Doors (Continued)

					TL (Transmission Loss), dB							
					Frequency, Hz							
315	400	**500**	630	800	**1000**	1250	1600	**2000**	2500	3150	**4000**	Test lab
24	25	**26**	26	25	**24**	23	23	**23**	22	19	**20**	NRCC
28	28	**29**	29	27	**25**	25	26	**26**	26	27	**28**	NRCC
31	30	**30**	30	28	**27**	27	28	**30**	33	34	**34**	NRCC

					TL (Transmission Loss), dB							
					Frequency, Hz							
315	400	**500**	630	800	**1000**	1250	1600	**2000**	2500	3150	**4000**	Test lab
15	16	**16**	17	17	**17**	17	18	**18**	17	19	**20**	NRCC
24	25	**25**	26	26	**26**	28	29	**30**	32	33	**34**	NRCC
27	29	**30**	31	31	**30**	29	31	**36**	38	40	**39**	NRCC

APPENDIX 5.5   Doors (Continued)

5.5c   Hollow-Core Steel Door and Solid Wood Door in Single Frame

			TL (Transmission Loss), dB						
					Frequency, Hz				
Description	STC	R_w	**63**	80	100	**125**	160	200	**250**
Solid-core wood door [4.9lb/ft² (24kg/m²)] and hollow-core steel door, 18 ga. steel faces [5.4lb/ft²(26kg/m²)] mounted in same frame; 2.5"(65mm) space between doors; no seals around perimeter	**29**		**18**	18	12	**16**	15	19	**21**
Solid-core wood door [4.9lb/ft² (24kg/m²)] and hollow-core steel door, 18 ga. steel faces [5.4lb/ft²(26kg/m²)] mounted in two frames with 8"(228mm) between inner faces; no seals around perimeter	**34**		**13**	16	19	**23**	27	27	**29**
Solid-core wood door [4.9lb/ft² (24kg/m²)] and hollow-core steel door, 18 ga. steel faces [5.4lb/ft²(26kg/m²)] mounted in same frame; 2.5"(65mm) space between doors, 1"(25mm) polyurethane foam on one inner door face; foam tape seals around perimeter	**37**		**18**	18	14	**20**	24	25	**28**
Solid-core wood door [4.9lb/ft² (24kg/m²)] and hollow-core steel door, 18 ga. steel faces [5.4lb/ft²(26kg/m²)] mounted in same frame; 2.5"(65mm) space between doors, 1"(25mm) polyurethane foam on one inner door face; foam tape seals around perimeter	**39**		**18**	18	21	**24**	32	31	**30**
Solid-core wood door [4.9lb/ft² (24kg/m²)] and hollow-core steel door, 18 ga. steel faces [5.4lb/ft²(26kg/m²)] mounted in same frame with no seals; 2.5"(65mm) space between doors, 1" (25mm) polyurethane foam on one inner door face; no seals around perimeter	**41**		**18**	17	19	**24**	28	31	**33**
Solid-core wood door [4.9lb/ft² (24kg/m²)] and hollow-core steel door, 18 ga. steel faces [5.4lb/ft²(26kg/m²)] mounted in same frame; 2.5"(65mm) space between doors; magnetic seals perimeter	**41**		**17**	19	25	**29**	33	33	**35**

APPENDIX 5.5 **Doors** (Continued)

					TL (Transmission Loss), dB							
					Frequency, Hz							
315	400	**500**	630	800	**1000**	1250	1600	**2000**	2500	3150	**4000**	Test lab
24	24	**25**	26	27	**28**	32	35	**34**	30	30	**31**	NRCC
36	36	**38**	37	35	**35**	34	33	**35**	32	32	**33**	NRCC
32	34	**34**	34	34	**36**	39	40	**42**	45	50	**53**	NRCC
36	35	**35**	36	37	**38**	41	42	**41**	42	46	**47**	NRCC
35	37	**38**	39	39	**40**	42	44	**47**	49	51	**50**	NRCC
38	38	**36**	37	39	**38**	42	45	**49**	51	51	**48**	NRCC

5.d   Hollow-Core Steel Door and Solid Wood Door in Separate Frames

| | | | TL (Transmission Loss), dB | | | | | | |
| | | | Frequency, Hz | | | | | | |
Description	STC	R_w	63	80	100	125	160	200	250
Solid-core wood door [4.9lb/ft² (24kg/m²)] and hollow-core steel door, 18 ga. steel faces [5.4lb/ft²(26kg/m²)] mounted in two frames with 8"(228mm) between inner faces; 1"(25mm) polyurethane foam on each inner door face; no seals around perimeter	43		15	17	20	26	25	29	33
Solid-core wood door [4.9lb/ft² (24kg/m²)] and hollow-core steel door, 18 ga. steel faces [5.4lb/ft²(26kg/m²)] mounted in same frame; 2.5"(65mm) space between doors, 1"(25mm) polyurethane foam on inner door faces; magnetic seals around perimeter	43		17	20	27	33	36	39	40
Solid-core wood door [4.9lb/ft² (24kg/m²)] and hollow-core steel door, 18 ga. steel faces [5.4lb/ft²(26kg/m²)] mounted in same frame; 2.5"(65mm) space between doors, 1"(25mm) polyurethane foam on one inner door face; magnetic seals around perimeter	43		17	17	25	31	32	37	39
Solid-core wood door [4.9lb/ft² (24kg/m²)] and hollow-core steel door, 18 ga. steel faces [5.4lb/ft²(26kg/m²)] mounted in two frames with 8"(228mm) between inner faces; magnetic seals around perimeter	49		25	26	30	35	38	41	44
Solid-core wood door [4.9lb/ft² (24kg/m²)] and hollow-core steel door, 18 ga. steel faces [5.4lb/ft²(26kg/m²)] mounted in two frames with 8"(228mm) between inner faces; 1"(25mm) polyurethane foam on each inner door face, magnetic seals around perimeter	51		26	27	32	34	39	43	45
Solid-core wood door [4.9lb/ft² (24kg/m²)] and hollow-core steel door, 18 ga. steel faces [5.4lb/ft²(26kg/m²)] mounted in two frames with 8"(228mm) between inner faces; 1"(25mm) polyurethane foam on each inner door face; magnetic seals around perimeter	52		26	26	32	36	40	43	46

APPENDIX 5.5   Doors (Continued)

					TL (Transmission Loss), dB							
					Frequency, Hz							
315	400	**500**	630	800	**1000**	1250	1600	**2000**	2500	3150	**4000**	Test lab
39	42	**44**	44	42	**43**	43	45	**48**	46	46	**46**	NRCC
39	40	**39**	39	40	**39**	43	46	**49**	51	53	**51**	NRCC
39	40	**39**	39	40	**39**	43	45	**47**	49	51	**50**	NRCC
46	47	**48**	47	45	**44**	47	48	**54**	56	61	**62**	NRCC
46	48	**49**	49	47	**47**	53	55	**57**	59	63	**65**	NRCC
47	49	**49**	49	48	**47**	54	56	**57**	59	63	**65**	NRCC

6

Structureborne Sound Insulation

A. C. C. Warnock

INTRODUCTION

Structureborne sound in a building is sound that originates as vibration or an impact communicated to the building structure, as illustrated in Fig. 1.3. For example, the structure may be set into vibration by a source which operates continuously (such as an electrical transformer); it may be set into vibration by a source which is of a periodic character (such as that produced by unbalanced rotating machinery); or it may be set into vibration by a source that is random in nature (such as the turbulent flow of water in a pipe).

Structureborne sound may also originate by an impact. An *impact* is a force of short duration (for example, footsteps, the slamming of a door, or the dropping of an object on the floor) which causes the structure to vibrate. If the falling object and the floor are hard, the resulting sound is heard as a sharp crack or click that is rich in high frequencies. If the falling object is resilient or if the floor is covered by a resilient surface, the peak force of the impact is greatly reduced in magnitude although its duration is increased. This greatly lessens the high-frequency energy communicated to the building structure. Thus, the quality of sound produced by footsteps on a floor depends not only on the hardness and area of the heel of the shoe but also on the hardness of the surface layer of the floor.

This chapter describes how structureborne sounds are propagated from their sources to other areas in the building, how sound insulation against impacts is rated, and methods of controlling structureborne sound. This chapter also includes tables of data for both airborne and solidborne sound insulation for various types of constructions. Additional data and guidance for the selection of appropriate constructions for various applications is given in Chap. 10.

HOW STRUCTUREBORNE SOUND IS
PROPAGATED IN BUILDINGS

Once vibratory energy is communicated to a building structure, it can propagate to other locations in the building and there set surfaces into vibration—thereby radiating noise. Structureborne sound then is perceived by a listener as airborne sound radiated directly from vibrating surfaces such as wall panels or chinaware. Some common sources of structureborne sound and the paths along which they travel are depicted in Fig. 1.3. For example, plumbing noises—water supply and waste pipes—and plumbing fixtures are prominent sources and carriers of structureborne sound (see Chap. 8).

In buildings, there are many paths along which solidborne noise may propagate. This is illustrated in Fig. 6.1 which shows a building whose walls and floors are of solid concrete and are rigidly connected. On the right of this illustration, sound energy caused by an impact (by a hammer striking the concrete floor) is transmitted along a direct path indicated by the letter **D,** through floors, ceilings, and walls of the structure to reach adjacent rooms. Structureborne noise may also be transmitted along so-called flanking paths, represented by the letter **F.** A *flanking path* for sound transmission is a path other than that through the common partition between two spaces (some sound is transmitted through the common partition). Flanking paths in buildings are discussed further in Chap. 10.

Once vibratory energy is imparted to a structure, it can travel throughout the structure for considerable distances, well over 100 feet (35 m). It may be transmitted to a relatively light-weight partition, some distance away, which is then set into vibration, thereby becoming a source of noise.

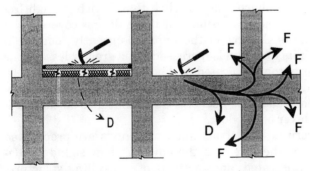

FIG. 6.1 Paths for structureborne sound in a concrete building. The paths marked with **D** are "direct paths" for the transmission of impact sounds; the paths marked **F** are "flanking paths." The floating floor on the left of the diagram reduces the transmission of the impact to the structure.

The magnitude of the vibratory energy, and hence the noise radiated by a structure, generally decreases (i.e., attenuates) with increasing distance from the source. This is primarily because the vibratory energy spreads throughout the structure and, to a lesser extent, because of energy dissipation through internal damping in the structure. Attenuation due to distance alone, however, cannot be relied on to reduce structureborne sound to acceptably low levels either in concrete buildings or in wood-joist construction.

A floor construction that provides good structureborne sound insulation does not necessarily assure a low noise level in the room in which the noise originates—i.e., the "source" room. For example, on the left side of Fig. 6.1, a wood floor is installed over fiberglass laid on the solid concrete building slab. This construction greatly improves the structureborne sound insulation. However, the noise level resulting from impacts of the hammer striking the floor of the source room may actually *increase* by as much as 10 dB or more. This is because a light-weight wood floor surface is a more efficient radiator of sound than the heavy concrete surface. An increase in noise level of this type usually can be minimized by applying a resilient surface, such as carpet, over the wood flooring.

RATING IMPACT SOUND INSULATION: IMPACT INSULATION CLASS (IIC)

Impact insulation class (IIC) is a single-number rating[1,2] which is a measure of the impact sound isolation provided by a floor/ceiling construction.* In general, the higher the impact insulation class (IIC) rating, the greater the impact noise insulation provided by the construction. IIC ratings for various types of floor/ceiling constructions are given in Table 6.1.

IIC Ratings for Various Constructions

Table 6.1 gives typical results for two major types of floor: wood joist or truss floors and concrete slabs. Values are given for different floor toppings. This information is intended to illustrate some basic principles, not to provide definitive test data.

A construction that provides good insulation against airborne noise reduction does not necessarily provide good insulation against solid-

---

*The impact insulation class for different types of floor-ceiling constructions is obtained using a "standardized tapping machine."[2-5] This device has five steel-faced hammers that strike the floor ten times per second. The lower the noise levels produced by this device *in the room below the tapping machine,* the higher the rating of the floor in terms of impact insulation class.

TABLE 6.1   **Approximate Sound Transmission Class and Impact Insulation Class Ratings for Typical Floor Structures**

Floor	Description	Sketch	STC	IIC
1	6-inch (150-mm) thick concrete slab		52	25
2	As 1 with carpet and underlayment on top		52	86
3	Plywood floor and gypsum board ceiling directly attached to wood joists		38	37
4	As 3 with carpet and underlayment on top		42	65
5	Plywood floor and gypsum board ceiling resiliently suspended from wood joists; cavity filled with sound absorptive material		45	43
6	As 5 with carpet and underlayment on top		48	73
7	As 1 with wood slab on furring floating on compressed fiberglass board		61	63

TABLE 6.1   Approximate Sound Transmission Class and Impact Insulation Class Ratings for Typical Floor Structures   (Continued)

Floor	Description	Sketch	STC	IIC
8	As 1 with concrete slab floating on compressed fiberglass board		62	71
9	As 1 with concrete slab floating on soft rubber pads; sound-absorptive material in the cavity		62	64
10	As 5 with wood slab on furring floating on compressed fiberglass board		57	51
11	As 5 with concrete slab floating on compressed fiberglass board		60	58
12	As 5 with concrete slab floating on soft rubber pads; sound-absorptive material in the cavity		59	57
13	As 5 with concrete slab laid directly on top		59	40
14	As 13 with carpet and underlayment		59	84

borne noise, and vice versa. For example, consider the 6-inch (150-mm) thick concrete slab shown in Table 6.1 (Floors 1 and 2 in Table 6.1). In each of these cases the airborne sound transmission class (STC) rating is about 52, which is fair. (See Tables 10.1 and 10.2 for recommended STC and IIC ratings for party walls and floors.) The IIC rating for the bare floor is only 25, which is very poor. Adding an underlayment and a carpet to the floor will provide no significant increase in STC rating but will increase the IIC rating to over 85. The floor then provides fair airborne sound insulation and good solidborne sound insulation.

In contrast, Floor 3 in Table 6.1 (a wood-joist floor) has very poor STC and IIC ratings. The IIC rating is easily increased to 65 simply by adding a soft carpet and underlayment (i.e., Floor 4 in Table 6.1). The STC rating is also slightly improved. This floor does not give adequate airborne sound insulation primarily because the gypsum board is not resiliently-hung and because there is no sound-absorptive material in the cavity. Floor 5 in Table 6.1 shows the improved STC and IIC ratings that result when the gypsum board is resiliently-hung and sound-absorptive material is added to the cavity. Floor 6 is the same as Floor 5, but with carpet and underlayment added to increase the IIC rating to over 70.

In concrete buildings, sometimes a hard floor surface is required for ease of cleaning (for example, in a kitchen or bathroom). In such a case, if excellent structureborne noise insulation is required, a floating floor (described in detail in a following section) should be used whenever practical. Floors 7, 8, and 9 in Table 6.1 show typical results for a $1^{1}/_{2}$-inch (40-mm) thick concrete floating slab and a $^{5}/_{8}$-inch (16-mm) thick floating plywood slab on a 6-inch (150-mm) structural slab. The IIC ratings are not as good as those provided by the carpet and underlayment in Floor 2, but the constructions would be very good for use in multifamily homes.

The addition of a floating floor to a joist or truss floor (as in Floors 10, 11, and 12) increases the impact sound insulation, but the increase is not as great as that obtained with the addition of the same floating floors to the concrete slab. Nevertheless, these three floors would be acceptable for use in multifamily dwellings according to the criteria given in Tables 10.1 and 10.2.

Increasing the mass of the floor layer in joist or truss construction improves the impact and airborne sound insulation. One common way of achieving a higher rating is to increase the mass of the floor by adding a layer of light-weight or normal-weight concrete on top of the floor. Floor 13 in Table 6.1 shows that additional concrete improves the sound transmission class (STC) rating by about 10 relative to Floor 5 without the concrete. However, the IIC rating is slightly worse than that for Floor 5 because the hard upper surface generates structureborne sound more efficiently. Adding a carpet and underlayment increases the IIC rating to over 80 (Floor 14), which is acceptable.

Wood-joist and truss floors perform quite differently from concrete floors. When finished with carpet and underlayment, the IIC rating of light-weight wood-joist and truss floors can be quite high. However, such light-weight floors may transmit enough low-frequency noise to be judged unacceptable by many occupants. This conflict between subjective reactions and IIC ratings arises because the impact insulation class rating system does not give adequate weight to low-frequency sound. Thus, the ratings for light-weight wood-joist and truss floor systems tend to be overly optimistic evaluations of their value in insulating impact sounds. Occupants living below such floors often complain of "thumps," creaking sounds, or rattling sounds when people walk on the floor above.

The energy dissipated in a building structure is inversely proportional to the mass of the structure and its damping. Thus, a light-weight structure which has little damping responds more vigorously (and radiates more noise) than a massive structure which is highly damped. Typically, concrete floors generate about 10 dB less noise at low frequencies than do lighter joist or truss systems. For this reason, in critical applications, the more massive constructions usually are preferable.

METHODS OF CONTROLLING STRUCTUREBORNE SOUND

Structureborne sound can be controlled at its source, along its transmission path, and at its point of reception. In general, it is more difficult to control structureborne noise than airborne noise. To control structureborne sound effectively, the following techniques (a number of which are described in greater detail in sections that follow) are recommended:

- Locate the source of vibration as far as possible from the area where low noise levels are required. *Examples:* Locate elevators and garbage chutes away from bedrooms in apartments; avoid placing a gymnasium above a school library.

- Reduce the power of a source of vibration by changing its operating conditions or by selecting a different model of machine—one that performs the same function but introduces less vibration into the structure. *Example:* Use well-balanced rotating machinery instead of reciprocating equipment.

- Provide vibration isolation between the source and the structure.

Examples: Mount a machine on springs or on an inertia block which rests on springs (see Fig. 9.18). Insert soft rubber or neoprene pads or vibration isolators under washing machines, dryers, loudspeakers, pianos, etc., to reduce the transfer of vibrational energy to the building structure.

- Strengthen the building structure at points of vibration excitation. *Example:* Under a rooftop air-conditioning unit, increase mass and stiffness of the building structure.

- Do not permit vibrating equipment to contact light-weight partitions in a building. *Example:* Support equipment resiliently on columns of the building rather than on the floors or roof.

- On floors that are subject to impacts, cover the floor surface with a layer of resilient material such as carpet and underlayment, as described below.

- If a resilient floor covering is not appropriate and if high-impact insulation is required, use a floating floor construction as described in a following section.

- Suspend the ceiling resiliently from the floor construction above it.

- If the ceiling is resiliently hung from the floor above, fill the cavity between them (at least $3/4$ full) with sound-absorptive material.

- Use breaks (for example, expansion joints) in an otherwise solid building construction to impede the transmission of solidborne noise.

It is important to recognize that merely improving the floor/ceiling construction (between a room above and a room below) may not significantly reduce noise from a source located on the floor. This is because significant impact noise may travel down the walls, from the floor above to the room below, as a result of flanking. Such flanking sound transmission is discussed further in Chap. 10.

Effect of a Resilient Floor Covering on Impact Insulation

A soft, resilient floor covering laid on a floor will cushion impact forces and reduce the impact energy transferred to a building structure. Hence carpeting and underlayment laid on a bare floor will improve the impact insulation class (IIC) rating of the floor. The improvement depends on the characteristics of the floor covering and the characteristics of the floor structure. Thus, the same carpet applied to a heavy concrete floor and to a light wood-joist floor does not necessarily provide the same improvement in impact sound insulation. However, for structural floors of similar construction, the same floor covering usually gives about the same improvement.

Although the addition of a resilient floor covering on a bare floor usually will improve the floor's impact noise insulation (particularly at high frequencies), it usually will not improve the floor's airborne sound insulation.

In remedial work where the floor is already carpeted but the impact noise insulation is inadequate, it may be necessary to add a floating floor, described in the following section.

Table 6.2 gives some approximate values of the improvement in impact insulation class produced by some floor coverings and floating floors on light-weight wood-joist and on heavy concrete floors. These values are intended only as a guide to the relative merits of the different floor toppings. (Test data for various floor constructions are given in Table 6.1.)

The amount of improvement in airborne sound insulation provided by an additional layer of heavy material on top of the floor depends on the weight of the additional layer relative to the weight of the existing structure. For example, adding a layer of plywood on top of a 6-inch (150-mm) concrete slab will have practically no effect. However, the same layer of plywood added to one layer of plywood on top of a wood-joist floor will increase the airborne sound insulation by about 4 dB.

Floating Floors

A *floating floor* is one that is supported by a structural floor but is completely isolated from it (by resilient supports, for example). It is usually the most effective method of controlling structureborne noise at its source and therefore is used in critical applications (for exam-

TABLE 6.2   Improvement in Impact Insulation Class (IIC) for Different Floor Coverings

Floor covering	Wood-joist or truss floors	Concrete floors
Vinyl or linoleum	5	5
Carpet	10	45
Carpet and underlayment	25	60
Floating floors:		
Concrete	10	40
Wood slab on furring strips	3	35

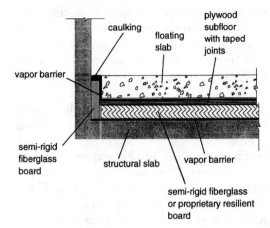

FIG. 6.2 A floating floor using a layer of resilient material to support a concrete slab. The resilient material can be semi-rigid fiberglass or proprietary material.

ple, in a mechanical room located above an executive dining room). The essential elements of a floating floor are illustrated on the left side of Fig. 6.1, and shown in greater detail in Fig. 6.2. There are several ways of constructing a floating floor:

- The floor slab can be supported by a continuous layer of resilient fiberglass board (usually precompressed) (see Fig. 6.2).

- The floor slab can be supported on a continuous layer of commercially available resilient material that may or may not be sound-absorptive.

- The floor slab can rest on relatively small resilient pads or vibration isolators, usually spaced at regular intervals under the slab (see Fig. 6.3). The airspace between the floating slab and structural floor may or may not contain sound-absorptive material. One variant of this approach is to use commercially available "screw-jack" vibration isolators. These isolators are placed in position on the structural floor and then used to lift the floating slab a few inches after it has been poured and cured. Unless special steps are taken, such floors do not have sound-absorptive material between the floating floor slab and the structural slab.

Floating floor slabs are most effective if they are relatively heavy, for example at least 2 inches (50 mm) of concrete. In large mechanical rooms, the concrete slab is often 4 inches (100 mm) thick. Lighter slabs, of thick plywood, for example, are often useful in remedial work where the structure of the building cannot support much additional weight, or for reasons of economy.

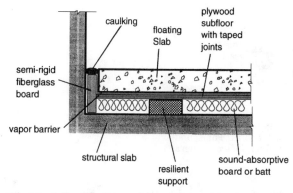

FIG. 6.3 A floating floor using resilient pads to support a concrete slab. The sound-absorptive material is usually fiberglass or mineral wool batts.

Examples of floating wood slabs are shown in Figs. 6.4 and 6.5. Such light-weight floating slabs are usually less effective than the slabs of heavier concrete shown in Fig. 6.2 and 6.3 (at very low frequencies, they may even decrease the structureborne sound insulation). Adding carpeting and underlayment on top of a floating slab will improves its impact sound insulation rating.

Design of Floating Floors. In designing a floating floor, take the following steps:

- Design the floating slab to have adequate structural strength for the load it is to support. In a concrete slab, usually a thickness of 2 to 4 inches (5 to 10 cm) is adequate. The 4-inch (10-cm) thickness is used where the loading is heavy—as it often is in a mechanical equipment room; then the concrete slab may be reinforced.

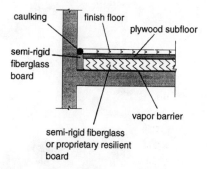

FIG. 6.4 A wood floating floor supported by layer of resilient material. The resilient material can be semi-rigid fiberglass or proprietary material.

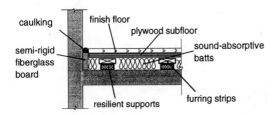

FIG. 6.5 A wood floating floor supported by wood furring strips resting on resilient supports. The sound-absorptive batts are usually of fiberglass or mineral wool.

- Select a resilient support whose load-bearing characteristics are appropriate for the floating slab. For example, precompressed fiberglass floor isolation board used to support a concrete floating floor slab usually has a density of 4 to 9 lbs/ft^3 (64 to 192 kg/m^3).

- Ensure that the resilient support has the required life expectancy for both static and dynamic design loads.

- Ensure that the floating slab will not contact the building structure. For example, fill the gap between the floating slab and the wall with a resilient material such as low-density fiberglass to prevent contact between the edge of the floating slab and the wall. Figures 6.2, 6.3, 6.4, and 6.5 show edge details. The fiberglass at the edge of the floating slab is recessed to leave a space for the caulking. The caulking, when applied in the recessed groove, is then protected against wear.

- Avoid penetrations of the floating slab by pipes, ducts, and so on, but where a penetration is essential (as, for example, a drainage pipe), ensure that it does not form a rigid connection between the floating slab and the structural slab or walls (see Figs. 6.6 and 6.7 for examples).

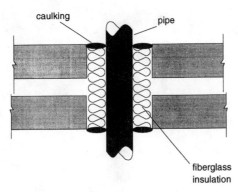

FIG. 6.6 A pipe penetration of a floating floor structure.

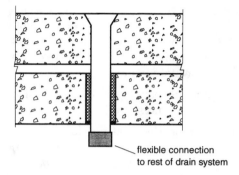

flexible connection
to rest of drain system

FIG. 6.7   A drain penetration of a floating floor
structure. Note that the drain may provide a
significant sound path from the upper to the
lower room.

- Protect fiberglass material from possible water damage. For example, if precompressed fiberglass floor isolation board is used as the resilient support, protect the fiberglass with a plastic sheet to prevent moisture from the concrete structural slab from damaging the fiberglass.

- Ensure that the resilient support provides uniform deflection of the floating slab by proper placement of the isolators even though the floating slab may not be uniformly loaded.

- If it is not practical to provide uniform deflection, then use several smaller slabs, each of which is uniformly loaded.

- Inspect the surface and the perimeter of the surface on which the concrete is to be poured to ensure that they are not damaged before pouring the floating slab.

- Ensure that the structural floor is clean and smooth before laying down the resilient supports. This avoids short-circuiting of the floating slab to the structure by debris, for example (see Fig. 6.8a).

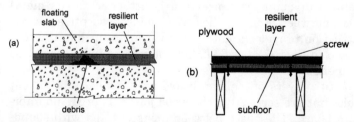

FIG. 6.8   (a) Debris beneath a floating slab can "short-circuit" the resilient layer, thereby resulting in decreased sound insulation. (b) Screws or nails that are too long can "short-circuit" the resilient layer in wood floating floors, thereby resulting in decreased sound insulation.

- Before pouring a floating concrete slab, cover the resilient material or supports with plywood (or fiberboard); tape the joints between plywood sheets; cover top surface of plywood with an impervious plastic sheet to provide a surface on which to pour the floating slab and a hard surface to walk on during construction.

- Provide sufficient ventilation during the pouring and setting of a large concrete floating slab to carry away moisture.

- Where there are no connections between the floating slab and the structural floor, avoid a situation (such as that shown in Fig. 6.8b) where the isolation is negated by screws that connect the floating slab to the structural floor.

Floor-Ceiling Constructions

In Fig. 6.9, the airborne sound insulation (STC ratings) for various floor/ceiling constructions are compared with the solidborne sound insulation (IIC ratings). The basic floor assembly consists of a plywood floor supported on wood joists. In Fig. 6.9a, b, and c, wood strapping (battens) is fastened to the joists and gypsum board is attached to the strapping.

The construction shown in Fig. 6.9a is inadequate from the standpoint of sound insulation; the addition of sound-absorptive material in the cavity between the gypsum board and the plywood flooring will not improve the construction sufficiently to make it acceptable.

In Fig. 6.9b, furring strips are added to the ceiling, and resilient metal channels are attached to the furring strips; a second layer of gypsum board is screwed into the resilient metal channels. The cavity between gypsum board layers is filled with sound absorptive material. Note that while both the airborne sound insulation (STC) ratings and the solidborne sound insulation (IIC) ratings are significantly higher than for the construction shown in Fig. 6.9a, they are not acceptable.

In Fig. 6.9c, metal studs are screwed to the joists (through the strapping), and a layer of gypsum board is attached to the metal studs; the space between studs is filled with sound-absorptive material. This construction provides greater sound insulation than the constructions shown in Figs. 6.9a or 6.9b, but the impact insulation class is still not good enough.

In Fig. 6.9d, two layers of gypsum board are fastened to resilient metal channels that are screwed to the wood joists. There is no intervening gypsum board. The space between joists is filled with sound-absorptive material. This construction provides STC and IIC ratings that are as good as the construction in Fig. 6.9c. It is much more eco-

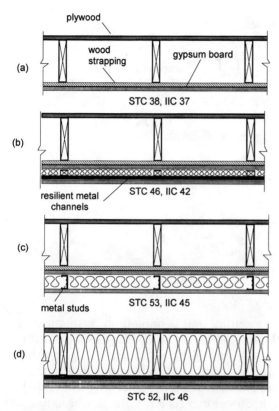

FIG. 6.9 Sound insulation data for various floor/ceiling constructions. (*a*) A floor consisting of $^5/_8$-inch (16-mm) plywood, wood joists, $^3/_4$-inch (19-mm) wood strapping, and $^1/_2$-inch (13-mm) gypsum board; this floor provides inadequate sound insulation. (*b*) The same construction as (*a*) with the addition of: $1^1/_2$-inch (38-mm) wood strapping (i.e., battens), sound-absorptive material, and an additional layer of gypsum board. (*c*) The same construction as (*a*) with the addition of: $2^1/_2$-inch (65-mm) metal studs, sound-absorptive material, and an additional layer of gypsum board. (*d*) A floor consisting of $^5/_8$-inch (16-mm) plywood supported on wood joists, as in (*a*), but with the two layers of gypsum board supported from the joists by resilient metal channels; the space between the joists filled with sound-absorptive material.

nomical to select such a design initially than it is to select an inadequate design (such as Fig. 6.9*a*) and then attempt to upgrade the sound insulation it provides. Note, however, that none of these floors provide high enough IIC ratings without a carpet and carpet underlayment.

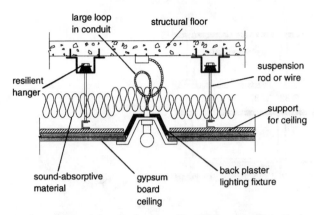

FIG. 6.10 Design details for a resiliently-hung ceiling that provides excellent insulation against both airborne sound and solidborne sound.

Resiliently-Hung Ceilings

A resiliently-hung ceiling is a ceiling that is hung from resilient hangers by wires or rods, as illustrated in Fig. 6.10. This type of ceiling provides greater structureborne and airborne sound insulation than the structural floor alone; this is accomplished by reducing the transmission of structureborne sound from the structural floor to the resiliently-hung ceiling. To achieve such good results, it is essential to ensure: (1) that sound cannot "leak" through holes in, or cracks around, lighting fixtures—note that the lighting fixture in Fig. 6.10 is back-plastered—and (2) that the resiliently-hung ceiling is not "bridged" by any solid connections to the overhead slab (e.g., by electrical conduit or air diffusers) or to the side walls. To prevent bridging, a small gap must be left around the periphery of the resiliently-hung ceiling, and this gap must be filled with a nonhardening caulking.

In most applications, excellent results can be achieved with neoprene or rubber isolators which are neither under- nor overloaded. However, where high values of sound insulation must be obtained at low frequencies (say, below 100 Hz), isolators must be used that have a larger "static deflection" than can be obtained with neoprene or rubber isolators. In this case, isolators composed of metal coils are used, of the type shown in Fig. 8.12.

The following steps are taken in designing a ceiling of this type:

- Select an appropriate ceiling material.
- Estimate the weight of ceiling.

- Choose the type of resilient support.
- Calculate spacing of supports required to obtain the specified loading per resilient support.
- Seal the holes and cracks around all light fixtures.
- Back-plaster light-weight lighting fixtures (i.e., coat the rear surface of the fixture with plaster).
- Provide a loop in the electrical cable (BX cable) to minimize transmission along it.
- Avoid any rigid connections between the resiliently-hung ceiling and the floor slab above or the side walls.
- Fill the gaps between the suspended ceiling and the surrounding walls with a low-density fiberglass, and then caulk the fiberglass surface with an acoustical caulking.
- Fill the cavity between the ceiling and the structure (about $^3/_4$ full) with sound-absorptive material, for example, fiberglass having a density of about 1 to 2 pounds per cubic foot (16 to 32 g/m^3).

Impact Sound Transmission through Walls

The transmission of sounds through walls due to impacts on them can be reduced by the following noise control measures:

- Avoid mounting telephones, piping, and other sources of noise directly on walls.
- Avoid mounting kitchen or bathroom cabinets directly on walls. Support them resiliently from the floor, or use a resilient support system.
- Install resilient pads on the doors of cabinets to reduce the impact when the doors slam.
- Install pneumatic door-closers on external doors to prevent slamming.

Resiliently-Mounted Wall Panels.   Resiliently-mounted wall panels usually are constructed of sheets of gypsum board or plywood that are supported from a wall surface by commercially available resilient metal channels. This type of mounting reduces the radiation of sound from a vibrating wall, thereby increasing both the solidborne and airborne sound insulation of the wall. (If the panel is directly attached to the wall, rather than being resiliently attached, the additional panel in some cases may actually increase the radiation of sound into the room.)

Following the principles discussed in Chap. 5, the additional sound insulation provided by a resiliently-supported wall panel increases with:

- An increase in the depth of the airspace
- A reduction in the stiffness of the supports
- An increase in the mass per unit area of the panel
- The insertion of sound-absorptive material in the airspace between the panel and the wall

The resilient metal channels should be supported from the wall by wood furring strips to increase the depth of the cavity, say, to $1^1/_2$ inches (40 mm). Otherwise, the cavity between the panel and the wall usually will be too small; as a result, the added panel may actually decrease the sound insulation at low frequencies rather than improve it.

Discontinuities in Building Construction

An effective method of controlling the propagation of structureborne sound is by the use of structural discontinuities (for example, see Fig. 6.11):

- The most effective discontinuity is a gap in the building structure. For example, in constructing a space where an unusually low background noise level is essential, it is good practice to provide a completely separate building to house mechanical and electrical equip-

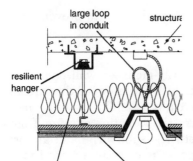

FIG. 6.11 An expansion joint in a concrete slab increases the attenuation of structureborne noise.

ment as well as elevators and water fountains. The two buildings are usually separated by a gap of 1 inch (25 mm).

- Pipes, conduits, ducts, or other rigid connections must not form a solid bridge across the gap.

- Debris must not be permitted to fall into the gap, thereby greatly reducing its effectiveness. To prevent the accumulation of debris in the gap during construction, the gap is usually filled with a resilient material, such as a semirigid board of polyurethane or fiberglass. Asphalt-impregnated board is usually used between on-grade slabs, foundations, and footings for this purpose.

- Expansion joints (usually incorporated into large buildings to allow for thermal expansion and contraction) can be used to isolate noisy and quiet areas, for example, in a theater to separate the mechanical equipment room and the stage shop from the performing and rehearsal areas.

REFERENCES

1. ASTM E989, "Standard Classification for Determination of Impact Insulation Class (IIC)."†
2. ISO 717, "Rating of Sound Insulation in Buildings and of Building Elements—Part 2: Impact Sound Insulation."
3. ASTM E492, "Standard Test Method for Laboratory Measurement of Impact Sound Transmission through Floor-ceiling Assemblies Using the Tapping Machine."
4. ASTM E1007, "Standard Test Method for Field Measurement of Tapping Machine Impact Sound Transmission through Floor-ceiling Assemblies and Associated Support Structures."
5. ISO 140/VI, "Laboratory Measurements of Impact Sound Insulation of Floors."
6. ISO 140/VII, "Field Measurements of Impact Sound Insulation of Floors."

†ASTM standards are available from the American Society for Testing and Materials, 1916 Race Street, Philadelphia, PA 19103-1187. ISO standards are available from the International Organization for Standardization, CH-1211 Geneva 20, Switzerland.

Chapter

7

Part 1: Noise Control in Heating, Ventilating, and Air-Conditioning Systems

Robert M. Hoover
Warren E. Blazier, Jr.

INTRODUCTION

Part 1 of this chapter considers the major sources of noise in heating, ventilating, and air-conditioning (HVAC) systems, how noise from these sources is communicated to the rooms being served, and how such noise transmission can be controlled. Major topics include:

- The planning of HVAC systems, showing how space limitations influence the noise that is produced
- Fans and fan noise
- Ducts and ductwork
- Sound attenuators (i.e., sound traps or duct silencers)
- Sound-absorptive plenums
- Air terminal devices (such as diffusers, grilles, acoustical louvers)
- Built-up fan equipment including: packaged fan equipment (air-handling units) and plenum fan equipment
- Packaged rooftop air-conditioning units
- Packaged air-conditioning systems, variable-air-volume systems, and air terminal control units (such as fan-powered terminals)
- Air-balancing procedures
- Conversion between sound power level of air terminal devices in a room and the resulting sound level in the room

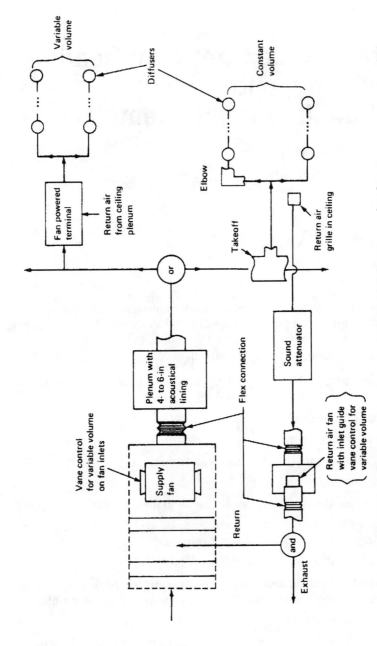

FIG. 7.1 Line diagram illustrating the major components of an HVAC system, related to the generation and control of noise.

Part 2 of this chapter describes methods for rating and specifying noise produced by HVAC systems and provides acceptability criteria for background noise in various types of rooms served by HVAC systems.

Typical Schematic Diagram and Terminology

The major components of an HVAC system, related to the generation and control of noise, are depicted in Fig. 7.1. These include the *fans* in the air supply and return systems, *inlet guide vanes* for regulating the volume of airflow at the fans, *air terminal devices* such as diffusers and grilles used to distribute air, lined and unlined ducts, duct elbows, sound attenuators, and volume control terminal units such as mixing boxes, variable air valves, and *fan-powered boxes*. Figure 7.2 illustrates many of the terms used in this chapter.

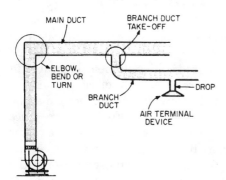

FIG. 7.2   Terminology used to describe HVAC ductwork.

PLANNING HVAC SYSTEMS IN BUILDINGS

In designing an HVAC system whose noise output is acceptable to the occupants of a building, there is usually close interaction between the HVAC system designer, architect, and structural engineer; in addition, the owner and the building management staff may become involved in the resolution of some noise-sensitive issues. With proper planning of an HVAC system, not only can costs be controlled but a quieter system can be obtained.

Sufficient space must be allotted in a building for the HVAC system so that energy-efficient fan equipment may be utilized and so that the various components of the system, described in detail below (such as ductwork, system controls, sound attenuators, and air terminal devices) may be appropriately sized to minimize noise produced by these components, as air flows through them.

Consider two general types of HVAC systems:

1. A *centrally-located* system in which the fans are located in a large, central location remote from the areas served by the fans; air is supplied from the fans to these areas by ductwork. The larger the volume occupied by ductwork, the smaller the revenue-producing space in the building.

2. A *distributed* system composed of "packaged" fan equipment [i.e., an assembly of air-conditioning components (cooling coils, filters, fan, humidifier, dampers, etc.) which is integrated into a self-contained package and installed as a single unit] located on each floor—usually in the building core (which may contain other non-revenue-producing services such as toilets, stairs, and elevators).

A distributed system is attractive to a building owner in that it provides greater revenue-producing space than a centrally-located system; this is because extensive ductwork is not required to carry air to various parts of the building. However, packaged fan equipment, located on each floor, is less energy-efficient than centrally-located equipment. Furthermore, the use of separate fan equipment on each floor may lead to a noise problem where such equipment is located in a room adjacent to an area in which relatively quiet conditions are required. In this case, expensive and complex constructions may be required to provide the necessary noise isolation. Furthermore, since the ducts between the fans and the air outlets or returns in the rooms supplied with air are relatively short because of the proximity of the fans and the spaces served, there may be another noise problem—the acoustically lined ducts may not provide sufficient attenuation to reduce the fan noise to an acceptable level in the room. For this reason, it may be necessary to add *sound attenuators* (i.e., also called *sound traps* or *duct silencers*) of the type described in this chapter. Such sound attenuators not only add to the cost of the system but increase the pressure drop in the fan system, thereby increasing electric power consumption of the fan equipment.

   For the above reasons, in many cases it is useful to determine the extent to which the allocation of inadequate space for an HVAC system affects the *total* cost of *both* the noise control solutions *and* the electrical energy required to operate the system over an arbitrary time period. Such an analysis may show that the estimated economic advantage of cutting down on the space allotted for the HVAC system and increasing the net revenue-producing area may be offset by the higher *first* cost of the noise control solutions and the projected higher *permanent* costs of operating the system.

FANS; FAN NOISE

In an HVAC system, the components that generate the most sound power are the *supply fan* (in the air supply system) and the *return fan* (in the return air system). By definition, a *fan* is a device for moving air which utilizes a power-driven rotating impeller. A fan has at least one inlet opening and at least one outlet opening. The openings may or may not be provided with connections to ductwork.[1]* The rotating impeller transfers mechanical energy from the fan shaft to the airstream; the energy in the air appears in the form of air velocity and air pressure. It is important to note that all of the energy added to the air is added by the power-driven rotating impeller. This section describes various types of fans; fan noise characteristics; *blade-passage noise* (i.e., the noise produced every time a blade passes a given point and gives the air an impulse); effect of operating efficiency on noise generated; and, airflow conditions at fans and the importance of smooth airflow.

Types of Fans

General fan construction and commonly used nomenclature for the various parts are shown in Fig. 7.3 for centrifugal fans and in Fig. 7.4 for axial-flow fans.[4]

Different fan applications require fans with different performance characteristics. The operating characteristics, including the noise characteristics, of a fan are determined primarily by the design of the rotating impeller. The types of fans described in this chapter are centrifugal fans and axial-flow fans normally used in central station air-conditioning systems, industrial ventilating systems, and industrial process applications. These different performance characteristics of fans result in different noise characteristics for the various types. Once the fan type, size, and speed have been selected to meet the specified performance and structural requirements, the noise characteristics for that particular fan are established.

Centrifugal fans may be characterized by the type of blades used, such as *airfoil, backward-curved,* or *backward-inclined blades* illustrated in Fig. 7.5.

---

*References appear at the end of Part 1.

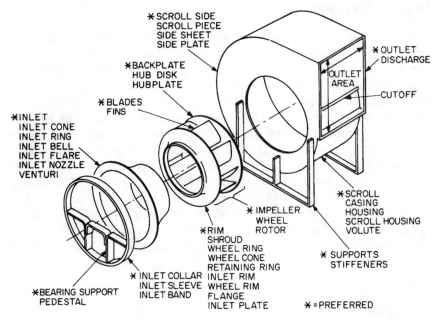

FIG. 7.3 Components of a centrifugal fan.

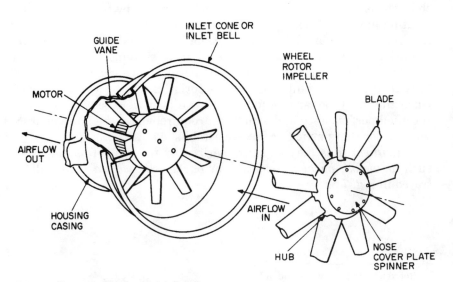

FIG. 7.4 Components of an axial-flow fan.

 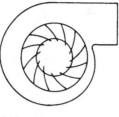 

AIRFOIL
BLADES

BACKWARDLY CURVED
BLADES

BACKWARDLY INCLINED
BLADES

FIG. 7.5   Three principal types of high-efficiency centrifugal fans.

Axial-flow fans are divided into the three major categories shown in Fig. 7.6:

1. Vaneaxial fans
2. Tubeaxial fans
3. Propeller fans

It is impossible to give general recommendations for the "best fan." In each application, the specific requirements for the fan must be considered; the best fan is determined on the basis of these specific requirements.

The primary selection criterion for a fan is based not on its acoustical characteristics but on its ability to move the required amount of air against the required pressure. The fan must do so at a reasonable initial cost. Once the operating requirements have been met, the type, size, and speed of the fan are completely determined; then the noise characteristics of the fan also are determined. In most cases it is not practical to substitute a fan that generates less noise since a quieter design of the same type probably will not meet the other operating specifications for the fan. Therefore, sound power levels generated by a correctly selected fan must be accepted as the sound power levels to be used in acoustical design calculations. Then the engineering approach to controlling the duct-transmitted noise is to provide sufficient sound attenuation in the duct installation to meet the specified acoustical requirements.

Fan Noise Characteristics

The broadband noise characteristics of typical fan designs are compared in Table 7.1. This table provides a rough comparison of the relative noisiness of well-designed centrifugal and axial fans of comparable size, when operating at or near their peak efficiency.

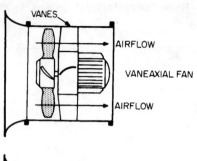

VANES

AIRFLOW

VANEAXIAL FAN

AIRFLOW

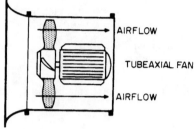

AIRFLOW

TUBEAXIAL FAN

AIRFLOW

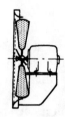

PROPELLER FAN

FIG. 7.6 Three major categories of axial-flow fans.

TABLE 7.1   The Relative Noisiness of Various Types of Fans in Air-Conditioning Systems That Operate at or near Peak Static Efficiency for Each Type of Blade
On this Scale, NNNNN Is the Noisiest; NNNN Less Noisy, and N Is the Least Noisy.*

Fan type	Noisiness
Centrifugal Fans	
Airfoil or backwardly-curved or backwardly-inclined	N
Radial fans:	
Low pressure	NNN
Medium pressure	NNNN
High pressure	NNNNN
Forward-curved	NN
Axial Fans	
Vaneaxial:	
Hub ratio 0.3–0.4	N
Hub ratio 0.4–0.6	N
Hub ratio 0.6–0.8	NN
Tubeaxial	NNN
Propeller	NNNN

*For specific details regarding fan selection, see Chap. 41 of Ref. 1.

7.8

For the acoustical design of critical spaces, actual noise data on the fans to be installed in the system should be obtained from the manufacturer. Octave-band noise levels should be used in air-handling system calculations; single-number ratings for evaluating fan noise should be avoided. The values of sound power level given by manufacturers for their various types of fans may represent the power radiated into the inlet duct or the outlet duct, or both.

Blade-Passage Frequency (Blade Frequency).   Every time a blade passes a given point, the air at that point receives an impulse. The repetition rate of this impulse—usually called the *blade-passage frequency,* also called the *blade frequency*—determines the fundamental tone that is produced. Doubling the number of blades of a fan, or doubling the rate at which it rotates, doubles the frequency of the fundamental, i.e., the blade-passage frequency. In addition to this fundamental, various harmonics may be produced, depending on the shape of the air impulse.

The tones that a fan generates are extremely important in the noise control of a fan system. In many noise problems related to fans, the major problem is the discrete frequency component contributed by the blade frequency. Special emphasis should be given to the octave band containing the blade-frequency component, since the ear has the ability to detect a tone in a general noise background. Therefore, one tends to be annoyed by it. The attenuation characteristics of the system must be completely adequate in that octave band.

The blade-passage frequency is given by:

$$f_B = n \times N \qquad (7.1)$$

where f_B = blade-passage frequency, hertz
  n = fan speed, number of revolutions per second
  N = number of blades in fan rotor

The approximate fan speed can be obtained from the catalog being used for fan selection, and the number of blades can be obtained from the catalog or manufacturer.

An analysis of fan noise is shown in Fig. 7.7. The octave-band spectrum is rather uniform; in contrast, the one-third-octave-band spectrum shows significant peaks. Since one-third-octave-band sound power level data are not available from all fan manufacturers, it should be assumed that such tones are present and should be taken into consideration in system design.

The fans most frequently encountered in HVAC systems for buildings are the backward-curved and forward-curved centrifugal fans and the vaneaxial fan. Although the characteristics of each fan type

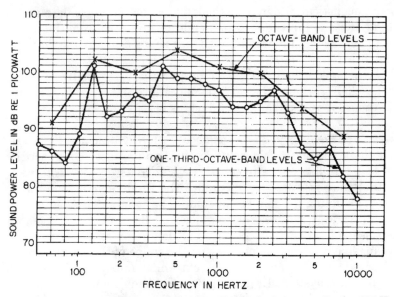

FIG. 7.7 A spectrum analysis of fan noise. The blade frequency (in the 125-Hz band) is evident in one-third-octave-band analysis but not in the octave-band analysis.

differ in terms of noise level as a function of frequency, they have one factor in common; by far, the lowest noise levels are produced when the fan is operated in the region of peak efficiency on its performance curve, as indicated by the optimum selection zone in Fig. 7.8.

Centrifugal fans generally produce noise across the entire audio-frequency spectrum, having the highest levels in the low-frequency octaves from about 31.5 to 250 Hz. Partly because of this, centrifugal fans in a typical HVAC system usually set the low-frequency noise limits in an occupied space.

Effect of Operating Efficiency on Noise Generated

The sound power level L_W of a fan at its discharge or inlet may be provided by the manufacturer of the fan for a specific operating condition, or it may be determined from tabular data and methods given in Chap. 41 of Ref. 1. The values, so obtained, apply only when the fan operates near its maximum efficiency and the velocity is relatively uniform across the cross section of the duct to which the fan is attached.

When inlet control dampers or guide vanes are used to control flow in a HVAC system, the operating point of the fan will be changed, and

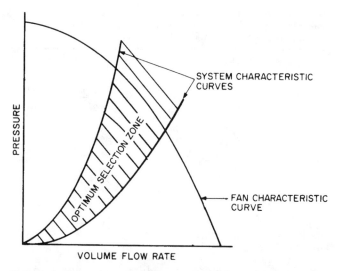

FIG. 7.8 A curve of pressure versus volume flow rate, illustrating an optimum selection zone of a fan.

the fan efficiency will be reduced; then, the sound power level in each octave-frequency band will increase by an amount that can be determined as follows:

Step 1. First, determine the static efficiency:

$$\text{static efficiency} = \frac{\text{flow rate} \times \text{static pressure}}{k \times \text{input power}} \qquad (7.2)$$

If the *flow rate* (i.e., rate of flow of air volume) is expressed in cubic feet per minute, and if the static pressure is expressed in inches of water, then the numerical constant k is equal to 6354 and the input power (i.e., the power developed by the fan shaft) is expressed in brake horsepower. In SI units, if the flow rate is expressed in L/s, and if the static pressure is expressed in pascals, then the numerical constant k is equal to 1, and the input power is expressed in kilowatts.

Step 2. Using the value of static efficiency obtained in Eq. (7.2), determine the increase in sound power level from Table 7.2 for the type of fan blade. *Note:* For vaneaxial fans, the pressure in Eq. (7.2) should be the total pressure; i.e., the sum of the static pressure and the velocity pressure (*velocity pressure* is the dynamic pressure due to the velocity of the moving airstream). For example, a velocity in the discharge duct of a fan equal to 4000 feet per minute (20 m/s) results in a velocity pressure of 1 inch of water (249 pascals); it varies as $[v/(4000 \text{ ft/min})]^2$, i.e., as $[v/(20 \text{ m/s})]^2$.

TABLE 7.2   Fan Efficiency Adjustment, i.e., the Number of Decibels by Which the Sound Power Level of a Fan Should Be Increased Because of Its Operation at Other Than Peak Efficiency (These Values Are for Different Types of Fans.)

Airfoil centrifugal and vaneaxial fan		Backward-curved centrifugal fan		Forward-curved centrifugal fan	
Efficiency, %	Increase, dB	Efficiency, %	Increase, dB	Efficiency, %	Increase, dB
80 to 72	0	75 to 67	0	65 to 58	0
71 to 68	3	66 to 64	3	57 to 55	3
67 to 60	6	63 to 56	6	54 to 49	6
59 to 52	9	55 to 49	9	48 to 42	9
51 to 44	12	48 to 41	12	41 to 36	12

Airflow Conditions at Fans; Importance of Smooth Airflow

If an HVAC system does not have good aerodynamic design and efficient operation of the various components, the noise level of fan noise sources described above may increase in level, and their spectra may broaden as well (particularly toward the low-frequency range), especially if the fans operate at low efficiency or under unstable operating conditions. Thus the airflow at the entrance and exit of a fan should be as smooth as possible to minimize the generation of turbulence; turbulence results in the generation of noise and an increased static pressure drop in the system. This is illustrated in Fig. 7.9 which shows examples of good and bad airflow conditions at the outlet of the fan; the noise generation in the latter case may be 10 to 30 dB higher than the former case. It is recommended that:

- Fittings (such as elbows and transitions) should not be placed closer than 3 to 6 duct diameters downstream from a fan.

- For an HVAC system having a constant volume of airflow, operate the fans generally close to their maximum efficiency.

- For a variable-volume system. a variable-speed drive should be considered to maintain operating efficiency for low volume.

- Avoid any obstruction close to the fan inlet or fan outlet.

- Provide a minimum space of $1^1/_2$ duct diameters at the fan inlet or fan outlet.

- Consider the installation of a bell-shaped inlet to provide better airflow conditions at the fan.

- Avoid offsets, abrupt or nonsymmetrical transitions, or offset flexible duct connectors in ductwork since they will be a source of turbulence and therefore noise sources.

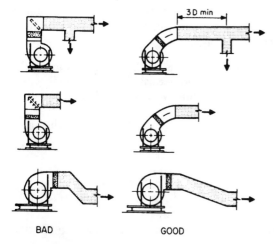

BAD   GOOD

FIG. 7.9 Examples of good and bad fan outlet conditions.

Fan Specifications

Specifications covering the noise generated by a fan may be written in either of two general forms:

Specification Form Number 1. *This form contains specifications of test procedures and the reporting of data for the sound power levels generated by the fan when it is operating at the specified performance.*

With this information it is possible to calculate the resulting sound pressure level for a particular fan installation. If these pressure levels are too high, appropriate sound attenuation facilities must be added to the system. A specification taking such a requirement into consideration may be written as follows:

Noise generated by the fan when operating at the specified volume flow rate and pressure shall be determined according to the conditions of AMCA Standard 300, Reverberant Room Method for Sound Testing of Fans,[2] and shall be reported in terms of sound power level in decibels re 1 picowatt in the specified octave bands.

Specification Form Number 2. *This form contains specifications of the upper limit of the octave-band sound power levels generated by the fan that will be permitted under the operating conditions.*

Such a specification is used in those cases where the sound power level that can be permitted on that particular job has been determined. The maximum sound power levels for the fan are specified. The fan manufacturer then must provide the necessary attenuation as a part of the fan assembly to meet these levels. The addition of such attenuation adds to the cost of the fan. Specifications based on this approach may be written as follows:

> Noise generated by the fan when operating at the specified volume flow rate and pressure shall be determined according to the conditions of AMCA Bulletin 300, Reverberant Room Method for Sound Testing of Fans,[2] and shall be reported in terms of sound power level in decibels re 1 picowatt in the specified octave bands and shall not exceed the values shown below:

Center frequency, Hz:	63	125	250	500	1000	2000	4000	8000
Maximum L_W, dB:	X	X	X	X	X	X	X	X

(The maximum permissible sound power levels are inserted in place of the X's.)

DUCTS

This section describes the following topics related to ductwork in HVAC systems: the recommended maximum velocity of airflow through ducts; ducts as a source of "cross-transmission" of noise between rooms; the penetration of walls and floors by ducts; attenuation of sound in unlined and lined ducts; division of sound power at duct branch points; attenuation of sound at elbows; end reflection losses; and enclosure for ducts (duct chases).

In installing, from the standpoint of noise control, it is advisable to specify that ducts should be attached from structural slabs, beams, and columns, or other massive and stiff structural components. Furthermore, it is important to specify and to check in the field to ensure that all ducts are hung so they are independent of other trades (e.g., a duct should *not* be hung from piping). In installations where a low noise level is a prime consideration, vibration isolation of the duct should be considered in accordance with the principles outlined in Chap. 9.

Airflow Conditions in Ducts; Recommended Maximum Velocity of Airflow

The flow of air through ductwork should be as smooth as possible to minimize the generation of turbulence, which not only results in an increased noise level but also in an decrease in system efficiency. Such turbulence increases significantly with increased velocity of airflow. In most applications, aerodynamic noise created by airflow through ducts will not be significant if the velocities through ducts do

TABLE 7.3 Recommended Maximum Velocity of Velocities through Rectangular and Circular Ducts under Various Conditions

Lowest RC or NC rating served by duct system	Square	Radius	Square, short vanes	Square, long vanes	Radius with vanes
	Maximum velocity in FPM				
50+	2000	2500	2500	2800	2800
45	1600	2000	2000	2400	2400
40	1300	1700	1700	2300	2300
35	1000	1300	1300	1700	1700
30	800	1000	1000	1200	1200
25	600	800	800	1000	1000
20 or less	—	500	500	600	600

SOURCE: Courtesy of ASHRAE, Ref. 4.

TABLE 7.4 Recommended Maximum Velocity of Airflow through Various Types of Elbows in Rectangular and Circular Ducts As a Function of the Criterion To Be Met

Duct location	RC or NC rating in adjacent occupancy	Max. airflow velocity in feet per minute	
		Rectangular	Circular
In shaft or above solid drywall ceiling	45	3500	5000
	35	2500	4500
	25	1700	2500
Above suspended acoustical ceiling	45	2500	4500
	35	1750	3500
	25	1200	2000

SOURCE: Courtesy of ASHRAE, Ref. 4.

not exceed the SMACNA duct design and construction guidelines given in Table 7.3 for elbows and Table 7.4 for ducts.

In medium-velocity and high-velocity systems, turning vanes usually are specified in rectangular duct elbows to promote smooth airflow, and hence to reduce the generation of noise.

Attenuation of Sound in Ducts

Noise is attenuated in a duct system by propagation losses: (1) in unlined ducts, (2) in lined ducts, (3) at lined elbows, (4) at branch points resulting from the division of power, (5) as a result of end reflection, (6) in sound attenuators, and (7) in plenums having a sound-absorptive lining.

TABLE 7.5   Attenuation in Decibels per Meter (dB/m) in Unlined Rectangular Sheet-Metal Ducts*

Perimeter/area ratio (P/A) in/in^2 (cm/cm^2)	Octave-band center frequency, Hz			
	31.5†	63	125	250
Over 0.12 (0.31)	0.3	0.3	1.0	0.3
0.12 to 0.05 (0.31 to 0.13)	0.3	1.0	0.3	0.3
Under 0.05 (0.13)	1.0	0.3	0.3	0.3

*The values given in this table must be doubled if the ducts are externally insulated.
†Extrapolated values.
SOURCE: Adapted from Ref. 4.

Unlined Ducts. Noise in an *unlined* duct is attenuated primarily by transmitting acoustic energy through the duct walls (by setting the duct walls into vibration) and then reradiating the noise into the space surrounding the duct; this mechanism provides attenuation since the sound being transmitted down the duct is decreased in level. The attenuation provided by unlined sheet-metal ducts is given in Table 7.5; these data are for ducts having different sizes and different shapes (expressed as the ratio of the duct perimeter to the area of the cross section, P/A).[4,5] If an unlined duct passes through an occupied space where a low noise level is a requirement, excessive low-frequency sound may be transmitted from the duct into the space—especially if the location is a short distance from the fan. The power level of this radiated sound depends on (1) the power level of the sound within the duct, (2) the cross-sectional area of the duct, (3) the length of the duct in the occupied space, and (4) the so-called "breakout" transmission loss (TL) of the duct walls described in the footnote for Fig. 7.12.

Large sheet-metal panels in rectangular ducts having a high aspect ratio (i.e., where one cross dimension is greater than 3 times the other cross dimension) may be excited into vibration by turbulent flow at the discharge of a fan, or near branch takeoffs. Such a source produces noise in the low-frequency range from 16 to 125 Hz. When this condition occurs, it is often difficult to separate or identify the contribution of individual sources.

Lined Ducts. The attenuation of sound provided by a duct lined with sound-absorptive material is given in Table 7.6. Figure 7.10 shows the attenuation versus frequency for a duct with a 1 inch (25 mm) and 2 inch (50 mm) thickness of duct lining. At 63 and 125 Hz, the attenuation is partially due to duct wall radiation. Attenuation in the low-frequency range is small compared with the attenuation in the high-frequency range. Therefore, an unbalanced noise spectrum may result, characterized by a rumble in spaces served by the air-conditioning system.

TABLE 7.6   Attenuation in Decibels per Meter (dB/m) for Ducts

These Values Are the Sum of the Losses Due to Duct Lining 1 in (25 mm) Thick, 1.5 to 3 lb/ft^3 (24 to 48 kg/m^3), and Losses Due to Duct Radiation.

				Octave-band center frequency, Hz						
				63	125	250	500	1000	2000*	4000*
Rectangular Duct										
Dimensions		Perimeter/area ratio								
in × in	(cm × cm)	in/in^2	(cm/cm^2)							
4 × 8	(10 × 20)	0.75	(0.3)	0.7	2.1	3.3	8.2	22.4	21.2	8.4
6 × 12	(15 × 30)	0.5	(0.2)	0.6	1.9	2.6	6.3	17.3	15.7	7.6
8 × 12	(20 × 30)	0.42	(0.17)	0.6	1.8	2.4	5.8	15.9	16.3	8.7
10 × 16	(25 × 41)	0.33	(0.13)	0.5	1.7	2.1	4.9	13.5	13.3	7.9
12 × 12	(30 × 30)	0.33	(0.13)	0.6	1.7	2.3	5.4	14.8	14.9	8.8
12 × 24	(30 × 61)	0.25	(0.10)	1.2	0.8	1.8	4.1	11.1	9.5	6.5
12 × 36	(30 × 91)	0.22	(0.09)	1.2	0.8	1.6	3.6	9.8	5.8	4.2
15 × 15	(38 × 38)	0.27	(0.11)	1.2	0.9	2.0	4.7	12.7	12.6	8.3
15 × 30	(38 × 76)	0.20	(0.08)	1.2	0.8	1.6	3.5	9.5	8.1	6.1
18 × 28	(46 × 71)	0.18	(0.07)	1.2	0.8	1.5	3.4	9.3	8.8	7.0
18 × 36	(46 × 91)	0.17	(0.07)	1.2	0.7	1.4	3.1	8.5	7.1	5.8
24 × 36	(61 × 91)	0.14	(0.05)	1.1	0.7	1.3	2.9	7.8	7.3	6.6
24 × 48	(61 × 122)	0.13	(0.05)	1.1	0.6	1.3	2.6	6.3	5.8	5.5
30 × 30	(76 × 76)	0.13	(0.05)	1.1	0.7	1.4	3.0	8.2	7.6	7.0
30 × 60	(76 × 152)	0.10	(0.04)	0.4	0.6	1.3	2.2	4.4	4.9	5.1
36 × 36	(91 × 91)	0.11	(0.04)	0.4	0.7	1.3	2.7	6.6	6.7	6.7
36 × 72	(91 × 182)	0.08	(0.03)	0.4	0.6	1.0	2.0	3.3	4.3	4.9
42 × 42	(107 × 107)	0.10	(0.04)	0.4	0.6	1.2	2.4	5.2	5.9	6.5
48 × 48	(122 × 122)	0.08	(0.03)	0.4	0.6	1.1	2.2	4.3	5.4	6.2
Circular Duct										
Diameter, in (cm):										
6 (15)				0.7	1.6	3.3	5.9	7.2	7.2	6.6
12 (30)				0.5	1.0	2.3	4.9	7.2	7.2	4.9
24 (61)				0.3	0.7	1.6	3.3	5.6	3.0	1.6
48 (122)				0.1	0.3	1.0	2.0	2.0	1.6	1.6

*These values apply for ducts up to 10 ft (3 m) in length. For greater lengths, the attenuation per unit length will be smaller than values indicated.

SOURCE: Refs. 4 and 6.

Specifications for Duct Lining.   Duct lining shall be a glass fiber material made up of bonded fibers with a neoprene-coated facing on the airstream side. The density of the lining material shall be between 1.5 and 3 pounds per cubic foot (24 to 48 kg/m^3), and the thickness shall be 1 inch (2.5 cm) or 2 inches (5 cm) thick. The sound absorption coefficients of the material shall be provided for each octave band with center frequencies ranging from 125 to 4000 Hz, as determined according to the current ASTM C423 test procedure, using Type F mounting of the material.

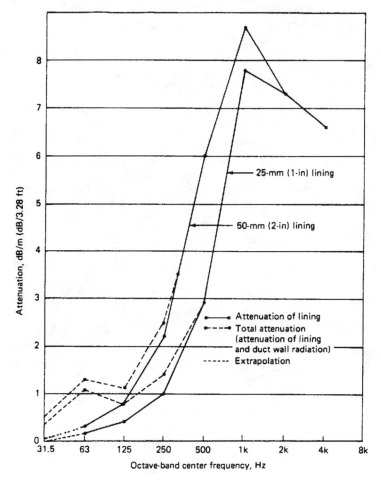

FIG. 7.10 Attenuation provided by sound-absorptive linings 1 inch (25 mm) and 2 inches (50 mm) thick in a duct 24 × 36 inches (610 × 914 mm).

Division of Sound Power at Duct Branch Points

When a branch duct leaves (i.e., branches off) from a main duct, as illustrated in Fig. 7.2, the sound power which is transmitted along the main duct is divided between the branch duct and the continuation of the main duct in approximately the same ratio as the area of the branch duct to the area of the main duct ahead of the branch. This division of power results in attenuation at the branch point. For example, if a duct branches off into two ducts having equal cross sections, then half the sound flows through each at the branch point.

The sound attenuation that results from the division of power can be expressed as:

$$\text{attenuation} = 10 \log_{10} \left(\frac{\text{area of branch duct}}{\text{area of main duct}} \right) \quad \text{dB} \quad (7.3)$$

This equation indicates the number of decibels that must be subtracted from the sound power level in the main duct to obtain the sound power level in the branch duct; this relationship is shown in Table 7.7. For example, if the branch duct has 4 percent of the area of the main duct, 4 percent of the sound is transmitted down the branch; therefore, according to Table 7.7, the sound power level of noise in the branch duct is 14 dB lower than the sound power level in the main duct.

TABLE 7.7 Division of Sound Power between a Main Duct and a Branch Duct*

Ratio (area of branch duct/ area of main duct)	0.01	0.02	0.04	0.06	0.08	0.1	0.2	0.4	0.6	0.8
Decibels to be subtracted	20	17	14	12	11	10	7	4	2	1

*This division provides an effective attenuation at the branch point. Thus the numbers in this table are to be subtracted from the sound power level in the main duct to obtain the sound power level in the branch duct.

Attenuation at Elbows in Ducts

Right-angle elbows reflect some sound back toward the source, resulting in attenuation of sound propagating along the duct. Approximate values of attenuation are given in Table 7.8 for elbows with and without lining.[6] At high velocities [2000 feet per minute (10 m/s)] an elbow may be a source of noise as a result of turbulent airflow generated at the elbow. The turbulence is less in circular ducts than in square ducts. The generation of turbulence at elbows may be reduced by the

TABLE 7.8 Attenuation of Sound for 90° Rectangular Duct Elbows with and without Fiberglass Lining 25 mm (1 in) Thick, with Turning Vanes, in Decibels (dB)

Width of duct in the plane of the turn, inches (cm)	Octave-band center frequency, Hz						
	63	125	250	500	1000	2000	4000
Lined elbows							
5 to 10 (12.5 to 25)	0	1	1	2	3	4	6
11 to 20 (27 to 51)	0	1	2	3	4	6	8
21 to 40 (53 to 102)	1	2	3	4	5	6	8
41 to 80 (104 to 203)	2	3	3	5	6	8	10
Unlined elbows							
All sizes	0	1	2	3	3	3	3

SOURCE: Adapted from Ref. 4.

use of turning vanes, which promote good aerodynamic airflow; turning vanes must be installed carefully since they can be a source of noise if the edges of the vanes are bent during installation.

End Reflection Losses in Ducts

When a duct opens into a room, some of the sound is reflected back into the duct, toward the fan, thereby providing losses at the duct opening. This reflection at the end of the duct is most pronounced for small ducts at low frequencies, where the wavelength of sound is large compared with the dimensions of the duct. The attenuation is a function not only of frequency and the size and shape of the opening but also of the position of the opening relative to nearby walls. The effect of position of the source is discussed in Chap. 4 (see Table 4.3). The end reflection loss is given in Table 7.9 for a range of duct sizes for situations in which the duct opening is in free space or is flush-mounted to an acoustical ceiling.

These data for end reflection losses also apply for the case of an air diffuser or grille attached to the duct opening. However, when the duct is attached to a linear diffuser (sometimes called a "strip diffuser"), the end loss may be approximately one-half that given for the size of the duct connected to the plenum.

Penetration of Walls and Floors by Ducts

Where a duct penetrates a partition and is in mechanical contact with it, several undesirable effects may occur: (1) There may be cracks around the duct, and sound may travel from one room to the other through these openings. (2) Vibration of the duct can be transmitted to the partition, which will then vibrate and radiate noise. (3) If the partition vibrates, this vibration will be communicated to the duct and possibly be radiated as noise elsewhere in the HVAC system. To avoid these undesirable effects, the duct should be isolated from the

TABLE 7.9   Attenuation of Sound in Ducts Resulting from End Reflection Losses, in Decibels (dB)

Square duct size, circular duct diameter, inches (cm)	Octave-band center frequency, Hz				
	63	125	250	500	1000
6 (15)	18	12	8	4	1
12 (30)	13	8	4	1	0
24 (60)	8	4	1	0	0
48 (120)	4	1	0	0	0

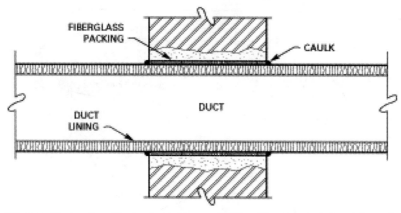

FIG. 7.11 Design for a duct penetrating a partition. The duct is isolated from the partition by a layer of fiberglass to minimize the transmission of structureborne energy between the two. Nonhardening caulking on both sides of the partition is essential to prevent leakage of sound from one side of the partition to the other.

wall by a resilient material such as fiberglass, as illustrated in Fig. 7.11; note that the nonhardening sealant on both sides of the partition is *essential*.

Ducts As a Source of "Cross-Transmission" of Noise between Rooms

Cross-transmission is the communication of noise between adjacent rooms via a supply or return duct which is common to the two rooms, as is illustrated in Fig. 10.15a. In this illustration, noise from one room may enter an air outlet, travel along the duct, and then be radiated through an outlet in the adjacent room. Lining the duct that interconnects the rooms will reduce this effect, but if this duct length is relatively short, the attenuation provided by the lining may be insufficient to decrease the sound transmission to an acceptable level. In that case, sound attenuators may be required as illustrated in Fig. 10.15b.

Where a duct passes through a noisy room, noise may be transmitted *through the walls of the duct*. The noise may then travel down the duct and be radiated from air terminal devices in an adjacent rooms. This is because the sound insulation provided by the walls of a sheet-metal duct (whether lined or unlined) is not large. For example, the "breakout" transmission loss* of the walls of rectangular and circular ducts walls is given in Fig. 7.12. When this transmission loss is not sufficient,

---

Break-out is the transfer of acoustic energy from the interior of a duct, through the duct walls, to the exterior of a duct.

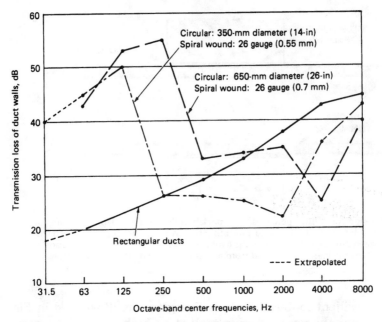

FIG. 7.12   The "breakout" sound transmission loss for sound propagated from the interior of a rectangular and circular duct through the duct walls to the exterior.[3]

the sound insulation of the ducts should be increased—for example, by lagging, as illustrated in Fig. 7.13. The transmission loss for a rectangular duct also can be increased by: (a) spot cementing fiberglass board to the duct and securing the insulation with mechanical fasteners, (b) wrapping the fiberglass board with hardware cloth, (c) applying vapor-barrier tape over joints and breaks, and (d) applying a heavy coat of plaster on the hardware cloth. Although the use of this method may be less effective in the low-frequency range than the use of circular ducts, it provides a practical means for increasing the sound insulation value of rectangular duct wall in an existing HVAC system.

Shafts for Ducts (Duct Chases)

Enclosures for ducts in a building should provide sufficient sound insulation to prevent the undesirable transmission of noise from duct-work to the areas adjacent to the duct enclosures. (Sound insulation of partitions is considered in Chap. 5.) The most effective and most economical method is to locate such enclosures in areas away from any noise-sensitive areas.

In the same shaft, do not run ducts that service noisy areas along side of ducts that service areas where quiet is essential. This is because noise may be communicated through the walls of the "noisy

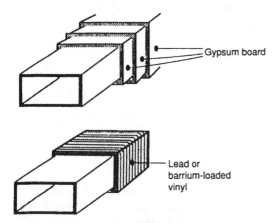

FIG. 7.13 (*a*) One or more layers of gypsum board screwed directly to the duct. (*b*) Lead or barium-loaded vinyl wrapping taped around fiberglass blankets; usually with a minimum weight of 2 pounds per square foot (10 kg/m²). (*Courtesy of American Society of Heating, Refrigerating and Air Conditioning Engineers, Inc.*[10])

duct" to and through the walls of the "quiet duct"; it may then travel along the quiet duct to the area where quiet conditions are important. The ducts should not be permitted to contact the walls of the duct enclosure since these walls will then be set into vibration and become a new source of noise. Instead, adequate clearance should be provided. A useful rule of thumb is to provide a clearance between a duct and the duct enclosure of 10 percent of the larger duct dimension or 6 inches (15 cm)—whichever is larger.

SOUND ATTENUATORS (SOUND TRAPS)

A *sound attenuator* (also called a *sound trap, duct silencer,* or *prefabricated silencer*), abbreviated SA on engineering drawings, is a commercially available device that is inserted in an HVAC duct to provide more attenuation than a lined duct of equal length. A sound attenuator has a cross section equal to (or greater than) the duct in which it is installed. As illustrated in Fig. 7.14, its cross section is subdivided into smaller ducts that are lined with (dissipative) sound-absorptive material to provide attenuation over a wide range of frequencies. Sound attenuators usually are fabricated in modular form in cross section, and in lengths of 3, 5, 7, and 10 ft (0.9, 1.5, 2.1, and 3.0 m). They are also available for circular ducts in lengths which are typically 2 to 3 times the duct diameter.

A sound attenuator has three important characteristics which are a function of the air velocity at the face of the attenuator: (1) insertion

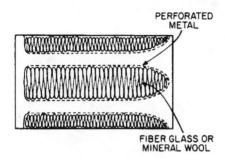

FIG. 7.14 Section through a sound attenuator.

loss, (2) pressure drop, and (3) self-noise. The relationship between these factors is shown in Table 7.10 for a typical attenuator 5 feet (1.5 m) long and 1 × 1 ft (0.3 × 0.3 m) in cross section.

The manufacturer's data and specifications for sound attenuators should be based on test procedures of the latest version of ASTM 477.[2] This information applies when the attenuator is installed in a straight duct with uniform flow to and from the unit. If these conditions are not provided in a field application, the pressure drop may increase, and the acoustical performance may decrease. Thus, sound attenuators should be separated from a fan discharge, or from duct elbows, by 2 to 3 duct dimensions. Manufacturers provide guidelines for predicting the actual pressure drop for a variety of unit locations within a duct system.

Insertion Loss

The *insertion loss* of a sound attenuator is the difference in sound power level (or the difference in sound pressure level) in decibels at a point in the duct system (beyond the sound attenuator or at some measurement location) due solely to the placement of the sound attenuator in the transmission path between the sound source and the given location. In general, sound attenuators which provide a low pressure drop also have a low insertion loss. The insertion loss varies with air velocity. *Dynamic insertion loss* of a sound attenuator is the insertion loss with air flowing through the attenuator. Figure 7.15

TABLE 7.10 Attenuation and Self-Noise Generation for a Typical Sound Attenuator* for a Face Velocity of 1000 ft/min (5.1 m/s) and a Pressure Drop of 0.4 in Water (100 Pascals)

	Octave-band center frequency, Hz							
	63	125	250	500	1000	2000	4000	8000
Insertion loss, dB	4	11	20	37	44	44	38	22
Self-noise L_W, dB	48	42	39	35	36	37	35	30

*5 ft (1.5 m) long, and 1 × 1 ft (0.3 × 0.3 m) in cross section.

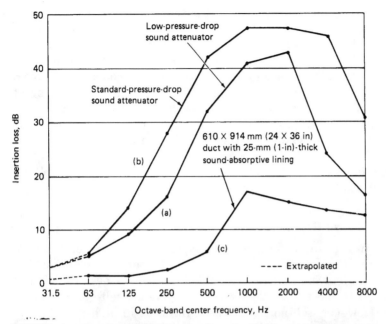

FIG. 7.15   A comparison of the insertion loss provided by a sound attenuator 7 feet (2.1 m) long. (*a*) A low-pressure-drop unit; (*b*) a standard-pressure-drop unit; (*c*) duct of the same length and cross section, lined with a fiberglass blanket 1 inch (25 mm) thick.

compares the insertion loss for a sound attenuator 7 feet (2.1 m) long for a standard-pressure-drop unit and a low-pressure-drop unit; also shown is the insertion loss of a duct (of the same length) lined with a fiberglass blanket 1 inch (25 mm) thick. This illustration shows that in the octave bands centered at 125 and 250 Hz, a sound attenuator provides much greater insertion loss than a lined duct of the same length. It would require about 50 feet (15 m) of the lined duct to equal the attenuation, in these two octaves, provided by a 7-foot (2.0-m) long sound attenuator. In the octave band centered at 63 Hz, the attenuator provides an insertion loss only about 5 dB more than the duct, and in the octave band centered at 31.5 Hz, their attenuations are approximately the same. However, the attenuation which results from the radiation of noise by the lined duct walls may have a negative aspect if such a duct is located in an occupied space. Such radiation of sound is unusual for sound attenuators because their construction is both heavier and stiffer than a typical duct.

Pressure Drop

The aerodynamic performance of a sound attenuator may be expressed in terms of the drop in air pressure in pascals (inches of water) across the attenuator. In some cases, the pressure drop across the attenuator may equal or exceed the total pressure drop in the remainder of the system. Therefore, this characteristic may govern the choice of attenuator. The pressure drop is a function of the open area at the face of the attenuator. For example, consider a typical sound attenuator, 5 feet (1.5 m) long, through which air is flowing at a velocity of 1000 feet per minute (304 m/min). The pressure drop across a low-pressure-drop unit (having an open area of 45 percent) is about 0.10 inches of water (25 pascals), and the pressure drop across a standard-pressure-drop unit (having an open area of 32 percent) is about 0.50 inches of water (125 pascals). Data are available giving the pressure drops for different face velocities.

Self-Noise (Noise Regeneration)

Self-noise in a sound attenuator is the noise that is generated as a result of the flow of air through the attenuator (for example, see Table 7.10). Most manufacturers publish such data as a function of air velocity. In most low-velocity HVAC systems, self-noise is not a problem. However, self-noise may be significant in high-velocity systems or in systems where the background noise in the space served must be very low, as is the case in a concert hall or drama theater.

In some instances, poor entrance and exit conditions may increase the self-noise and pressure drop produced by a sound attenuator for a given airflow. This can result in decreasing the insertion loss of the attenuator; it may also change the operating point of the fan and change its noise output. For these reasons, it is recommended:

- That there be a straight run of duct having a minimum length of two duct diameters ahead of a sound attenuator

- That transitions between a sound attenuator and a fan outlet or inlet be gradual and symmetric

Typical Sound Attenuator Installations

Figure 7.16 shows a centrifugal fan, with sound attenuators on both the inlet and the outlet, used in the supply system of a central station ventilating system. The outlet of the fan is fitted with a sound attenuator to reduce the flow of acoustic energy from the discharge of the fan to the supply air ductwork. The required insertion loss (IL) of this sound attenuator is determined by using the sound power levels of the fan (without the sound attenuator) to calculate the sound level that would result in the room with the most critical noise criterion. The amount by which the calculated sound level exceeds the allowable sound level determines the required amount of IL that the atten-

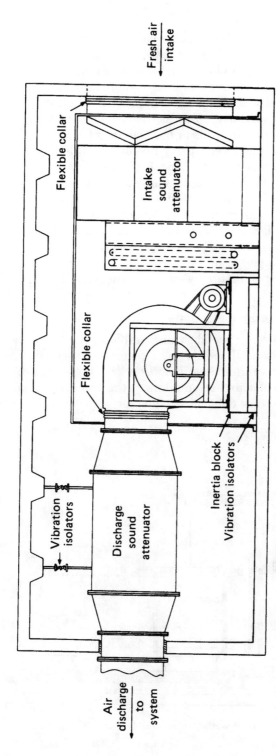

FIG. 7.16 Sound attenuation system for a centrifugal fan installation.

7.27

uator must furnish. There is no rule of thumb for selecting such attenuators—each attenuator must be selected on the basis of actual requirements. The sound attenuator on the fan intake system shown in Fig. 7.16 is used to reduce noise radiated on the inlet side of the fan (outside the fresh-air intake) to an acceptable value. This attenuator is selected in the same way as the attenuator used in the fan discharge. While different criteria may be used (such as an A-weighted sound level at either the property line of the building or at the nearest adjacent building or residence), the requirement for the sound attenuation should be determined for each octave band.

Figure 7.17 shows sound attenuators attached directly to both the upstream and downstream sides of an axial-flow fan; the sound attenuators and the fan are treated as a single unit which is separated from both the inlet and discharge ductwork by flexible collars. The entire unit is supported on an inertia block which, in turn, is isolated from the building structure by vibration isolators.

Sound Attenuator Specifications

Sound attenuators, or prefabricated mufflers, shall provide the specified *insertion loss* in dB, while not exceeding the specified pressure at the specified air volume flow. Insertion loss, pressure drop, and self-noise properties of sound attenuators at the specified air volume flows shall be submitted as determined in accordance with the procedure of ASTM E477.

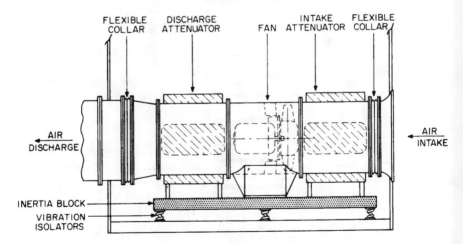

FIG. 7.17 Sound attenuation system for an axial-flow fan installation.

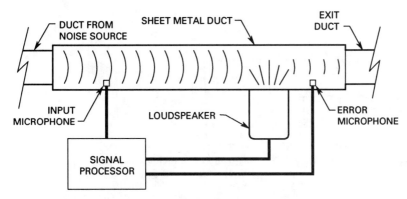

FIG. 7.18 Principle of operation of an active sound attenuator.

Active Sound Attenuators

An *active sound attenuator* is a special type of attenuator that incorporates a sound source (i.e., a loudspeaker) which generates sound waves equal in amplitude and out-of-phase with the unwanted sound (i.e., the noise) being propagated down the duct, as illustrated in Fig. 7.18. This "sound-cancellation" technique is usually limited to plane waves of low frequency whose wavelengths are larger than the largest dimension of the duct. Therefore, its application generally is limited to frequencies below approximately 250 Hz.

In such a sound-cancellation system, an input microphone detects the primary sound (i.e., the noise being propagated down the duct); the electrical signal from the microphone is then fed to an electronic signal processor. This processor generates and sends an electrical signal which is transmitted to a loudspeaker(s) mounted in a wall of the duct. The loudspeaker then radiates a secondary sound wave into the duct which is equal in amplitude and 180° out-of-phase with the primary sound wave, thereby producing cancellation. If an exact cancellation is not achieved, an "error microphone" sends a signal back to the processor to adjust the signal to the loudspeaker.

With the application of adaptive, digital signal processing, it is possible to cancel broadband noise, as well as sound at the blade-passage frequency, by application of this technique.

SOUND-ABSORPTIVE PLENUMS

In an air-conditioning *supply system,* a *plenum* is an enclosed volume which is at a slightly higher pressure than the atmosphere and is connected to one or more branch supply ducts; in a *return system,* a plenum is at a slightly lower pressure than the atmosphere and is

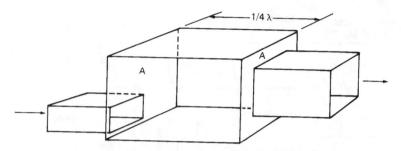

FIG. 7.19 Schematic diagram of an acoustically lined plenum, designed to provide low-frequency attenuation. The interior walls of the entire plenum should
be lined with fiberglass having a thickness of 4 to 6 inches (10 to 15 cm),
depending on the amount of low-frequency attenuation required. The areas *A*
of the two walls should be 4 to 6 times the cross-sectional areas of the ducts
that penetrate these walls; λ is the wavelength of the lowest frequency to be
attenuated.

connected to a number of return grilles. Examples of plenums
include:

- An expansion chamber, inserted in a duct system, which has a
  cross-sectional area at least 4 to 6 times the area of the duct, as
  shown in Fig. 7.19

- The volume of air in the space between a suspended ceiling and the
  structural slab above it, used as a plenum in a return air system

- A sheet-metal enclosure provided on the discharge or intake of a
  fan to smooth out turbulent airflow

- The space below the raked floor of an auditorium which forms part
  of the return air system for the auditorium

A plenum can provide significant attenuation if the interior surfaces of the plenum are lined with very thick sound-absorptive material. For example, if a plenum is lined with fiberglass 4 inches (10 cm)
thick, the IL can be as large as 12 dB in the octave bands as low as
31.5 Hz.[7] Plenums also can be useful in providing significant insertion loss at high frequencies.

In such an application, the fiberglass [usually 4 to 6 inches (10 to
15 cm) in thickness] should be neoprene coated. In general, it is convenient to fasten the fiberglass to the walls of the plenum with stick
clips. *Stick clips* are sheet-metal discs [about 1 inch (25 mm) in diam-
eter] having a sharp metal rod perpendicular to the disc. The disc at
the base of the stick clip [usually on about 1½-foot (0.5-m) centers] is
cemented to the plenum wall with an epoxy. The fiberglass blanket is
impaled on the stick clips; a washer is then slipped over the end of
sharp rod, which is then bent over to secure the blanket.

TERMINAL DEVICES (AIR DIFFUSERS, GRILLES, ACOUSTICAL LOUVERS)

An *air terminal device* is a device at the end of a duct through which air is delivered to, or removed from, a room. In an air supply system, air terminal devices (usually called *diffusers*) supply air to the space and distribute it in a more or less predictable manner. In a return air system, air terminal devices are usually called *registers, grilles,* or *mushrooms,* depending on their shape; air is removed from the space served through such devices.

Air diffusers are usually round, rectangular, or long narrow strips (the last are called *linear diffusers*), as illustrated in Fig. 7.20. The spectrum and level are strongly dependent on the type of air diffuser and the type of deflector. For example, Fig. 7.21 shows the octave-band spectrum for three air diffusers, each of which delivers 800 cfm (0.4 m³/s): a circular air diffuser 12-inch (30-cm) diameter; a square, perforated plate grille; and a sidewall grille 1 square foot (0.09 m²), 82 percent open area.

Effect of Air Deflectors on Noise Output of Air Diffusers

Air diffusers usually incorporate air *deflectors,* such as vanes, fins, and cones, to help distribute the air evenly throughout the space being served. The greater the deflection, the higher the noise level the deflectors produce. The noise generated by the flow of air through a diffuser increases significantly with the velocity of airflow through it. For example, the power level L_W generated by air flowing through an air diffuser usually increases 16 dB for each doubling of the velocity in the octave bands centered at 500 Hz and below, and 18 to 24 dB for the octave bands centered at 1000 Hz and above.

Effect of Dampers on Noise Produced by Air Diffusers.   Dampers which regulate the quantity of airflow may be an integral part of an air outlet or may be installed directly behind air diffusers or grilles to control the volume of airflow through them. The dampers increase the radiated noise (usually in the range from 1000 to 8000 Hz)—the more a damper restricts the flow of air, the higher the noise level. For example, if the volume of air supplied per second is cut to one-half its value, the sound power level of the noise radiated from the combination of the diffuser and damper may increase as much as 10 to 20 dB. Thus, when obtaining data from manufacturers, it is important to determine whether the data apply to only the diffuser or to a diffuser-damper combination. The manufacturer's data generally apply only when there is uniform air delivery to the air diffuser; if the airflow is

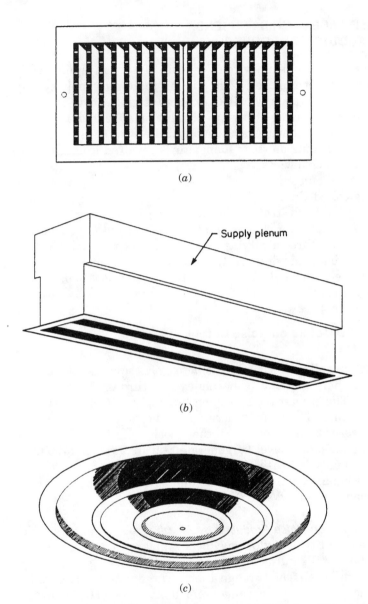

(a)

(b)

(c)

FIG. 7.20 Various types of air diffusers. (a) Rectangular diffuser; (b) linear diffuser; (c) circular diffuser.

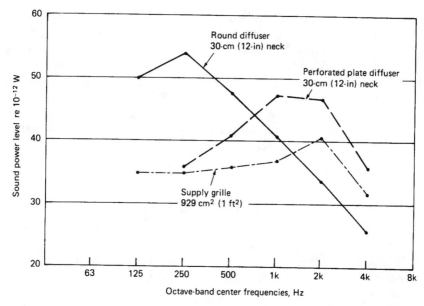

FIG. 7.21   Examples of octave-band sound level spectra for three types of air outlets.

not uniform, the noise level will be higher than predicted on the basis of the furnished data. In the high-frequency range, air terminals and their associated dampers often determine the level of sound produced in a room by an HVAC system.

Because air diffuser noise is produced at or near the air terminal device in an occupied space, there is no sound attenuation in the path (between this source of noise and the observer) to reduce its level. Therefore, from the standpoint of noise control, it is preferable to control the flow of air by a damper located in the duct upstream for a air supply duct, and downstream for an air return air duct—for example, at a junction with the main branch duct—rather than at the air diffuser. Then, lining the duct between the damper and diffuser can be effective in reducing damper noise.

Published Data on Noise Ratings of Air Diffusers and Grilles.   It is almost always necessary to use manufacturers' data for the noise produced by air diffusers as well as supply and return grilles. Some manufacturers do provide such information in terms of power levels in octave bands and/or the NC levels they predict will not be exceeded if there is only a single air diffuser in the room; this prediction is based on the assumption that the *space factor,* also called a *room correction factor* $(L_W - L_p)$, is equal to 10 dB. In contrast, the value of $(L_W - L_p)$ for typical residential rooms usually is smaller than 10 dB[1,3]; for example, in a small office, the value of $(L_W - L_p)$ may be as little as 5 dB. Thus, the published NC levels for air diffusers may predict sound pressure levels 5 dB below the actual levels that will be experienced. For this reason, when the published NC values for air outlets are used, these values should be increased by 5 NC. For larger rooms, the value of $(L_W - L_p)$ should be estimated by using Fig. 4.8 or Eq. (4.9) and adjusting the manufacturer's NC value accordingly.[3] Furthermore, manufacturers' data typically assume:

- That the duct is straight near the air diffuser; bends will increase the noise level.

- That the nearest listener is far from the grille; if the listener is closer than assumed, the air diffuser will be perceived as being noisier.

- That the blades on the air diffuser are set for zero deflection; at other angles of deflection, the noise output will increase significantly.

- That there is no damper close to the face of the air diffuser; a damper at, or close to, the face of a damper will raise the noise output.

- In the case of a linear diffuser, the data are given for a specified length of diffuser; for longer lengths, the noise level in the space will increase.

Flexible Duct Connection to an Air Diffuser

A flexible duct provides a convenient means of connecting an air diffuser to a branch duct, for it allows some flexibility in locating the diffuser in a suspended ceiling. However, if the air diffuser is misaligned (see Fig. 7.22) or if the drop to the diffuser is too short, the air delivery will not be uniform across the diffuser; then the velocity on one side of the diffuser will be substantially higher than the average value. This will result in substantially higher noise levels than the published data.

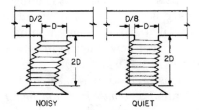

FIG. 7.22 Correct and incorrect installation of a flexible duct connection between a branch duct and an air diffuser.

For example, a misalignment of 1 diameter in 2 diameters of duct length may result in an increase in sound power level of 15 dB. For this reason it is advisable that ducts which serve an air diffuser be straight for at least 3 duct diameters upstream of the diffuser's duct collar.

If low-frequency sound is present, a flexible duct will permit sound to be radiated directly into the ceiling plenum (in which it is located); then the low-frequency sound will be transmitted through the acoustical ceiling and into the occupied space.

Acoustical Louvers

Acoustical louvers are a series of streamlined, perforated metal baffles having an airfoil shape, which are filled with a sound-absorptive material such as fiberglass, as illustrated in Fig. 7.23. Such devices

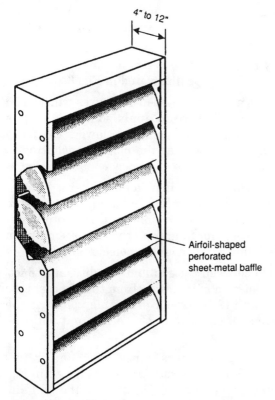

FIG. 7.23   An acoustical louver. The perforated sheet-metal baffles are filled with fiberglass. (*Courtesy of American Society of Heating, Refrigerating and Air Conditioning Engineers, Inc.*[10])

are sometimes used where one part of an HVAC system opens directly to the outdoors (for example, at a fresh-air intake), providing an
insertion loss as much as 10 to 15 dB in the mid-frequency range
between 500 and 2000 Hz. They are sometimes used to ventilate an
enclosure that contains a noise source.

MECHANICAL EQUIPMENT ROOMS

The following guidelines are recommended:

- Maximize the distance between mechanical equipment rooms and
  noise-sensitive areas.

- The walls of a mechanical equipment room should be of solid, high-
  density construction to reduce transmission of airborne noise from
  the mechanical equipment room to adjacent spaces. Where the
  adjacent areas are noise sensitive, double walls, described in Chap.
  5, should be used.

- Where there are nearby noise-sensitive areas, it may be necessary
  to install a "floating floor" of the type illustrated in Fig. 6.2.

- In buildings where there is a major noise-sensitive area (such as an
  auditorium), it is often cost-effective to apply sound-absorptive
  material in a mechanical equipment room; this lowers the noise
  level in the room [see Eq. (4.6)] so that the noise transmitted to
  adjacent spaces is reduced.

- Support the entire fan assembly on an inertia block that is isolated
  from the equipment room floor by vibration isolators, as illustrated
  in Fig. 7.17. This is important from a noise control standpoint
  because without this isolation, vibration from the fan assembly can
  be transmitted to the building and can create noise problems.

- Install flexible collars (1) between the fan and the discharge ductwork to reduce the transmission of vibration from the fan casing to
  the attached ductwork and (2) between a flexible collar at the
  fresh-air intake to prevent direct contact of the fan unit with the
  building structure.

- Wall or floor penetrations (by conduits, pipes, ducts, or drains)
  should be isolated from the building structure as illustrated in Fig.
  7.11: (1) to prevent the transmission of vibration to the building
  structure and (2) to prevent the leakage of sound through cracks
  around such penetrations.

- Avoid flanking transmission, described in detail in Chap. 5.

BUILT-UP FAN EQUIPMENT

Built-up fan equipment is the term usually applied to HVAC systems where the fan is selected as an individual component and integrated in the installation with other separate elements of the system such as coils, air filters, and control dampers for regulating the proportioning of outside, exhaust, and return air. The use of a built-up fan system provides the best opportunity to optimize the fan selection so that the fan operates in the most efficient region of its air performance curve, thus minimizing electric power consumption and fan-generated noise. The principal advantages of built-up fan systems are a result of operation at higher fan efficiencies: (1) lower energy cost and (2) lower operating noise level. The principal disadvantages are (1) increased space requirements in the mechanical room and (2) higher initial cost.

There are two types of built-up fan configurations commonly used: the *draw-through* and the *blow-through*. The differences are illustrated in Fig. 7.24. In the draw-through configuration, the air entering the supply fan is drawn through the heating and cooling coils, and the

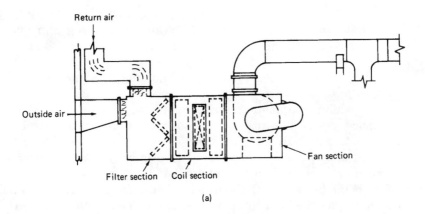

(a)

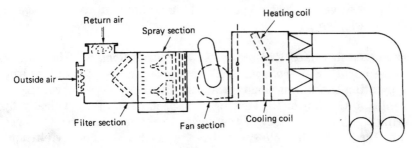

FIG. 7.24   Built-up fan. (*a*) Draw-through unit; (*b*) blow-through unit.

discharge side of the fan is directly connected to the main distribution ductwork. In this arrangement, a sound attenuator is usually required in the main duct as the first element in the noise control design. In the blow-through configuration, the air entering the supply fan passes through the filters; the discharge side of the fan supplies air through a transition section to the heating and cooling coils and the plenum, before connection to the main air-distribution ductwork. If the plenum has a sound-absorptive lining, it can provide an attenuation of 5 to 10 dB; therefore, at low frequencies, the sound power level will be lower than for the same fan used in a draw-through configuration. Furthermore, it can provide even higher attenuation at high frequencies.

A blow-through configuration, in general, couples significantly less fan noise to the main duct system than the draw-through geometry. In some cases, this may reduce or eliminate the need for a sound attenuator in the main duct connected to the supply fan, as is customary with a draw-through configuration.

Packaged Fan Equipment (Air-Handling Units)

An *air-handling unit* is an assembly of air-conditioning components (cooling coils, filters, fan, humidifier, dampers, etc.), integrated into a self-contained package and installed as a single unit which is connected to the air distribution system. Air-handling units are also called *packaged fan equipment.*

Packaged fan equipment, installed in a location adjacent to an occupied space, may constitute a source of both airborne and structure-borne noise, generally at frequencies below 500 Hz. The character of this noise may be either broadband or primarily discrete-frequency components associated with the fan-blade frequency or speed of rotation of (1) the fan shaft, (2) the drive-motor shaft, or (3) the drive belt. The use of packaged fan equipment is advantageous where there is no central air distribution system for the building; each floor of the building is served by its own packaged fan equipment, usually located in the interior core.

Constant-Speed versus Variable-Speed Air-Volume Control. The flow of air in a *variable-air-volume* (VAV) *system* usually is regulated by (1) operating the fan at constant speed with variable-vane control at the inlet to the fan or (2) varying the speed of the fan, typically by varying the line frequency of the power to the drive motor. Of these two methods, the variable-speed drive is much more energy efficient and results in significantly (as much as 15 dB) lower noise levels.

A majority of the applications for such equipment is in variable-air-volume systems discussed in the next section; many noise control problems that occur with such systems are the result of an over-sized fan which becomes unstable as the airflow is modulated (by using variable-inlet-vanes, rather than by modulating the fan speed). Other problems occur with packaged fan equipment furnished with forward-curved fans which use variable-inlet-vanes for modulating airflow. Whenever fans of this type become unstable, there may be a 10- to 15-dB increase in the level of fluctuating noise and vibration, usually at low frequencies (31.5 Hz or lower). Generally, it is not fea-sible to correct noise problems of this nature except by making modi-fications to stabilize the fan. The commonest solution is to remove the inlet vanes and install a variable-speed drive.

Plenum Fan Equipment

A plenum fan uses a backward-curved airfoil impeller that is *not* enclosed in a typical volute scroll; instead, it is housed in a rectangu-lar plenum which has ducted inlet and outlet connections. The dimen-sions of the plenum usually are about 2 impeller diameters; the inte-rior sidewalls of the plenum are lined with a sound-absorptive mater-ial. A typical plenum fan installation is illustrated in Fig. 7.25. Although the operating efficiency of a well-designed plenum fan is slightly less than that of an equivalent, scrolled, airfoil centrifugal at the same duty (3 to 5 percent), there are several advantages realized in using a unit of this type in certain applications. For example, pack-aged equipment using a plenum fan instead of a scrolled centrifugal is inherently significantly shorter in the longitudinal dimension. This makes it very attractive for use in cramped quarters such as the typi-cal mechanical room in buildings having separate HVAC systems on each floor. It is also possible to select a more efficient fan, within the

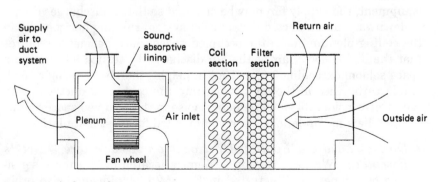

FIG. 7.25   A plenum fan.

same space constraints, and realize savings in the electric power required to operate the system. Furthermore, because of the absorption introduced by its enclosing plenum, the plenum fan produces significantly less noise on the discharge side of the system than the equivalent direct-connected scrolled centrifugal fan. However, the noise radiated from the inlet of a plenum fan is essentially the same as that of a scrolled centrifugal, so similar noise control measures are required on the return side of the air distribution system.

Packaged Rooftop Air-Conditioning Systems

A packaged rooftop air-conditioning system is a complete air-conditioning unit, intended for rooftop installation, which is assembled in a single casing and which usually discharges conditioned air either directly in the room below it or into nearby spaces through short ductwork. Rooftop units are frequently utilized in low-rise buildings (1) to minimize the initial cost of the HVAC system, (2) to ease the problems of installation, and (3) to gain increased revenue-producing floor space by eliminating interior mechanical equipment rooms. A rooftop location permits the use of a direct-expansion cooling coil and an air-cooled compressor-condenser system which eliminates the need for a cooling tower and the associated pumps and piping required with water-cooled equipment. In direct-expansion systems it is highly desirable to keep the refrigerant lines between the condenser and evaporator as short as possible; this dictates that the supply and return fans of the building air distribution not be remotely located but be integrated as a part of the equipment package.

The use of rooftop units of this type may result in noise and vibration control problems that are difficult and expensive to solve—particularly if the unit is located above or adjacent to a noise-sensitive space or where the unit is mounted on light-weight building construction. For example, to minimize the longitudinal dimension of most packaged equipment, the supply fan may be oriented so that it discharges directly downward into a ducted distribution system running horizontally in the ceiling plenum above the occupied space. Such geometry requires that the high-velocity air at the fan discharge be turned 90°, within a space seldom exceeding 3 feet (1 m) in height, thereby creating considerable turbulence in the air flowing into the connected ductwork and radiating considerable low-frequency noise in the occupied space below.

The following guidelines are recommended for most installations:

- *Do Not Locate a Rooftop Unit over an Area Where Quiet Is Essential:* Where a rooftop system is located over a noise-sensitive occupancy, as illustrated in Fig. 7.26, significant noise prob-

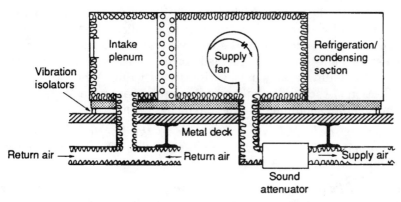

FIG. 7.26   Rooftop unit.

lems may result. Such noise problems are particularly apt to occur if (1) the rooftop unit is located near the edge of a building having a window curtain-wall or (2) the ceiling of the space below is a lay-in system of acoustical tile, which provides very little sound insulation from sources of noise above the acoustical ceiling—particularly in the low-frequency region association with the rumble radiated by ducts carrying highly turbulent airflow. Furthermore, the typical roof on which a rooftop air-conditioning system is mounted usually does not provide adequate sound insulation.

■ *Locate the Rooftop Unit in an Area of Maximum Stiffness of the Roof:* (Locating the unit directly over a column is best; across a major beam—as near to a column as possible, is next best, etc.) In the location of the rooftop unit, consider (1) the addition of additional beams to increase the stiffness of the roof and/or the addition of a heavy housekeeping pad beneath the rooftop unit to increase the mass and stiffness of the roof.

■ *Avoid Locating the Rooftop Unit near the Perimeter of the Building:* This is especially important where the exterior walls are curtain walls, which provide relatively little sound insulation.

■ *Provide Efficient Vibration Isolation of the Entire Packaged Rooftop Unit Utilizing the Methods of Chap. 9:* The casing of a typical rooftop unit is generally not stiff enough to be supported on individual external vibration isolators. The base of the unit should be mounted on stiff rails; otherwise, the unit will usually be subject to excessive flexural bending. Such rails should be mounted on vibration isolators of the type shown in Fig. 9.13—a combination metal-coil spring on a neoprene pad. In general, the static deflection of the vibration isolators should be somewhat greater than the value indicated in Fig. 9.15, which is applicable only when the isolators are carried by a supporting structure that deflects no more than 10 percent of the deflection of the vibration isolators. Therefore, when the static deflection of the roof is known, the static deflection of the springs should be at least 10 times this value. When the static deflection of the roof is unknown, the static deflection of the vibration isolators should be at least 2.0 inches (5 cm).

- *Ensure that the Vibration Isolation of the Rooftop Unit Is not Compromised by Electrical Connections:* Provide adequate slack, as illustrated in Fig. 9.11.

- *Avoid All Penetrations of the Room in Noise-Sensitive Areas:* For example, avoid conduits, piping, ducts, and drains.

- *Use a High-Density Backing on Any Suspended Acoustical Ceiling Which Is below a Rooftop Unit:* It should have a high-density backing which has a minimum surface weight of 1.5 lb/ft^2 7.3 kg/m^2. With lay-in acoustical ceilings, this may be provided by a gypsum board backing $^1/_2$ inch (12.5 mm) thick.

- *Increase the Sound Insulation of Main Ductwork Which Passes over Noise-Sensitive Areas by Means of Duct "Lagging" or a Duct Enclosure:* However, in the region where the main ductwork is close to the rooftop unit, the vibration of the ductwork (due to aerodynamic turbulence) usually must be reduced before the duct lagging or duct enclosure can be effective. This is typically accomplished by screwing a $^5/_8$-inch (16-mm) gypsum board to the sidewalls of the duct. After stiffening the walls of the ductwork, the lagging generally takes the form of an exterior wrapping of fiberglass blanket 2 to 4 inches (25 to 50 mm) thick plus a plaster skin or gypsum board enclosure weighing at least 2 lb/ft^2 (9.8 kg/m^2). Where the main ductwork is a sufficient distance downstream of the unit that is the source of duct wall vibration, the stiffening of the duct sidewalls may be omitted. Where ductwork is not encased, it is highly advantageous to use round, rather than rectangular ductwork. These measures will reduce the transmission of noise through the walls of the ductwork occupied areas.

- *Install Sound Attenuators and Lined Plenums:* Where possible, sound attenuators should be above the roof so that the noise level within the ducts is reduced before the duct enters the building.

- *Consider the Use of Acoustical Louvers on Air Intakes and Air Outlets Located on Rooftop Units Where Sound Transmission through Ordinary Louvers May Be a Source of Annoyance to Neighbors.*

VARIABLE-AIR-VOLUME SYSTEMS AND AIR TERMINAL CONTROL UNITS

A *variable-air-volume system* is an HVAC system that controls the temperature in the space served by varying the volume of air supplied (at constant temperature). The control units for such systems are located in the duct distribution system in the areas served to control the volume of air delivered to the various outlets. A *variable air valve* (VAV) is a control unit consisting of a metal box containing a damper, damper-position control equipment, a controller, and a sensor. The box is usually supplied with "primary" air through a circular duct from the main distribution system which is isolated from the box by a flexible connector. The output of the box is connected through a flexible connector to a duct that delivers air to one or more air diffusers located in the space being served. Such a unit should not be located in an area where quiet conditions are required; instead, select a location such as a corridor.

Mixing Boxes

A *mixing box* is a device used to reduce the air velocity in the duct of a medium- or high-pressure, high-velocity system; it incorporates a valve which controls the volume of flow for distribution within a room and is used to mix hot and cold air. A mixing box (1) provides an insertion loss, (2) is a source of noise, predominantly in the mid-frequency range from 250 to 2000 Hz, and (3) radiates noise from its housing. In general, the larger the box and the more air it handles, the more noise it radiates.

Fan-Powered Terminals (FPTs)

A *fan-powered box* is a variable air valve provided with an auxiliary fan to mix induced air from the ceiling plenum with the primary air. Thus, in some variable air valves, one or more auxiliary fans are installed in the box along with the damper system to supplement the delivery of air by mixing induced air from the ceiling plenum with the primary air. Such a unit is designated as a fan-powered terminal (FPT). FPTs are available in two different types: (1) constant-volume FPT, in which the fan operates constantly and both the primary and return air are mixed and discharged by the fan, and (2) variable-volume FPT, in which the fan handles only the induced air from the space served and functions only when it is necessary to mix warm return air with the primary air. Since operation of the fan is not continuous, this can lead to increased awareness of the control unit.

In a FPT, the *damper* and the auxiliary fans are sources of noise

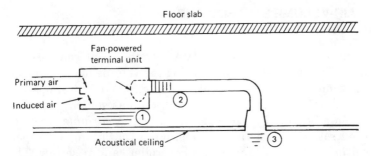

FIG. 7.27   An air terminal unit in a ceiling plenum. (1) Casing-radiated sound generated by fan-powered terminal unit; (2) discharge sound generated by fan-powered terminal unit; (3) discharge sound generated by air outlet.

that may propagate into the occupied space (1) through the discharge duct connecting the unit, with its damper blade, to an air outlet, as shown in Fig. 7.27, and (2) via radiation of sound directly from the walls of the FPT to the space in which it is located above a suspended ceiling, and then through the suspended ceiling or through openings in the ceiling for return air.

Manufacturers publish data giving the sound power level of (1) the noise emitted to the discharge duct and (2) the noise radiated by the casing as a function of the capacity of the unit and the static pressure drop across the unit. These data are measured in accordance with Air-Conditioning and Refrigeration Institute (ARI) Standard 880.[8] The manufacturer's data do not distinguish between (1) noise radiated from the air intake port through which the fan draws air from the ceiling plenum and (2) noise radiated from the casing. The sound levels in spaces served by such HVAC systems can be estimated by the method described in ARI Standard 885[9] and outlined in Chap. 42 of Ref. 1.

AIR-BALANCING PROCEDURES

Air balancing is a procedure used in the field to adjust the flow of air in an HVAC system so as to meet the design goals for airflow in the system; if the system is properly designed, the acoustical design goals also should then be met. The acoustical design of the system is based on the sound power level of a fan at its operating point on the system curve. If air balancing is not performed properly, the system resistance may be higher than anticipated. As a result, the fan speed must be increased to obtain the required air quantity; then the fan will operate at a higher pressure than anticipated, at a less efficient point on its air performance curve. The result may be a substantial increase in fan noise and a correspondingly higher noise level in the spaces being served.

Balancing a Constant-Volume HVAC System

The following sequence of steps is recommended for balancing a constant-volume system:

Step 1. Open all dampers in the system, including those at the air diffuser terminals.

Step 2. Adjust the fan so as to obtain approximately the correct airflow.

Step 3. Adjust the dampers in each of the branches of the system so as to obtain the design value of airflow in each branch. The ratio of the airflows in all the branches to the total airflow must be the same as that scheduled. In a duct branch, it is essential to adjust the damper nearest the fan first. Then the next nearest damper should be adjusted, etc.

Step 4. Adjust the dampers at the air diffusers to "fine-tune" the flow of air so that each diffuser provides its specified air volume. The dampers within the diffuser terminals should *not* be used to obtain the required air volume without first using the branch dampers in the system to achieve a coarse balance; the damper at the diffuser terminal should not be used for this purpose since diffuser noise will then be significantly increased.

Step 5. Recheck the total air delivery at the fan, and readjust the fan speed, if necessary.

Balancing a Variable-Air-Volume HVAC System

A variable-air-volume HVAC system contains two mechanisms not found in a constant-volume HVAC system: (1) a means for controlling the amount of air being delivered by the fan at any given time (this is generally accomplished using variable-inlet-vanes or by variable-fan-speed control) and (2) variable-volume boxes, installed in various zones of the building, which are controlled by the thermostat in each zone. Therefore, balancing a variable-air-volume system is more complex than balancing a constant-volume system.

The following balancing procedure is recommended for the variable-air-volume system:

Step 1.   Lock the fan-inlet-vanes in their fully open position.

Step 2.   Deactivate the controls on the variable-volume boxes so that each is in the wide-open air-delivery position.

Step 3.   Follow Steps 1 through 5 for balancing a constant-volume system, described above.

Step 4.   (When the above initial balance is completed, the adjustable dampers in the branch ducts and at the air diffuser terminals are in their correct positions, and the fan is operating at the correct speed.) Next, restore the system to its normal operating condition by unlocking the fan-inlet-vanes and activating the controls of the variable-volume boxes.

Step 5.   Check to ensure that the fan and zone control systems for varying the air delivery of the fan in response to the demand of the volume-control boxes in each zone are properly synchronized.

DETERMINING THE SOUND LEVEL IN A ROOM FROM THE SOUND POWER LEVEL OF THE SOURCE AND THE QUANTITY ($L_W - L_P$)

After the sound power level L_W of the supply units in a room has been determined, the sound pressure level L_p in the room can then be determined by subtracting $(L_W - L_p)$ from the quantity L_W according to the methods of Chap. 4 [See Eqs. (4.9) and (4.10)].

REFERENCES

1. C. M. Harris, ed., *Handbook of Acoustical Measurements and Noise Control,* 3d ed., McGraw-Hill, 1991.
2. "Reverberant Room Method for Sound Testing of Fans," AMCA Standard 300, Air Movement and Control Association, Arlington Heights, IL 60004.
3. W. E. Blazier, Jr., "Revised Noise Criteria for Application in the Acoustical Design and Rating of HVAC Systems," *Noise Control Engineering,* vol. 16, 1981, pp. 64–73.
4. *ASHRAE Handbook, HVAC Systems and Applications,* Chap. 52, "Sound and Vibration Control," American Society of Heating, Refrigerating and Air Conditioning Engineers, Inc., Atlanta, GA 30329, 1987.
5. I. L. Ver, "A Review of the Attenuation of Sound in Straight and Unlined Ductwork of Rectangular Cross Section," *ASHRAE Trans.,* vol. 84, pt. 1, 1978, p. 122.
6. R. M. Hoover and H. L. Kuntz, "The Interrelationships between the Physical Properties of Fibrous Duct Lining Materials and Lined Duct Sound Attenuation," *ASHRAE Trans.,* vol. 93, pt. 2, 1987, p. 449.
7. L. L. Beranek, *Noise and Vibration Control,* rev. ed., Chap. 12, Institute of Noise Control Engineering, Poughkeepsie, NY 12603, 1988, pp. 391–393.
8. *Air Terminals,* Standard 880–89, Air-Conditioning and Refrigeration Institute, 1501 Nelson Boulevard, Arlington, VA 22209.

9. *Procedure for Estimating Occupied Space Sound Levels in the Application of Air Terminals and Air Outlets,* Standard 885–90, Air-Conditioning and Refrigeration Institute, 1501 Nelson Boulevard, Arlington, VA 22209.
10. M. E. Schaffer, *A Practical Guide to Noise and Vibration Control for HVAC Systems,* American Society of Heating, Refrigerating and Air Conditioning Engineers, Inc., Atlanta, GA 30329, 1991.

Part 2: Noise Control Criteria for Heating, Ventilating, and Air-Conditioning Systems

Warren E. Blazier, Jr.

INTRODUCTION

Part 2 of this chapter considers the criteria used to establish noise control requirements in the design of heating, ventilating, and air-conditioning (HVAC) systems and/or in evaluating the performance of existing systems. The principal topics discussed are:

- Methods for rating and specifying noise produced by HVAC systems

- Criteria for, and table of values of, acceptable HVAC noise levels for various types of rooms in buildings

- A criterion which provides a recommended upper limit for noise in the low-frequency range to avoid *vibration* of light-weight walls and ceilings that may be set in motion by such acoustic excitation

HOW TO RATE NOISE PRODUCED BY HVAC SYSTEMS

This section describes several common methods of rating HVAC noise by a single number. The application of these methods is valid for only *continuous steady-state noise that exhibits no obvious fluctuations in sound level with time; HVAC noise which fluctuates in sound level is more annoying than noise of the same level that is steady.* Failure to recognize this effect usually leads to serious errors in rating the noise produced by an HVAC system. Fluctuating noise levels may occur as a result of the unstable operation of a fan or as a result of "beats" between two or more fans (or other rotating equipment in the system) which operate at nearly the same speed.

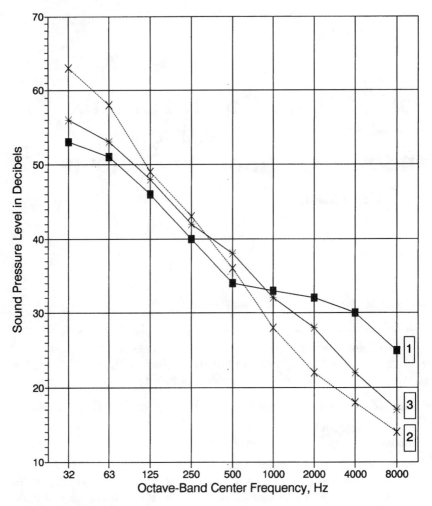

FIG. 7.28 Three typical HVAC spectra, each having an A-weighted sound level of 40 dB(A).

A-Weighted Sound Level for Rating HVAC Noise

The ear is not equally sensitive at all frequencies. For this reason, sound-level meters (described in Chap. 2) incorporate *frequency-weighting* which makes such instruments less sensitive at frequencies where the ear is less sensitive. The most commonly used frequency-weighting is called *A-weighting* (see Table 2.2); readings taken on a sound-level meter with this weighting are called *A-weighted sound levels* and are expressed in dB(A), as described in Chap. 2. Although A-weighted sound levels are very useful in evaluating many types of noises, their use can be unreliable for assessing HVAC noises. For example, Fig. 7.28 shows three arbitrary HVAC noise spectra having frequency distributions which differ markedly. They are similar in relative loudness; each has an A-weighted sound level of 40 dB(A). However, they differ markedly in the relative annoyance they produce.

For the above reasons, the use of A-weighted sound levels should be avoided in specifying the noise control objectives of HVAC systems for typical buildings. Furthermore, the use of A-weighted sound levels as a diagnostic tool in noise analysis of an HVAC system is not recommended; usually, the shape of the noise spectrum is required.

NC Method of Rating HVAC Noise

NC curves, illustrated in Fig. 7.29, have been widely used (1) to evaluate the noise in a room generated by an existing HVAC system and (2) to specify the upper limits of the octave-band levels of HVAC noise which are permissible in a room.[1]* For example, if the mechanical specifications indicate that the noise in an unoccupied room may not exceed NC 30 with the HVAC system in operation, the octave-band levels of the background may not exceeded the following values (which may be read directly from the NC 30 curve of Fig. 7.29): 63 Hz, 57 dB; 125 Hz, 48 dB; 250 Hz, 41 dB, 500 Hz, 35 dB; 1000 Hz, 31 dB; 2000 Hz, 29 dB; 4000 Hz, 28 dB; and 8000 Hz, 27 dB.

How to Determine NC Ratings.   The NC rating of noise in an unoccupied room, with all HVAC systems in operation, may be determined as follows:

Step 1.   Measure the octave-band level of the noise in the room, at the following octave-band center frequencies: 63 Hz, 125 Hz, 250 Hz, 500 Hz, 1000 Hz, 2000 Hz, 4000 Hz, and 8000 Hz.

Step 2.   Obtain the spectrum of the noise by plotting (on Fig. 7.29) the octave-band levels obtained in Step 1.

Step 3.   On Fig. 7.29, locate the lowest NC curve (these curves are plotted at 5-NC intervals) which is completely above the spectrum plotted in Step 2.

Step 4.   Shift the NC curve of Step 3 downward until it is just tangent to the spectrum. At 1000 Hz, determine the number of decibels this curve must be shifted downward to be tangent to the spectrum.

Step 5.   The NC rating is then equal to the numerical value of the NC curve of Step 3 minus the number of decibels downward shift of Step 4. For example, if the NC-40 curve is shifted downward 2 dB to be tangent to the spectrum, then the noise spectrum has an NC rating of 38 (that is, 40 − 2).

---

*References appear at the end of Part 2.

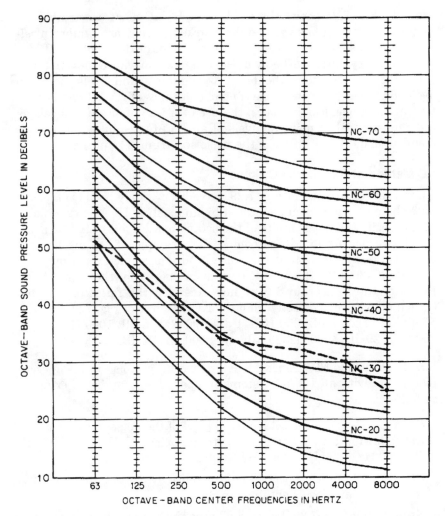

FIG. 7.29 NC curves. The octave-band spectrum of example 7.1 is superposed on these curves.

Example 7.1:   NC Calculations for the Spectra of Fig. 7.28.

Step 1. Spectrum 1 of Fig. 7.28 has the following octave-band levels: 63 Hz, 51 dB; 125 Hz, 46 dB; 250 Hz, 40 dB; 500 Hz, 34 dB; 1000 Hz, 33 dB; 2000, 32 dB; 4000 Hz, 30 dB; and 8000 Hz, 25 dB.

Step 2. On Fig. 7.29 plot the spectrum of the octave-band levels of Step 1, yielding the curve shown in Fig. 7.30.

Step 3. On Fig. 7.30, the lowest of the NC curves which is completely above the spectrum plotted is NC 35.

Step 4. When the NC-35 curve is shifted downward, it will be just tangent to the spectrum in the 2000-Hz octave band. The amount of downward shift at 1000 Hz is 2 dB.

Step 5.   Therefore, the NC rating of this noise spectrum is NC 35 − 2, that is, NC 33.

If the above procedure is applied to Spectrum 2 of Fig. 7.28, it will be found that this spectrum also has a rating of NC 33 because it is entirely below the curve for NC 33; the NC-33 curve touches this spectrum at 250 Hz.

If the above procedure is applied to Spectrum 3 of Fig. 7.28, it will be found that this spectrum also has a rating of NC 33 because it is entirely below the curve for NC 33; the NC-33 curve touches this spectrum at 500 Hz.

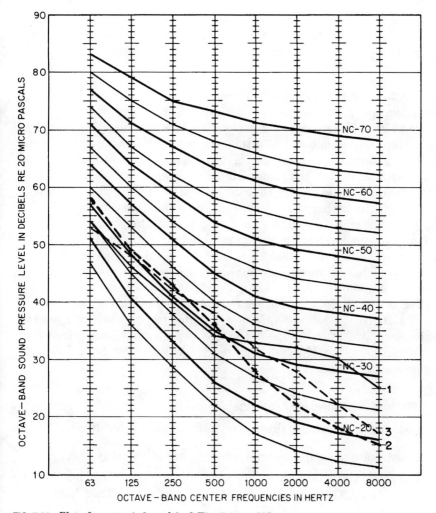

FIG. 7.30   Plot of spectra 1, 2, and 3 of Fig. 7.28 on NC curves.

Disadvantages of the NC Rating System. The three spectra of Fig. 7.28 and Example 7.1 all have a rating of NC 33. Yet, their spectra are quite different; they will sound quite different, and they will also produce different levels of annoyance. For example:

- Most listeners would judge Spectrum 1 to be *hissy* because there is a greater concentration of noise at high frequencies than there is in an acceptable HVAC system.

- Most listeners would judge Spectrum 2 to be *rumbly* because there is a greater concentration of noise at low frequencies than there is in an acceptable HVAC system.

- Most listeners would judge Spectrum 3 to be neither hissy nor rumbly. Therefore, it is defined as a *neutral* spectrum in that it is not likely to be objectionable as background noise at levels appropriate to the environment.

What NC Rating Is Acceptable? The choice of an acceptable NC rating for design purposes depends on the type of space use within a building that is being considered. For example, in a private office or conference room environment, the primary consideration is to ensure that the background noise (with the HVAC system in operation) does not interfere with speech communication; in open-plan offices, however, it is also important to ensure that the background noise is high enough to reduce the awareness of speech and other noises produced by neighbors nearby. In contrast, in a concert hall, the primary consideration is to ensure that the background noise (with the HVAC system in operation) does not "mask" (i.e., prevent one from hearing) the quietest passages of music. Acceptable NC levels for various types of rooms are given in Table 7.12. *It should be emphasized that meeting an NC criterion does not ensure that the "quality" of the background noise will be unobjectionable to a listener* (as a result of spectral imbalance) unless the shape of the noise spectrum being evaluated is approximately that of the designated NC curve for at least four contiguous octave bands.

RC Method of Rating HVAC Noise[2]

The RC curves which are illustrated in Fig. 7.31 are used:

1. To evaluate noise in a room from an existing HVAC system

2. To specify the octave-band levels of a neutral-sounding background noise (i.e., a background noise that sounds neither hissy nor rumbly)

TABLE 7.11   Criteria for Identifying the "Quality" of HVAC Noise As It Might Be Subjectively Described by an Observer

Letter designation	Octave-band levels at 500 Hz and below	Octave-band levels at 1000 Hz and above
(N) Neutral spectrum	Must not exceed octave-band levels of the reference spectrum by more than 5 dB.	Must not exceed octave-band level of the reference spectrum by more than 3 dB.
(R) Rumbly spectrum	Exceeds the octave-band levels of the reference spectrum by more than 5 dB.	Does not exceed octave-band level of the reference spectrum by more than 3 dB.
(H) Hissy spectrum	Does not exceed octave-band levels of the reference spectrum by more than 5 dB.	Exceeds the octave-band level of the reference spectrum by more than 3 dB.
(RV) Perceptible vibration	Levels in the 16-, 31.5-, or 63-Hz octave bands must not exceed 70 dB. At levels between 65 and 70 dB, such vibration is possible but is generally not a problem.	

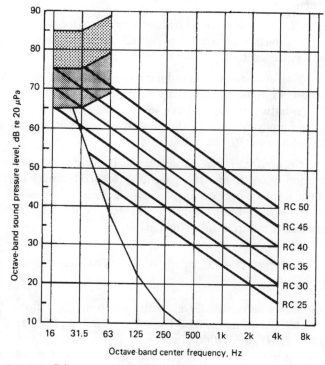

FIG. 7.31   RC curves. (*W. E. Blazier, Ref. 3.*)

The use of RC curves is the *preferred* alternative to the use of either NC curves (or modified versions of such curves) or to the use of A-weighted sound levels. This is because the RC rating system:

- Takes into account the influence of *both* the spectrum shape and level on the subjective assessment of the noise
- May include data in the octave bands centered at 16 and 33 Hz
- Takes into account the annoying effects of vibration in light-weight building construction resulting from operation of an HVAC system

Letter Designation of Noise Quality.   In addition to a numerical level, the RC rating of a noise includes a letter designation which describes the "quality" of the sound (noise) as defined in Table 7.11. These quality descriptors differentiate between those noises which are hissy, rumbly, neutral sounding (i.e., neither hissy nor rumbly) as well as noises which have sufficient low-frequency content to induce vibration that can felt in typical light-weight building construction:

Hissy Spectrum (H):   A spectrum is judged to be hissy as a result of a spectral imbalance created by relatively high octave-band levels at high frequencies.

Rumbly Spectrum (R):   A spectrum is judged to be rumbly as a result of a spectral imbalance created by relatively high octave-band levels at low frequencies.

Neutral Spectrum (N):   A spectrum is judged to be neutral in character when it is neither hissy nor rumbly. This is a result of an approximate balance between the relative loudness in the low-frequency and high-frequency regions of the spectrum over the range of recommended application (RC 25 to RC 50).

Rumbly Vibration Spectrum (RV):   A spectrum is judged to produce rumbly vibration when it has the potential for producing perceptible vibration of light-weight ceilings or walls. This is a result of high levels in the octave bands centered at 16.5 and 31.5 Hz. Such vibration is considered in a following section.

How to Determine RC Ratings.   The RC rating of an HVAC noise spectrum is obtained as follows:

Step 1.   Measure the octave-band level of the noise at the following octave-band center frequencies: 31.5 Hz, 63 Hz, 125 Hz, 250 Hz, 500 Hz, 1000 Hz, 2000 Hz, and 4000 Hz. Where there is the potential for acoustically-induced vibration which is perceptible, the 16-Hz octave band must be included.

Step 2.   On the RC curves of Fig. 7.31, plot the octave-band levels of Step 1.

Step 3.   Calculate the arithmetic average, in decibels, of the octave-band levels, measured in Step 1, for the bands centered at 500, 1000, and 2000 Hz. *This value corresponds to the numerical value of the RC rating.*

Step 4.   At 1000 Hz on the plot of the data in Step 2, at the average value obtained in Step 3, draw a line which has a slope of −5 dB/octave. This line is called the *reference curve* in the following steps.

Step 5.   Draw two lines parallel to the reference curve of Step 4. (1) The first line, between 31.5 and 500 Hz, is drawn 5 dB above the reference curve. (2) The second line, between 1000 and 4000 Hz, is drawn 3 dB above the reference curve. These two lines are the permissible limits of a neutral spectrum.

Step 6.   Assign a letter designator (which serves as an indicator of the "quality" of the sound) to the RC rating determined in Step 3. This letter is assigned following the criteria of Table 7.1, i.e., as follows:

- *The letter **N** is assigned*   if the spectrum being evaluated falls entirely within the reference curve and the two parallel lines drawn in Step 5, i.e., between the reference curve and the permissible limits of a neutral spectrum—between 31.5 and 500 Hz and between 1000 and 4000 Hz.

- *The letter **H** is assigned*   if the spectrum being evaluated: (1) is at least 3 dB above the permissible limit between 1000 and 4000 Hz, *and* (2) does not exceed the octave-band levels at 500 Hz and below by more than 5 dB (i.e., lies between the reference spectrum and the permissible limit).

- *The letter **R** is assigned*   if the spectrum being evaluated: (1) is at least 5 dB above the permissible limit between 63 and 500 Hz, and (2) does not exceed the octave-band levels at 1000 Hz and above by more than 3 dB.

- *The letters **RV** are assigned*   if the spectrum being evaluated: has an octave-band level in the 16-Hz and/or 31.5-Hz octave bands which is 70 dB or higher; between 65 and 70 dB, acoustically-induced vibration is possible but is generally not a problem.

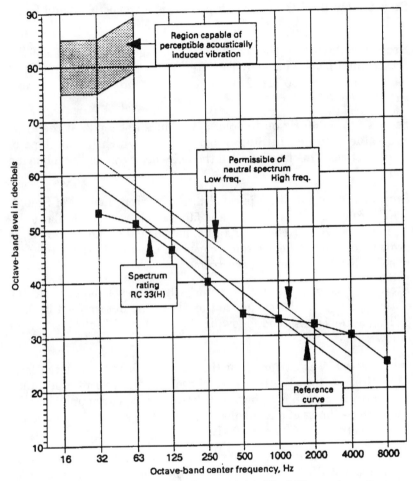

FIG. 7.32 Determining the RC rating of spectrum 1 in Fig. 7.28.

Example 7.2:   Determine the RC Rating of Spectrum 1 in Fig. 7.28.

Step 1. According to the data given in Fig. 7.28, the measured octave-band levels of the spectrum labeled *1* are: 31.5 Hz, 53 dB; 63 Hz, 51 dB; 125 Hz, 46 dB; 250 Hz, 40 dB; 500 Hz, 34 dB; 1000 Hz, 33 dB; 2000 Hz, 32 dB; 4000 Hz, 30 dB.

Step 2. Plotting the above octave-band levels on RC curves of Fig. 7.31 yields the spectrum shown in Fig. 7.32.

Step 3. The arithmetic average of the levels of the octave bands centered at 500, 1000, and 2000 Hz is $(34 + 33 + 32)\text{dB}/3 = 33$ dB. *Thus the numerical value of the RC rating in this example is 33.*

Step 4. At 1000 Hz on the plot of the data in Step 2, at the average value obtained in Step 3, draw the reference curve having a slope of -5 dB/octave, as illustrated in Fig. 7.32.

Step 5. Draw a parallel line at a level 5 dB above the reference curve, extending from 31.5 to 500 Hz, labelled "permissible limit of neutral spectrum at low frequencies." Now draw a second parallel at a level of 3 dB above the reference curve, extending from 1000 to 4000 Hz, i.e., the permissible limit at high frequencies.

Step 6. In this example, the spectrum exceeds the permissible limit of a neutral spectrum, in the octave bands above 1000 Hz, by more than 3 dB. Therefore, according to the rules given above, the appropriate letter designation is H, which is an indication of a hissy noise spectrum. Thus, the RC rating of this spectrum is RC 33(H).

Acoustically-Induced Perceptible Vibration. The shaded regions of the RC curves of Fig. 7.31, in the octave bands from 16 to 63 Hz, illustrate the frequency and amplitude ranges of octave-band sound pressure levels that may introduce perceptible vibration in the walls and ceilings of light-weight building construction. For example, Fig. 7.33 illustrates a noise spectrum having an RC rating of RC 31(RV). The spectrum of the noise greatly exceeds the assigned boundary limits, established in Table 7.11, in the octave bands at 500 Hz and below; furthermore, the sound pressure levels in the octave bands centered at 16 and 31.5 Hz are greater than 70 dB and extend well into the upper shaded region of the family of RC curves shown in Fig. 7.31. For these reasons, the spectrum is assigned a rating of RC 31(RV). (In a typical office with a suspended acoustical ceiling, a spectrum of this character would not only have an unpleasant rumbly sound but it would also be likely to induce audible rattles in lighting fixtures, air diffusers, and return air grilles.)

CRITERIA FOR ACCEPTABLE HVAC NOISE LEVELS IN ROOMS

To be acceptable, HVAC noise in a room must not prevent people from hearing sound they want to hear; furthermore, it must not be intrusive or annoying. Therefore, in an office environment, the acceptable level of background noise is generally established by requirements for speech communication, which can vary widely as a function of the type of space use. In contrast, in an auditorium, recital hall, or concert hall where the performance is unamplified, the acceptable level of background noise is generally established by the faintest sounds that are to be communicated clearly to the audience.

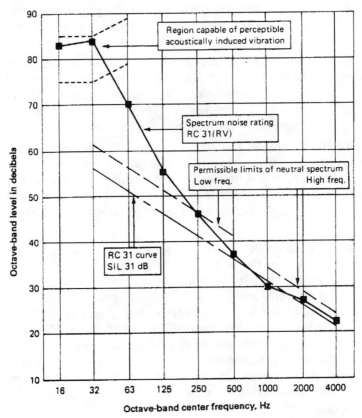

FIG. 7.33 RC rating of an HVAC spectrum capable of producing perceptible acoustically-induced vibration.

Table 7.12 provides recommended criteria for the acceptability of HVAC noise in various types of spaces in buildings. These criteria are expressed in terms of the two most commonly used procedures for noise rating, and it gives very approximate corresponding values of A-weighted sound levels. The "Preferred" column is based on the use of the RC curves; this criterion is recommended whenever the *quality* of space use dictates the need for a neutral (i.e., neither hissy or rumbly), unobtrusive background sound. The "Alternative" column is based on the use of NC curves; this criterion may be used when the quality of space use is not so demanding and can tolerate rumbly, hissy, or tonal characteristics in the background sound, *as long as it is not too loud.* However, whenever the alternative criterion is used, there is an inherently higher potential for occupant dissatisfaction.

The lower value in this table is intended for use as a goal in *system*

TABLE 7.12   Acceptability Criteria for Steady Background Noise in Unoccupied Rooms

Type of room	Recommended criterion		Approximate A-weighted sound level,* dB
	Preferred	Alternative	
Recording studios	RC 10–20(N)	NC 10–20	18–28
Concert and recital halls	RC 15–20(N)	NC 15–20	23–28
TV studios, music rooms	RC 20–25(N)	NC 20–25	28–33
Legitimate theaters	RC 20–25(N)	NC 20–25	28–33
Private residences	RC 25–30(N)	NC 25–30	33–38
Conference rooms	RC 25–30(N)	NC 25–30	33–38
Lecture rooms, classrooms	RC 25–30(N)	NC 25–30	33–38
Executive offices	RC 25–30(N)	NC 25–30	33–38
Private offices	RC 30–35(N)	NC 30–35	38–43
Churches	RC 30–35(N)	NC 30–35	38–43
Cinemas	RC 30–35(N)	NC 30–35	38–43
Apartments, hotel bedrooms	RC 30–35(N)	NC 30–35	38–43
Courtrooms	RC 35–40(N)	NC 35–40	43–48
Open-plan offices and schools	RC 35–40(N)	NC 35–40	43–48
Libraries	RC 35–40(N)	NC 35–40	43–48
Lobbies, public areas	RC 35–40(N)	NC 35–40	43–48
Restaurants	RC 40–45(N)	NC 40–45	48–53
Public offices (large)	RC 40–45(N)	NC 40–45	48–53

*A-weighted sound levels are not recommended for use in the design of HVAC systems.

design; the higher value is the recommended *limit* in specifying the performance of the system under actual operating conditions in the field.

PERCEPTIBLE VIBRATION OF PARTITIONS

Some HVAC systems produce considerable noise in the very low-frequency range (i.e., in octave-bands centered at 16, 31.5, and 63 Hz shown as the shaded region in Fig. 7.31). In this region, the low-frequency sound waves may force light-weight wall and ceiling construction into vibration. Such vibration may be perceptible to people within rooms bounded by these partitions. In fact, in light-weight partitions, it is not uncommon for HVAC systems to induce vibration levels which are 10 to 20 dB above the threshold of human perception. The effects of such vibration on people and structures is discussed in detail in Ref. 1. The acoustically induced vibration may also cause "secondary" noise radiation such as rattles in cabinet doors, pictures, ceiling fixtures, and other room furnishings in contact with the walls. In addition to the annoyance caused by such vibration, the low-frequency sound waves are also a source of annoyance since they are subject to large random or periodic fluctuations in level over short time intervals. The onset of problems of this nature usually occurs at vibration levels near, or somewhat above, the threshold of human perception.

Criterion: *To avoid noise-induced vibration in typical light-weight construction of metal studs and gypsum board, or for suspended ceilings with attached light fixtures and air terminal assemblies, and to minimize audible effects due to vibration of the surrounding partitions, in the octave bands centered at 16, 31.5, or 63 Hz, the octave-band level should not exceed 70 dB.* This criterion is the basis for the limits imposed at low frequencies, i.e., on the 16-, 31.5-, and 63-Hz octave-band sound pressure levels of the RC curves illustrated in Fig. 7.31.

Procedure for Estimating the Level in the 16-Hz Octave Band

In evaluating the probability of wall and ceiling vibration, sound pressure level data in the 16-Hz octave band are particularly important. If the octave-band analyzer being used in the measurements does not have a 16-Hz filter, the octave-band level in this octave band usually can be estimated (for a typical HVAC spectrum) as follows:

Step 1. Measure the sound pressure level of the noise spectrum with a sound-level meter/octave-band analyzer *without* frequency weighting, i.e., use the "linear" or "flat" setting.

Step 2. Measure the sound pressure level of the noise spectrum in the 31.5-Hz octave band.

Step 3. Subtract the 31.5-Hz octave-band level (Step 2) from the sound pressure level (Step 1).

Step 4. (a) If the level difference in Step 3 is less than **1 dB,** then the 16-Hz octave-band level usually is negligible. (b) If the level difference in Step 3 is **1 to 3 dB,** then the 16-Hz octave-band level is equal to, or within 5 dB of, the 31.5-Hz octave-band level. (c) If the level difference in Step 3 is **4 dB or more,** then the 16-Hz octave-band level is usually roughly the same as the sound pressure level measured in Step 1.

REFERENCES

1. L. L. Beranek, "Revised Criteria for Noise Control in Buildings," *Noise Control*, vol. 3, 1957, pp. 19–27.
2. W. E. Blazier, Jr., "Revised Noise Criteria for Application in the Acoustical Design and Rating of HVAC Systems," *Noise Control Engineering*, vol. 16, 1981, pp. 64–73.

8

Noise Control in Plumbing Systems

John J. Van Houten

INTRODUCTION

Noise is an unavoidable byproduct of plumbing systems within buildings. In multifamily and certain institutional buildings, noise generated by the operation of plumbing systems is a critical factor in architectural and mechanical design. Often it is a cause of embarrassment and annoyance, especially when heard from waste piping or when generated by a neighbor's lengthy shower late at night. When experienced by the occupants, its potential for annoyance may exceed that of other sources of noise which intrude at much higher levels.

This chapter first describes how noise is generated in plumbing systems. Next, methods of controlling each of these sources of noise is treated in detail. The sources of noise, paths along which the noise is communicated, and the control methods apply to any noise-sensitive building (commercial, theatrical, educational, medical, etc.) although emphasis is placed on multifamily residential structures such as hotels, motels, apartments, and condominiums. Finally, the chapter concludes with a checklist which will be of benefit to architects and engineers in avoiding many common plumbing noise problems.

MECHANISMS OF NOISE GENERATION IN PLUMBING SYSTEMS

Unsteady flow is usually the primary cause of noise generation in plumbing systems. It leads to noise radiation as a result of: *turbulence, cavitation, water splash, waste water flow,* and *water hammer*. In Table 8.1, these noise-generation mechanisms are related to components and equipment in plumbing systems.

TABLE 8.1   Sources of Noise in the Plumbing System of a Building, Their Generation Mechanisms, and Their Potential for Annoyance

Plumbing system component/equipment	Generation mechanism	Potential annoyance
Piping runs:		
Couplings	Turbulence	Minimal
Elbows	Turbulence	Minimal
Tees	Turbulence	Minimal
Fixtures:		
Bar sink	Cavitation/turbulence/splash/ waste flow	Minimal
Bathtub	Cavitation/turbulence/splash/ waste flow	Very significant
Bidet	Cavitation/turbulence/waste flow	Nominal
Flushometer	Cavitation/turbulence	Significant
Hose pipe valves	Cavitation/turbulence	Nominal
Laundry tubs	Cavitation/turbulence/splash/ waste flow	Nominal
Pressure regulator	Cavitation/turbulence	Nominal
Shower	Cavitation/turbulence/splash/ waste flow	Very significant
Sink	Cavitation/turbulence/waste flow	Significant
Valves	Cavitation/turbulence	Significant
Water closet, tank stool	Cavitation/turbulence/splash/ waste flow	Very significant
Urinal	Cavitation/turbulence/splash/ waste flow	Nominal
Appliances:		
Dishwasher	Vibration/cavitation/spray/ water hammer	Very significant
Drinking fountain	Cavitation/turbulence	Minimal
Washing machine	Vibration/cavitation/impact/ motor/water hammer	Very significant
Waste disposal	Vibration/waste flow	Very significant
Water heater	Cavitation/turbulence	Minimal
Supply and waste pumps:		
Booster	Rotational flow/cavitation/ motor	Significant
Recirculation	Rotational flow/cavitation/ motor	Nominal
Sewage	Rotational flow/cavitation/ motor	Significant
Sump	Rotational flow/cavitation/ motor	Significant

Turbulence

The flow of liquids in pipes generally is classified as *laminar flow* or *turbulent flow*. In laminar flow, as illustrated in Fig. 8.1*a*, the liquid moves in such a way that individual fluid particles move along paths parallel to one another and to the general direction of motion. In turbulent flow, there is an irregular, random motion of the particles in directions transverse to the direction of the main flow, as illustrated in Fig. 8.1*c*. The major factors which influence whether the flow is laminar or turbulent are (1) pipe diameter d, (2) density of the fluid ρ, (3) absolute viscosity μ, and flow velocity v. These variables are related by a dimensionless quantity known as the *Reynolds number*, which is defined as

$$R = \frac{d\, v\, \rho}{\mu} \qquad (8.1)$$

For Reynolds numbers less than about 2000, the flow is laminar. For Reynolds numbers greater than about 4000, the flow is usually turbulent. Between these two values lies a transition region in which the flow may be either laminar or turbulent, as illustrated in Fig. 8.1*b*.

Generally, noise generated by laminar flow is so low in intensity as to be of no concern, even under the most critical design conditions. In most practical plumbing systems, however, velocities are high enough to result in turbulent flow. For example, in domestic plumbing systems, typical velocities are on the order of 8 feet per second (2.5 m/s). For a standard copper pipe having an inside diameter of $^5/_8$ inch (1.6 cm) carrying water at 60°F (16°C) with the usual values of density and absolute viscosity, the flow has a Reynolds number of about 35,000. Therefore, the flow is turbulent and is a basic mechanism of noise generation within the piping runs and fixtures of the plumbing system.

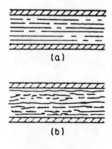

(a)

(b)

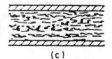

(c)

FIG. 8.1 Laminar and turbulent flow. (*a*) Laminar flow in which the flow is undisturbed; (*b*) transition region in which the flow is becoming turbulent; (*c*) turbulent flow.

Cavitation

Most of the noise in plumbing systems is usually caused by turbulent flow, but conditions sometimes exist, particularly in nearly closed valves, which give rise to the phenomenon of cavitation, which results in greatly increased noise levels. *Cavitation* is the formation and subsequent collapse of bubbles within the flow of water through and past a restriction in the flow. For cavitation to occur, a local restriction in the water flow must exist which results in localized high velocities and low pressures. At a particular velocity, the pressure is low enough so that vapor bubbles are formed. As these bubbles move past the restriction, the velocity decreases and the pressure increases, resulting in the sudden collapse of the bubbles, with extreme local pressure fluctuations which result in noise.

The cavitation phenomenon is illustrated in Fig. 8.2, which shows the pressure variation and velocity variation in a partially opened globe

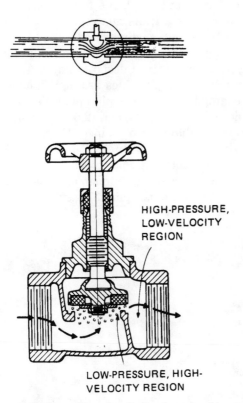

HIGH-PRESSURE,
LOW-VELOCITY
REGION

LOW-PRESSURE, HIGH-
VELOCITY REGION

FIG. 8.2   Formation of cavitation in a plumbing system containing a partially opened valve. Regions of high-velocity flow and low pressure lead to the generation of cavitation.

valve in a plumbing system. Such a variation in the pressure leads to the formation of cavitation within the flowing water. Cavitation develops downstream of the partially opened valve when the pressure at the minimum area (highest velocity) is reduced to the vapor pressure, about 0.26 psi (18 kPa) for water at 60°F (16°C). If the vapor bubbles are near or in contact with the pipe when they collapse, the forces exerted by the liquid rushing into the cavities create very high localized pressures on the pipe wall. Cavitation is accompanied both by vibration and noise. The forces exerted by the collapsing cavities may result in the pitting of the surfaces on which the cavitation occurs. Cavitation usually occurs at discontinuities within most plumbing systems, for example, at bathtub spouts, shower heads, and supply valves.

Water Splash

Water splash on sinks, bathtubs, and shower pans produces significant noise by the impact of the water as it strikes the surface. The predominant parameters in this noise-generation mechanism include:

1. The velocity of the water as it leaves the spout

2. The height of the spout above the surface

3. The size of the droplet that strikes the surface

4. The dynamic characteristics of the sink, tub, or shower pan surfaces (including: surface density, thickness, shape and size, and elastic properties)

Waste/Water Flow

The flow of waste products and water flow beyond the drain trap has an intermittent character. This is generally the case when the pipe has a long vertical run or an abrupt transition which is located in the wall of a neighboring or lower occupied space. Even though the sound level of the waste/water noise may be very low, its character may cause embarrassment and concern when experienced over the quiet background noise of a residential unit. For example, noise that is experienced in a lower-floor bedroom when a neighbor's toilet is flushed may only create a maximum sound level of 30 to 35 dB(A). However, when the sound level of the background noise is only 22 to 25 dB(A) in the room where the listener is located, the waste pipe noise will be heard clearly and will be objectionable.

Water Hammer

A sharp, intense noise known as *water hammer* occurs when steady flow in a plumbing system is suddenly interrupted, for example, by closing a quick-action valve. When the fluid is in motion throughout the whole piping system, the momentum, even at relatively low flow velocities, can be great. The sudden interruption of flow results in an extremely sharp pressure rise which propagates as a (shock) wave upstream from the valve. The steep wavefront of the excitation can be reflected numerous times back and forth through various parts of the water system until its energy is finally dissipated.

To some degree, water hammer occurs in a piping run whenever the flowing water is suddenly interrupted. Such an interruption occurs at the rapid closure of electrical, pneumatic, or spring-loaded (solenoid) valves. In residential structures, it is often experienced during wash and rinse cycles of a washing machine or dishwasher.

Plumbing Components and Equipment and Their Noise-Generation Mechanisms

Table 8.1 provides a summary of various components and pieces of equipment in plumbing systems that are sources of noise. For each, the basic mechanisms of noise generation are identified, and their potential for annoyance is indicated.

Piping Runs.   In piping runs, if the piping is in a straight line, the noise resulting from water flow is relatively insignificant. However, where there are elbows or tees and the velocity is significant, a noise problem may arise. The average flow velocity in a turn in a piping system is the same as that in a straight pipe of the same cross-sectional flow area. But because fluid recirculates in a turn, it may accelerate to a very high velocity, causing cavitation-generated noise at the higher velocity region on the inside of the turn.

Fixtures.   Fixtures such as sinks, bathtubs, showers, and toilets are predominant sources of noise which may create annoyance within buildings. The mechanism of noise generation which may penetrate the building structure involves (1) cavitation at the valves and spouts, (2) water splash on a large bathtub bottom and shower pan, and (3) the intermittent waste-water and particulate flow through, and beyond, the drain trap.

Appliances.   Appliances within a residential structure include dishwashers, washing machines, and waste disposal units. These appliances produce vibration which may be transmitted to a neighboring dwelling when the appliance is in contact with a common wall and/or placed directly on a floor separation assembly. Hence they provide a significant source of potential annoyance within a multifamily building.

Pumps.   The primary noise source of pumps involves the hydrodynamic pulsations which are inherent in all pumps. These pulsations are usually associated with the rotational speed of the pump's impeller blades. The fundamental frequency of pump noise is equal to the product of the rotational speed (in revolutions per second) and the number of blades. In addition, high-frequency pump noise results from cavitation caused by the vaporization of the water and the rapid collapse of the vapor bubbles which are shed by the impeller blades. Other sources of pump noise which may impart vibration to the pump's support structure and surrounding area include imbalanced motor bearings, the motor cooling fan, the gearbox, and an imbalanced impeller.

CONTROL OF NOISE IN PLUMBING SYSTEMS

The control of unwanted plumbing noise should be considered an integral part of building design. In addition, the building construction specifications should include minimum acceptable requirements for noise control.[1] The *checklist* that follows this section provides representative items which should be considered in the plumbing system installation specifications for multifamily and other noise-sensitive construction. These noise control elements of the design and specifications involve:

1. Water flow and piping characteristics

2. Radiation to the structure

3. Selection and mounting of fixtures

4. Pump system isolation

5. Water-hammer control

Quantitative evaluations of the performance of such plumbing installations are given in Ref. 2.

Control of Noise from Water Flow in Piping

Water Pressure.   The water pressure in a plumbing system influences the flow noise generated by the piping runs and water supply valves. According to typical building code requirements, the water system supply pressure must be at least 15 psi (100 kPa) but no greater than 75 psi (500 kPa).[3] However, for acceptable system performance, the supply pressure usually must be between 35 and 55 psi (230 and 370 kPa). To minimize the generation of noise, regulation of the supply pressure to the lower value, about 35 psi (230 kPa), is desirable. However, other factors (e.g., building size, number of floors, and number of units) significantly influence plumbing system design and the required supply pressure.

Piping. Flow noise radiation from the piping runs can be minimized by reducing the number of pipe transitions (e.g., elbows, tees, and Y connections), thus minimizing turbulence and reducing the possible occurrence of cavitation. Pipe of $1/2$-inch diameter is most common in domestic plumbing systems in the U.S.A. However, to minimize noise, $3/4$-inch-diameter pipe is selected when noise control is given a high priority in the building design. The reduction in sound level obtained by the decreased velocity may be as much as 3 to 5 dB.

Control of Noise Radiation from Piping

Pipe Isolation. Noise resulting from the flow of water in pipes may be transmitted from the piping runs to the rooms of the building if the pipes are in direct contact with large radiating surfaces (i.e., walls, ceilings, and floors). Isolation of these piping runs from the structure provides significant noise reduction. For example, a reduction of 10 to 12 dB may be obtained if piping is mounted with foam isolation instead of being rigidly connected to the building structure. Table 8.2 illustrates the various mounting methods and shows the resulting relative reduction in noise radiated from a double-studded party wall. These data show the advantage of isolating the plumbing runs from the structure.[4-7]

All plumbing components should be isolated from the building structure. Resilient material, such as neoprene or fiberglass at least $1/4$-inch (6-mm) thick should be employed wherever the piping run passes through the structure (block, stud, joist, or plate) or is in contact in any way with the wallboard or masonry. In addition, it is important to seal around the perimeter of all pipes, faucets, and spouts which penetrate the walls and floors. A resilient caulking should be applied as generously as possible. Figures 8.3 to 8.6 indicate methods of ensuring good isolation. These techniques are well worth the increased cost of the plumbing installation.

Manufactured Isolators. Manufactured pipe isolators also improve the overall quality of the plumbing installation. However, to obtain this benefit, it is absolutely essential that: (1) the isolators have a resilient material between the pipe and structure, (2) the isolators are installed as specified by the manufacturer, and, (3) there be a follow-up inspection to ensure quality control.

TABLE 8.2 Piping-Run Mounting Methods and Noise Reduction Relative to a Rigid Attachment to the Structure
The Flow Noise Is Generated by a Standard Termination Fixture.[5]

Method of pipe mounting	Illustration	Noise reduction compared with rigid mounting, dB
Wood wedges: Two wood wedges forced between the pipe and stud	Wood	0
J-hook nail-ons: ¾-in J-hook nail-on at each pipe penetration of stud	Nail-on	0
Pipe insulator/foam insert: Plastic insulator with polyethylene foam insert (experimental)	Polyethylene foam	−11
Elastic mount: Isolated from studs by a resilient strip	Resilient strip	−19

8.9

Waste/Water Flow.   When polybutylene pipe is used in long vertical waste runs within a wall separation, unacceptable noise may be experienced within adjacent occupied spaces. This noise may be minimized or even eliminated by the use of cast-iron pipe runs which are isolated from the building structure. The methods of isolation are similar to those previously discussed (see Fig. 8.3 to 8.6).

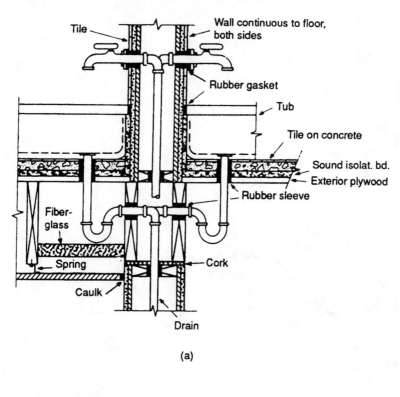

(a)

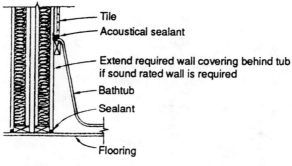

(b)

FIG. 8.3 Isolation of water supply and waste piping. (*a*) Within a party wall and floor/ceiling assembly; (*b*) detail showing isolation where bathtub or shower is adjacent to a party wall.

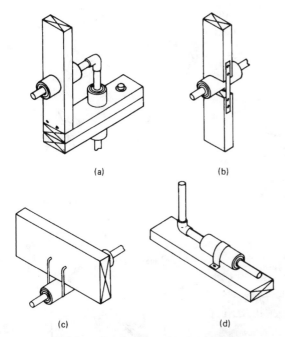

(a)   (b)

(c)   (d)

FIG. 8.4 Pipe isolation at (a) plates, (b) studs, and
(c) joists, (d) blocking by use of fiberglass jacketing or
neoprene pads in wood construction.

Pipe Lagging or Jacketing. Pipe lagging or jacketing, as shown in Figs.
8.7 and 8.8, is common in large commercial and industrial plumbing
systems, mainly as thermal insulation. When used for noise control,
reductions in sound level of approximately 6 to 10 dB may be
obtained when the lagging is properly applied. In general, the lagging
should consist of a foam or fiberglass insulation material covered with
an aluminum metal jacket $1/16$- to $1/8$-inch (1.5- to 3-mm) thick,
secured by adhesive or tape. A water-resistant mastic may be used in
place of the metal jacket; however, the thickness of the mastic should
provide a surface weight equal to the metal jacket application. Figure
8.8 shows an insulated pipe supported by a clevis hanger. The insulation reduces the sound transmission to the hanger and therefore to
the structure to which the hanger is attached.

Plumbing Wall Chase. Enclosing pipes within a pipe chase can be beneficial in controlling the propagation of noise radiated by piping.
Plumbing chases should be laid out with adequate space to ensure that
piping runs can be supported *so they are not in direct contact with the
walls of the pipe chase.* It is essential that this separation be maintained. For example, while a $2^{1}/_2$-inch (6.5-cm) waste pipe may be isolated within a 2- by 4-inch (5- to 10-cm) stud wall, a 3- to 4-inch (7.5- to
10-cm) waste pipe requires a correspondingly thicker wall construction.

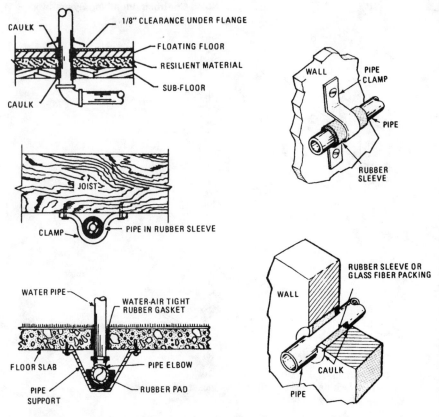

FIG. 8.5 Various techniques for isolating a pipe from the structure which supports it.

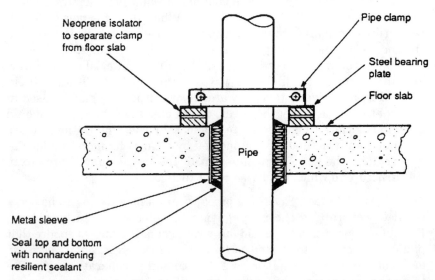

FIG. 8.6 Isolation of plumbing (waste and large-diameter supply piping) which penetrates a floor slab. (*After R. S. Jones.*[9])

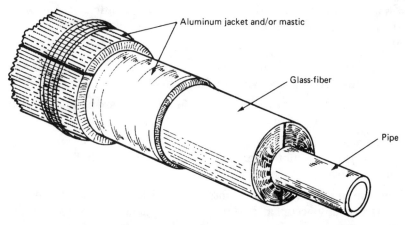

FIG. 8.7 Lagging or jacketing of pipe run to minimize the transmission of noise due to water flow. Mastic, if used in place of metal jacket, should have a thickness such that the surface weight is equal to that of a metal aluminum jacket, $^1/_{16}$ to $^1/_8$ inch (1.5 to 3 mm). Fiberglass insulation should be 1 to 2 inches (25 to 50 mm) thick, depending on the pipe diameter, and should have an insulation density of 3 to 5 pounds per cubic foot (50 to 80 kg/m^3).

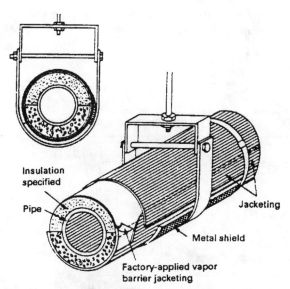

FIG. 8.8 An insulated pipe supported by a clevis hanger. The premolded fiberglass sleeve reduces the transmission of noise to the hanger and therefore to the structure which supports the hanger.

Low-Noise Fixtures. The following guidelines should be considered when selecting valves (see Chap. 11 of Ref. 1) and taps for the water supply:

- *Ball valves* are excellent for no-flow applications since they provide a straight-through flow with a minimum of turbulence.

- *Water taps* that incorporate an aerator in the spout may provide noise reductions up to 15 dB.[7]

- *Gate valves* offer practically no resistance to flow when fully opened; they are not recommended for throttling or flow modulation.

- *Globe valves* are ideal for throttling service; however, where close throttling may occur, as is the case for most valves, excessive noise will be generated.

Isolation of Fixtures and Appliances. The radiation of water splash noise generated by the impact of water on the bottom of a tub or shower pan may be minimized by isolation of the assembly from the wall and floor structure. Hence, bathtubs and shower pans should be set on resilient pads. Drywall should be installed and fitted as needed to form a well-sealed party wall assembly prior to the installation of the bathtubs and/or shower stalls. Water closets and stools should be isolated from the structure (for example, as in Figs. 8.9 and 8.10). Flexible hoses should be used to connect the appliances (e.g., dishwashers and washing machines) to the water-supply and waste-pipe runs.

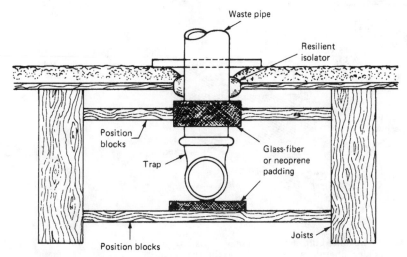

FIG. 8.9 Isolation of the stool or toilet fixture waste pipe to minimize the transmission of noise to the building structure.

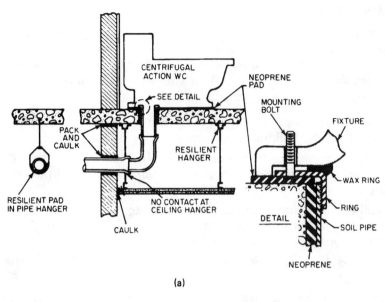

(a)

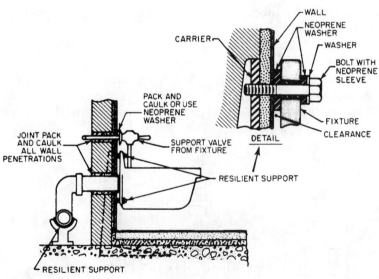

(b)

FIG. 8.10 (*a*) Isolation of a toilet for quiet operation. (*b*) Isolation of a sink from the structure which supports it. A detail is shown of a method of attachment that does not negate the mechanical isolation which is provided. (*After Ref. 6.*)

Control of Pump System Noise

The control of pump system noise may be achieved by the proper iso-lation of the pump, its support system, and associated piping and electrical services. This may be accomplished by the use of commercial hardware. The noise control measures included in the pump system design usually include the following:

1. Vibration isolators to support the pump and motor, thereby isolating it from the building structure
2. Flexible connectors between the pump and motor and associated piping and electrical connections, as described in Chap. 9 and shown in Fig. 8.11
3. Resilient hangers to support the piping from the overhead structure or resilient supports to attach the piping to walls or floors as illustrated in Figs. 8.12 and 8.13
4. Isolation of the piping where it penetrates the building walls or floors
5. Inertia blocks, described in Chap. 9, as one of the elements in the support system for the pump, motor, and the piping and electrical connections

Water-Hammer Noise Control

The destructive forces associated with water hammer may cause ruptured piping, leaks, weakened connections, damaged valves, etc.[8] Water-hammer pulsations associated with washing machines and

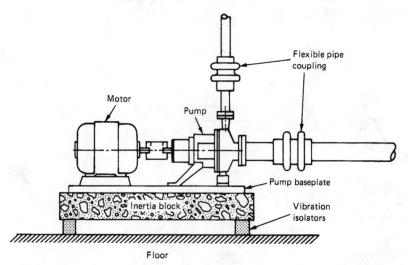

FIG. 8.11 Isolation of a pump system (on an inertia block) from the building structure.

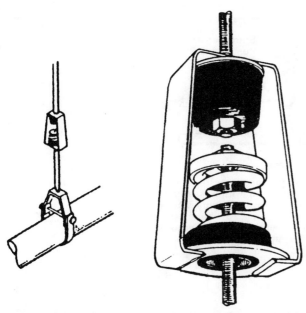

FIG. 8.12 Pipe isolation from a ceiling, by the use of a hanger with a vibration isolator which is a combination of a metal spring and an elastomer. (*Courtesy of Mason Industries.*)

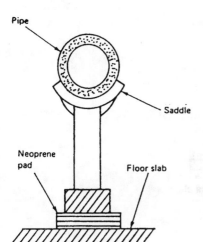

FIG. 8.13 Isolation of a pipe which is supported by a saddle on a neoprene pad.

dishwashers may be partially damped by connecting such machines to the water supply with an extra-long hose. Water-hammer arresters are considered advisable. In some building types they are required where polybutylene water distribution tubing is used in the plumbing system. Such tubing may burst when subjected to the sudden pressures generated by water hammer. Consideration should be given to

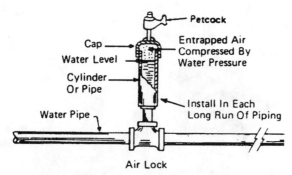

Petcock

Cap

Water Level

Cylinder
Or Pipe

Water Pipe

Entrapped Air
Compressed By
Water Pressure

Install In Each
Long Run Of Piping

Air Lock

FIG. 8.14 A capped pipe-nipple that serves as a water-hammer arrester. The volume of air within it is used to cushion the shock generated by water hammer. Should the air within the pipe-nipple be replaced with water, the petcock provides a means of venting; when opened, the water is released so the pipe-nipple is again able to serve as a water-hammer arrester.

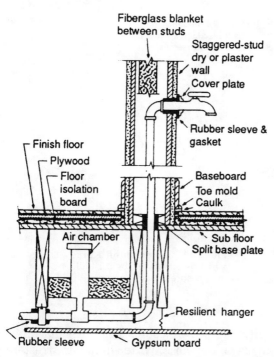

Fiberglass blanket
between studs

Staggered-stud
dry or plaster
wall

Cover plate

Finish floor

Plywood

Floor
isolation
board

Rubber sleeve &
gasket

Baseboard

Toe mold

Caulk

Air chamber

Sub floor
Split base plate

Resilient hanger

Rubber sleeve   Gypsum board

FIG. 8.15 A water-hammer arrester incorporated in a water line in a resiliently-hung ceiling. Note that the piping is isolated by resilient elements to minimize the transfer of noise to the structure.

their installation where there are solenoid or other quick-closing valves in the system.[3]

Figure 8.14 illustrates the use of a capped pipe which provides an air chamber for water-hammer suppression. The length of the pipe nipple is 12 to 24 inches (30 to 60 cm) long and may be of the same or larger diameter than the line it serves. The volume of the air chamber required to serve as an "air cushion" depends on the nominal pipe diameter, the branch line length, and the supply pressure. For example, $1/2$-inch (12.5-mm) pipe, 25 feet (7 to 8 m) in length, operating at a supply pressure of 60 psi (400 kPa) requires an air chamber having a volume of 8 cubic inches (130 cm^3). If the air chamber becomes filled with water, it will be ineffective. Commercial devices (called *water-hammer arresters*) that perform essentially the same function are not subject to this limitation because a metal diaphragm separates the air from the water. The arrester should be mounted near quick-acting valves. If such a valve is closed quickly, it generates a "shock wave" which propagates upstream in the piping. Water-hammer arresters should also be installed at the ends of long pipe runs. Isolation of the piping from the structure will minimize the transfer of noise to the structure, as illustrated in Fig. 8.15.

CHECKLIST FOR GOOD NOISE CONTROL PRACTICE IN PLUMBING SYSTEM DESIGN

The following checklist provides a useful supplement to the design principles described earlier. (*A* = affordable; *M* = moderate; and *L* = luxury.)

System Design

A   Water velocity shall not exceed 6 feet per second (2 m/s), and pipe size shall be adjusted for this maximum velocity.

A   Waste and water supply pipes shall not be installed in any walls enclosing bedrooms, living rooms, studies, or other rooms where privacy and quiet surroundings are essential.

A   Vertical drain pipes shall not be installed within bedroom walls or on the exterior wall of bedroom areas.

A   Restrictions on shower heads shall be used to limit the flow to less than 3 gallons per minute (0.2 L/s).

A   The number of pipe transitions (elbows, tees, Y connections, etc.) shall be minimized.

A   Regulators shall be installed as required to ensure that the water pressure is no greater than 50 psi (344 kPa) in main water supply lines.

A   Water-hammer arresters shall be placed close to quick-acting valves and shall be installed at the ends of long pipe runs. Quick-acting valves are associated with such appliances as washing machines and dishwashers.

M   All waste pipe shall be cast iron.

L   Plumbing penetrations on opposite sides of a sound-rated partition assembly shall be separated by a minimum distance of about 16 inches (40 cm).

Noise Control Items

A   Toilets, bathtubs, and shower pans in upper-floor units shall be set on resilient pads (e.g., neoprene or rubber).

A   Washing machines, dryers, and dishwashers in upper-floor units shall be placed on neoprene pads on isolation mounts as specified by the appliance manufacturer.

A   Tubs, showers, toilets, wash basins, and faucet fixtures shall be isolated from the supporting walls by means of resilient gaskets.

A   Voids between the wall, floor, and tub/shower units shall be completely filled with fiberglass insulation.

M   Flexible hose couplings for inlet and outlet water connections on washing machines shall be used so that no rigid connection exists with the building structure.

M   Flexible electrical (BX) cable shall be used with electrically operated pumps so that no rigid connection exists with the building structure.

M   Flexible connectors shall be used to couple the water pumps to the plumbing system.

L   Waste piping in noise-sensitive locations shall be wrapped in either (a) $1/32$-inch (0.8-mm) thickness of sheet lead, or (b) lagging consisting of foam or fiberglass insulation material covered with an aluminum metal jacket at least $1/16$-inch (1.6-mm), secured by adhesive or tape.

L   Large-diameter waste and supply pipes shall be (a) boxed in gypsum board enclosures and lined with open-faced fiberglass material or (b) enclosed in thick fiberglass jackets having a minimum density of 6 pounds per cubic foot (96 kg/m^3) and a minimum thickness of 3 inches (7.6 cm), with a heavy, impervious outer covering of plastic or leaded vinyl material weighing at least 1 pound per square foot (4.9 kg/m^2).

L   Spa-type or whirlpool-type tubs in upper-floor units shall be seated in $1/4$-inch (0.6-cm) neoprene. All pumps and blowers shall be isolated from the tub and floor/ceiling assembly by use of commercially available vibration isolators which have a minimum of $1/2$-inch (12-mm) static deflection.

Architectural Design

A   Fiberglass insulation shall be installed in spaces between joists (a) where a plumbing pipe penetrates a floor/ceiling assembly or (b) where such a pipe passes through the plane of the floor/ceiling assembly from within a wall. The insulation shall be installed to a point at least 16 to 24 inches (40 to 60 cm) beyond the pipe.

A   The stud bay or joist cavity surrounding the supply and waste piping shall be filled with open-faced fiberglass.

A   The floor/ceiling separation assembly beneath a tub and/or shower assembly shall be constructed consistent with the floor/ceiling specifications—in regard to noise control requirements.

A   The party wall behind a tub and/or shower assembly shall be constructed consistent with the party wall specifications in regard to noise control requirements. Wallboard shall be installed behind all tubs and/or showers which are adjacent to party walls.

M   Where waste piping and/or water supply piping is placed within a party wall of gypsum board construction, the party wall shall be constructed with two layers of gypsum board on each side, two rows of studs separated by at least 4 inches (10 cm), and a minimum of $3\frac{1}{2}$-inch (9- cm) insulation batts in both stud bays.

M   Where waste piping and water supply piping of an upper-floor unit is required in interior partition walls of the unit below, the partition wall shall be constructed of (a) 2- × 6-inch (5- × 15-cm) wood studs on a 2- × 6-inch (5- × 15-cm) plate, (b) one layer of fiberglass batts which completely fill the spaces between the studs, and (c) two layers of $\frac{5}{8}$-inch (16-mm) Type X gypsum board on each side of the partition.

Isolation

A   Waste piping and water supply piping shall be isolated from the building construction at points of contact with resilient sleeves, vibration isolators, or a minimum of $\frac{1}{4}$-inch (65-mm) of resilient material such as soft neoprene, rubber, felt padding, carpet, and carpet padding.

A   At locations where a pipe penetrates a wall construction, the size of the hole shall be kept to a minimum, but in no case shall the pipe make physical contact with the wall construction. The space around the pipe shall be filled with a resilient material and caulked so that there is a complete seal between the pipe and wall construction.

A   In residential housing, resilient hangers shall be used to support piping within horizontal runs.

M   Vertical drain pipes on the outside wall of a residential unit shall be structurally isolated from the building by inserting soft rubber or neoprene sleeves or collars around the drainpipes where they are supported by the wall.

L   Common water-supply piping directly across party walls shall not be permitted.

Equipment

A   Select plumbing valves of the ball-type which exhibit minimum noise when in use.

A   All faucets and taps shall have fully ported nozzles and be equipped with aeration or antisplash devices.

REFERENCES

1. C. M. Harris (ed.), *Handbook of Utilities and Services for Buildings,* Chap. 10, "Specifications," McGraw-Hill, New York, 1990.
2. *Research Project on Plumbing Noise in Multi-Dwelling Buildings, Project 177.891,* Canada Mortgage and Housing Corporation, Ottawa, 1990.
3. *Uniform Plumbing Code,* International Association of Mechanical and Plumbing Officials, Walnut, CA 91789-2825, 1988.
4. *A Guide to Airborne, Impact and Structureborne Noise Control in Multifamily Dwellings,* National Bureau of Standards, Washington, DC, 1963.
5. J. Hedden, *Plumbing for Old and New Houses,* Creative Homeowner Press, Upper Saddle River, NJ, 1980.
6. R. D. Berendt and E. L. R. Corliss, *Quieting: A Practical Guide to Noise Control,* National Bureau of Standards Handbook 119, Washington, DC, 1976.
7. *ASPE DataBook,* Chap. 15, American Society of Plumbing Engineers, Westlake, CA 91362, 1981–1982.
8. *Water Hammer Arresters,* The Plumbing and Drainage Institute, Indianapolis, IN, 1983.
9. R. S. Jones, *Noise and Vibration Control in Buildings,* McGraw-Hill, New York, 1984.

9

Part 1: Control of Mechanical and Electrical Noise*

Colin G. Gordon
Cyril M. Harris

INTRODUCTION

Part 1 of this chapter discusses general methods of noise control that are useful in reducing mechanical and electrical equipment noise and that do not require modification or redesign of the equipment itself. These methods usually fall into one of two classifications:

1. *Techniques Which Reduce Airborne Noise Transmitted through the Air, from the Source to a Listener:* These methods include the use of enclosures around the equipment (e.g., either complete enclosures or partial enclosures) and the application of sound-absorptive materials as described in Chap. 4.

2. *Techniques Which Reduce Structureborne Noise Originating as Vibration or Impacts at the Source and Which Are Communicated through the Building Structure:* Such vibration or impacts may travel as structureborne noise for long distances within a building. Therefore, it is important to reduce significantly the energy that is imparted by such equipment to the building structure.

Part 1 of this chapter first provides a checklist for the practical solution of common noise problems in buildings. It then describes how an enclosure around a sound source (both complete enclosures and partial enclosures) may be used to considerable advantage in noise control in buildings. Then, noise reduction by the application of vibration-damping materials is described. Finally, Part 1 concludes with

---

*References for Part 1 appear at the end of Part 1.

an example illustrating the process of developing a cost-effective solution to a noise problem.

Part 2 of this chapter describes the principles of vibration isolation, types and characteristics of vibration isolators used to prevent equipment vibration from being communicated to the building structure, the selection of vibration isolators for the usual vibration problems encountered in buildings, and practical considerations in installing vibration isolators.

CHECKLIST OF METHODS FOR CONTROLLING EQUIPMENT NOISE

Often the most effective method of solving a mechanical or electrical equipment noise problem is the obvious one of replacing the piece of equipment with a similar unit which produces less noise and/or vibration. Many times, this is neither economical nor practical. Then, the following noise control techniques should be considered, where appropriate. In this checklist, references are given to other chapters where more detailed information is provided:

1. Move noisy equipment to a new location in the building—farther from the area where quiet is required (Chap. 1).
2. Surround the noisy equipment with a partial or complete enclosure.
3. Line the interior of the enclosure with a sound-absorptive material.
4. Seal any openings that permit noise to "leak" around the edges of the enclosure or through the walls of the enclosure.
5. Connect ventilation openings in the walls of the enclosure either to ducts lined with sound-absorptive material or to sound attenuators.
6. Install acoustical material on the ceiling (and possibly on the walls) of the room containing the noisy equipment. This will reduce the noise level in the room, as indicated in Eq. (4.4).
7. Provide a solid acoustical barrier to shield, deflect, and (if faced with sound-absorptive material) absorb the noise that would otherwise be communicated from noisy equipment to a listener.
8. Apply wrapping or "lagging" (e.g., a preshaped layer of fiberglass with a heavy outer impervious cover, as in Fig. 8.7) to the exterior surfaces of pipes or ducts connected to noisy equipment; this will reduce the radiation of noise from these surfaces.
9. Mount equipment on vibration isolators to reduce the transmission of vibration from this equipment to the floor on which it is mounted. (See Part 2 of this chapter.)

10. Insert flexible connectors, of the type shown in Fig. 9.21, between vibrating equipment and pipes, ducts, conduits, or cables which are connected to it, as illustrated in Fig. 9.11.
11. Isolate the pipes, ducts, conduits, or cables from the surfaces on which they are mounted so that these surfaces are not set into vibration.
12. Install an inertia block under machinery that is mounted on vibration isolators, where appropriate, as illustrated in Fig. 8.11.
13. Apply vibration-damping materials to the housing of the equipment if the housing vibrates. (For example, to reduce the radiation of noise, vibration-damping material is routinely applied to the housings of dishwashers, washing machines, and the interiors of the hoods and trunks of automobiles.)
14. Reduce the "unbalance" of rotating machinery as described in Chap. 39 of Ref. 1. *Balancing* is a procedure for evenly distributing the mass of a rotor.

Many of these noise control techniques are applied in the example shown in Fig. 9.1; the numbers in this illustration correspond with the numbers in the above checklist. Figure 9.2 illustrates further application of these methods of noise control; correct and incorrect methods of mounting a water pump are illustrated.

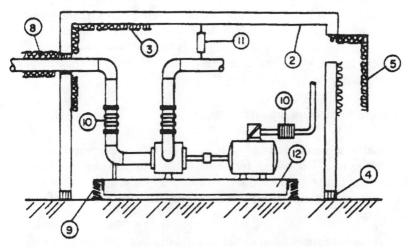

FIG. 9.1   Application of various noise control techniques to a piece of equipment that acts as a noise source. The numbers correspond with the numbers in the checklist. (*After Ref. 2.*)

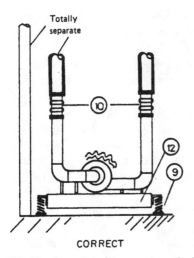
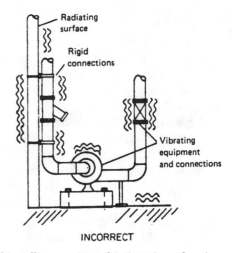

CORRECT   INCORRECT

FIG. 9.2 Correct and incorrect methods of installing a noisy, vibrating piece of equipment. The numbers correspond with the numbers in the checklist. (*After Ref. 2.*)

ENCLOSURES AROUND SOURCES OF NOISE

A well-designed enclosure around a noise source can be highly effective in reducing the level of noise in the surrounding areas. This section considers: (1) how much noise reduction can be provided by an enclosure which completely surrounds the source, (2) the effects of openings in the enclosure (for example, to provide ventilation for equipment within) in diminishing the noise reduction provided by the enclosure, and (3) the noise reduction provided by an enclosure which only partially surrounds a noise source. It is assumed throughout *this section* that the noise source is isolated from the floor so that noise is communicated to the listener only through the air.

A Complete Enclosure around a Noise Source

An enclosure, which completely surrounds a noise source, reduces the noise level around the source by **containing** and **absorbing** a significant fraction of the acoustic energy radiated by the source. For example, at the same point in a room, compare the sound levels for two conditions:

1. For the noise source open to the room (i.e., there is no enclosure)

2. For the noise source surrounded by an enclosure which has heavy, solid walls with no sound-absorptive lining

The difference between these two sound levels represents the noise reduction which is provided. In the typical example considered here, the difference is approximately 15 dB(A)). The accompanying footnote provides details on how the noise reduction varies with frequency.*

Now suppose a similar comparison is made—but this time the interior of the enclosure is lined with an efficient sound-absorptive material. In this case, the noise reduction is typically about 30 dB(A). The sound-absorptive material has increased the noise reduction by 15 dB(A). Because the acoustical lining can provide significant noise reduction at relatively little cost, wherever possible the interior of a solid enclosure around a noise source should be lined with sound-absorptive material.

Rules for Selecting the Sound Insulation Value of the Walls of an Acoustically Lined Enclosure:

- If the Enclosure Is Completely Lined with a Sound-Absorptive Material: The walls of the enclosure should have an STC rating at least 10 higher than the required noise reduction.

- If the Enclosure Is Partially Lined with a Sound-Absorptive

---

*In this example, Fig. 9.3 shows a comparison of the octave-band levels at the position of a listener in the vicinity of a noise source in a room for the following conditions:
1. For the noise source without an enclosure
2. For the noise source surrounded by a solid-wall enclosure in which there is no sound absorption
3. Same as Condition 1 but with the enclosure lined with a sound-absorptive material
4. For the noise source surrounded by a porous enclosure

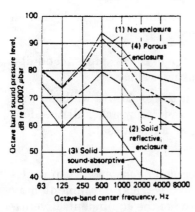

FIG. 9.3 The octave-band levels at the position of a listener for various type of enclosures.

The noise reduction provided in any octave band is the difference between the octave-band level for the noise source without an enclosure (i.e., Condition 1) and the specific condition for which a comparison is desired.

Material: The walls of the enclosure should have an STC rating at least 15 higher than the required noise reduction.

■ If the Enclosure Is Not Lined with a Sound-Absorptive Material: The walls of the enclosure should have an STC rating at least 20 higher than the required noise reduction.

Porous Enclosures. No significant noise reduction is provided by an enclosure constructed of a porous material. As explained in Chap. 5, a layer of porous material is ineffective in providing sound insulation because sound is communicated, from one side of the layer to the other side, through the pores. In the example considered here, the porous enclosure provides a noise reduction of less than 3 dB(A). Therefore, any type of enclosure having porous walls should be avoided.

Effect of Openings in an Enclosure Completely Surrounding a Noise Source

How "Sound Leaks" Degrade the Noise Reduction Provided by Enclosures. Suppose an enclosure completely surrounds a noise source, but there are cracks around the bottom edges of the enclosure. As shown in Fig. 5.5, such cracks greatly reduce the enclosure's effectiveness. Similarly, holes in the walls of the enclosure, which may be provided for ventilation, significantly decrease the noise reduction provided by the enclosure. For example, if the total area of the cracks and/or holes is equal to 1 percent of the area of the walls of an enclosure, the noise reduction provided by the lined enclosure cannot be greater than 20 dB(A) (assuming that the noise source radiates uniformly in all directions) no matter how massive the walls are.

To minimize the degradation of noise reduction caused by sound leaks, the following steps should be taken:

■ Seal all openings around the perimeter of ducts, pipes, conduits, cables, etc., which penetrate the enclosure walls.

■ Provide gaskets on all access doors in the enclosure walls so that the doors fit tightly; install locking handles which pull the door tight to the gasket, thereby providing an airtight seal.

The Use of Lined Ducts on Enclosures Requiring Ventilation. An enclosure around an item of mechanical or electrical equipment may require ventilation to prevent overheating of the equipment. If ventilation is provided by openings in the walls of the enclosure, as illustrated in Fig. 9.4a, the openings will substantially diminish the noise reduction provided by the enclosure. This effect may be mini-

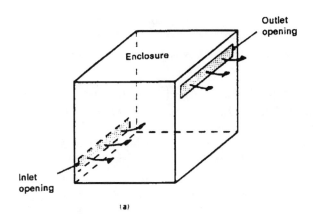

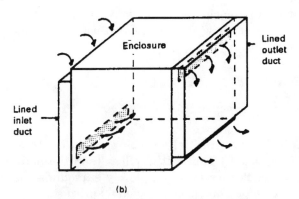

FIG. 9.4   Schematic drawing of an enclosure which is pene-
trated by ventilation openings. (*a*) Untreated air-inlet and
air-outlet openings; (*b*) openings with ducts lined with
sound-absorptive material.

mized by the use of lined ducts connected to the openings, as shown
in Fig. 9.4*b*.

Consider the following example. A noise source is contained within
an enclosure in which air-inlet and air-outlet openings have been cut
to provide ventilation. Each opening is 7 inches (18 cm) high, 36 inches (100 cm) wide, and is fitted with a sheet-metal duct 36 inches
(91 cm) long that is lined with fiberglass 1 inch (2.5 cm) thick.

Compare the sound levels (at a given distance from the source) for
the following conditions:

1. No enclosure
2. A lined enclosure having air-inlet and air-outlet openings (but
   without the ducts) as illustrated in Fig. 9.4*a*

3. An enclosure having lined ducts attached to the openings of condition 2, as illustrated in Fig. 9.4*b*

4. A lined, completely sealed enclosure with no air-inlet or air-outlet openings

The difference in sound levels between Conditions 1 and 2 represents the noise reduction provided by the enclosure with ventilation openings but no lined ducts. In this example, an attenuation of only about 15 dB(A) may be expected because of the ventilation openings—far below the 30 dB(A) quoted in the earlier example for the completely sealed enclosure. When lined ducts (Condition 3) are added, the noise reduction is increased by an additional 13 dB(A), providing almost the same noise reduction as the completely sealed enclosure shown as condition 4. The accompanying footnote provides detailed information describing how this noise reduction varies with frequency.[†]

If a fan is required within an enclosure to provide greater ventilation, a quiet fan should be selected so that it does not contribute significantly to the noise in the room.

PARTIAL ENCLOSURE AROUND NOISE SOURCES AND BARRIERS

Partial Enclosures

The noise reduction provided by a partial enclosure, such as one of those shown in Fig. 9.6, is usually substantially less than the noise reduction provided by an enclosure that completely surrounds the noise source. However, such a partial enclosure usually provides more

---

[†]In this example, Fig. 9.5 shows the octave-band levels at the position of the listener for each of the four conditions described in the text.

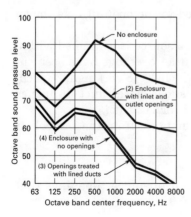

FIG. 9.5 Octave-band spectra at the position of a listener for different treatments of ventilation openings in an enclosure.

(a)

(d)

(b)

(e)

(c)

(f)

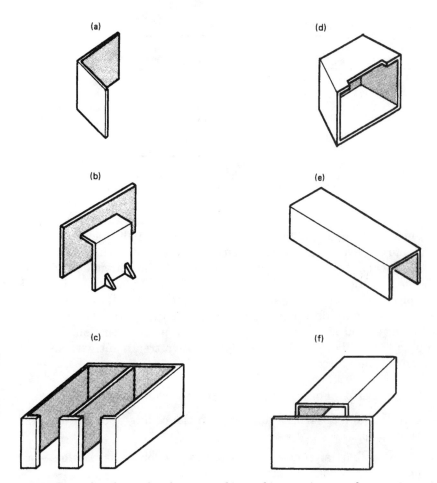

FIG. 9.6   Examples of partial enclosures used in machinery noise control.

noise reduction than a simple barrier which is intended to "shield" a listener from a noise source in a room. In indoors situations where the listener is far enough from the noise source so that direct sound is negligible compared to the reflected sound, the noise reduction provided by a partial enclosure, which is completely lined with sound-absorptive material, depends on the extent to which it surrounds the source. If the enclosure surrounds 50 percent of the source, a noise reduction of 3 dB(A) may be provided; if the enclosure surrounds 75 percent of the source, a noise reduction of 6 dB(A) may be provided. Other conditions and corresponding noise reductions are shown in Table 9.1. For these same conditions, if the partial enclosure is not lined with a sound-absorptive material, it will be almost totally ineffective.

TABLE 9.1   Effectiveness of a Partial Enclosure*

Sound energy enclosed and absorbed, %	Maximum achievable noise reduction, dB
50	3
75	6
90	10
95	13
98	17
99	20

*These values are based on the assumption that the source radiates uniformly in all directions and that the partial enclosure which surrounds it is fully lined with a sound-absorptive material.

Consider the partial enclosures shown in Fig. 9.6. Enclosures **a, b,** and **c** provide a noise reduction roughly equivalent to that of the solid barrier which is lined with sound-absorptive material as described in the next section. Enclosure **c** in combination with an acoustical ceiling provides a noise reduction similar to that provided by lined barriers in an open-plan office, as discussed in Chap. 10. Partial enclosures **d, e,** and **f,** in general, provide more noise reduction than the simple barrier because the sound-absorptive treatment extends over the top of the source.

Rules of thumb: For any type of partial enclosure:

- Install sound-absorptive material on the ceiling and nearby walls of the room.

- Place the partial enclosure as close to the source as possible—but not in contact with the source.

- Extend the partial enclosure beyond the line-of-sight of the source—both vertically and horizontally.

- Line the partial enclosure with sound-absorptive material having a noise reduction coefficient (NRC) of at least 0.8.

- Select a material for the partial enclosure (with no openings or holes) having a sound transmission class (STC) at least 10 dB higher than the required noise reduction and with a minimum STC value of 20 dB.

Barriers

Consider a barrier which separates a noisy piece of equipment from a listener in a room, as illustrated in Fig. 9.7 (also see Fig. 10.19 for the application of barriers in open-plan offices). In this example, as in the

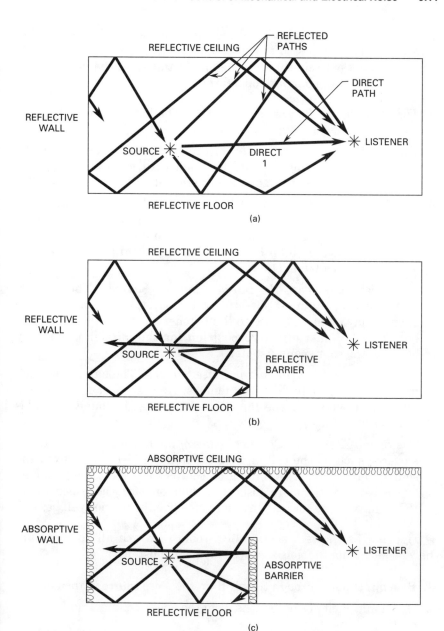

FIG. 9.7 A "ray diagram" showing the airborne paths of sound propagation between a noise source and a listener in a room. (*a*) All surfaces of the room are hard and reflective; there is no barrier between the noise source and listener. (*b*) All surfaces of the room are hard and reflective; there is a solid reflective barrier between the noise source and the listener. (*c*) Sound-absorptive material has been applied on the ceiling and wall surfaces and on the side of the barrier facing the noise source.

previous ones, it is assumed that the noise source is mounted on effective vibration isolators so that the sound which the listener hears is communicated entirely through the air. In this case, the noise reduction provided by the barrier depends on:

- *The Material the Barrier Is Made Of:*   The barrier should be solid (i.e., not porous) or have a solid center core.

- *The Acoustical Characteristics of the Barrier Surface Facing the Source:*   This surface should be lined with a sound-absorptive material having a noise reduction coefficient (NRC) of at least 0.8.

- *The Height and Width of the Barrier:*   The higher and wider the barrier, the greater its effectiveness. The barrier should completely block the line-of-sight between the source and listener. The barrier should have a minimum height of 5 feet (1.7 m) and a minimum width of at least 6 feet (1.8 m).

- *The Distance between the Barrier and the Source:*   The smaller this distance, the more effective the barrier. (Alternatively, the barrier may be placed close to the listener as shown in Fig. 9.7. In general, the least effective position for the barrier is midway between the source and listener.)

- *The Frequency Spectrum of the Noise Source:*   The barrier is much more effective at higher frequencies. At the lower frequencies, sound will bend over the top of the barrier and around the sides because of diffraction.

- *The Sound-Absorptive Characteristics of the Room Surfaces:*   Room surfaces such as the ceiling and walls may reflect noise from the source to the listener into the area that is supposed to be protected by the barrier—the more absorptive the room surfaces (especially in the vicinity of the source), the more effective the barrier will be.

Figure 9.7a shows a section of a room in which all surfaces are hard; sound from the noise source travels to a listener:

1. By a direct path through the air from the noise source to the listener

2. By a multiplicity of reflections from the walls, ceiling, and floor

In Fig. 9.7b, the solid barrier has some effect in reducing the sound traveling to the listener. In Fig. 9.7c, sound-absorptive material has been installed on the "source-side" of the barrier, as well as on the ceiling and walls. Under these conditions, the reflections are greatly reduced, and maximum noise reduction can be achieved.

A noise reduction of 10 dB(A) can reasonably be expected from a barrier that is well designed and properly installed.‡

VIBRATION ISOLATION

Vibration isolators (also called *vibration mounts*) are used to control (1) *vibration,* such as that produced by rotation of a pump, and (2) *mechanical shock,* such as that produced by the impact of a punch press bolted to the floor of a building. Part 2 of this chapter describes the principles of vibration isolation, properties of vibration isolators, and how to select and install vibration isolators.

Consider a machine, a source of vibration, which has been mounted on vibration isolators. This vibration isolation may be seriously compromised by mechanical connections (such as cables, conduit, and piping) connected to it. For this reason, it is essential to employ flexible elements which permit the isolated equipment to vibrate without transmitting this vibration through the mechanical elements to the building structure, as illustrated in Fig. 8.11. Note that in this illustration, the equipment is mounted on an "inertia block," a heavy mass on vibration isolators which may be effective in reducing the magnitude of vibration of the machine on its isolators and in helping stabilize the machine by lowering its center-of-gravity.

---

‡A comparison of the octave-band levels, at the position of a listener, is given in Fig. 9.8 when only direct airborne sound is significant (i.e., there are no nearby reflecting surfaces) for the following conditions: (1) no barrier, (2) porous barrier composed of a sound-absorptive material such as fiberglass, (3) solid, reflective barrier—such as gypsum board or sheet metal, and (4) solid, reflective barrier of Condition 3 above, lined with a sound-absorptive material on the side facing the source.

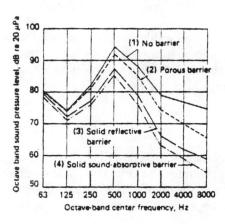

FIG. 9.8   Octave-band levels at the position of a listener for various types of barriers between the listener and the noise source.

The effectiveness of vibration isolation in providing noise reduction in a room depends on whether or not the noise which reaches the listener is primarily structureborne or airborne. In the former case, vibration isolation can be very effective; for example, a noise reduction of 10 dB(A) may be obtained. In contrast, if most of the noise reaches the listener by a direct airpath (as is often the case near the source), then the noise reduction provided by the vibration isolation may be only a few decibels. In most cases, when some type of enclosure surrounds (or partially surrounds) a source, it is necessary to mount the noise source on vibration isolators to achieve the full noise reduction potential of the treatment.

APPLICATION OF DAMPING TREATMENT

The vibration of large, relatively thin, sheet-metal panels which house mechanical and electrical equipment, such as washing machines, dishwashers, refrigerators, heating units, air-conditioners, and office equipment, often results in the generation of considerable noise. Such vibration often can be reduced effectively by the use of vibration damping. *Damping* is the removal of mechanical energy from a vibrating system (such as a vibrating panel) usually by converting the energy of vibration into heat. Although all materials exhibit some inherent damping, metal surfaces often require the application of a damping material in order to deaden them sufficiently for noise reduction purposes. Several general types of commercial damping materials are readily available (for example, many automobile supply stores carry vibration damping materials for application on automobile bodies). Of these, the most widely used are mastics which may be troweled or sprayed onto the metal surface. Commercial damping materials are also available in the form of self-adhesive sheets or tapes.

Damping materials can provide considerable noise reduction if they are applied to panels that form cabinet-like enclosures for machines or if applied to the backside of surfaces that are subject to impacts from hard objects, as is the case in refuse chutes.

How Much Damping Is Required? Where?

A typical damping material of the mastic type usually is applied in a thickness which is between $1/2$ and 2 times the thickness of the panel. To be most effective, the damping material of this type must be well bonded to the panel and should be applied where the amplitude of vibration of the panel is greatest (usually somewhere near the center of the panel); it is least effective where vibration of the panel is not significant (usually along the edges of a fixed panel). However, since some materials of this type are relatively inexpensive, it is not unusual for damping material to be applied over most of the panel surface. See Chap. 37 of Ref. 1 for further details.

COST-EFFECTIVE SOLUTIONS TO NOISE CONTROL PROBLEMS IN BUILDINGS

The transmission of noise in buildings, for example from mechanical or electrical equipment to a listener, usually can be represented by a diagram of the type illustrated in Fig. 1.4 in which there are three major components: (1) the noise **source,** (2) the **path** along which noise or vibratory energy travels, and (3) the **listener** who is exposed to the noise. This section first considers these components in terms of an example of a typical office noise problem illustrated in Fig. 9.9. Then, an outline is given of the steps that can be taken to obtain a cost-effective solution.

Source

In the example described here, the source of disturbance is a copying machine in an office. This machine has several distinct sources of noise:

- Sound energy radiated as airborne noise from the housing of the copying machine

- Sound energy radiated as airborne noise from the openings in the housing through which the copying machine is ventilated

- Vibratory energy (structureborne noise) communicated through the feet of the copying machine to the floor on which it rests, and then propagated along the building structure

Each of these sources will have different characteristics in terms of its magnitude and frequency spectrum. For example, ventilation noise produced by the machine is typically dominated by aerodynamic noise associated with the ventilation fan and with the flow of air through filters, dampers, and other constrictions. Noise radiated by the machine's housing may be due to a combination of effects, including excitation of the housing by mechanical equipment and transformers. Sources of structureborne energy are often associated with the dynamic unbalance of rotating equipment such as motors and fans.

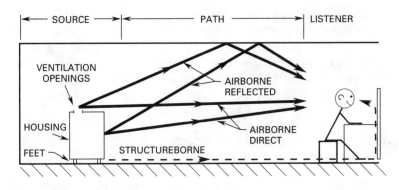

(a) THE PROBLEM

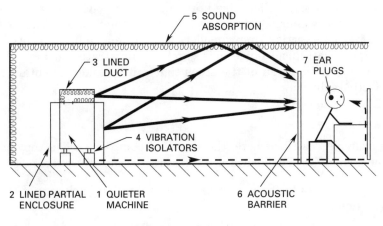

(b) POSSIBLE SOLUTIONS

FIG. 9.9 Schematic diagram of (*a*) a noisy copying machine in the same office as an employee; no noise control measures have been applied. In (*b*), various noise control measures are applied to provide acceptable conditions at the listener's position.

Path

Three paths of noise propagation, from the source to the listener, are illustrated in Fig. 9.9*a*:

1. *Airborne Direct:* Noise radiated by the housing and by the ventilation openings travels through the air to the listener by a direct path, i.e., without reflections from any room surface.
2. *Airborne Reflected:* Noise radiated by the housing and by the ventilation openings travels through the air to the listener by a

reflected path, i.e., by a path that involves reflection from one or more surfaces of the room. Although there may be a number of such reflected paths (as illustrated in Fig. 9.7), for simplicity, only a single reflected path is shown for each of the two airborne noise sources.

3. *Structureborne:*   Vibration travels through the feet of the copying machine along the floor, and sets partitions, furniture, etc. into vibration. Additional airborne noise is then radiated from these vibrating surfaces.

The efficiency with which each of these paths transmits noise to the listener depends upon a number of factors, including: the distance between the source and the listener, the characteristics of the room surfaces (for example, the sound absorptivity and geometry), and the characteristics of the floor structure (e.g., its mass per unit area and its stiffness). The efficiency of each path also depends on the frequency characteristics of the noise sources.

Listener

The listener in Fig. 9.9 is assumed to be an office worker. In other situations the listener may be the occupant of a dwelling, a factory worker, etc. Alternatively, the "listener" could be a delicate item of equipment, such as an electron microscope whose operation can be affected adversely by noise and vibration.

Developing a Cost-Effective Solution

Chapter 1 indicated that two quite different approaches may be used in solving noise control problems: (1) the empirical approach, and (2) the analytical approach. The latter method is considered here.

To find a solution to a typical noise problem in a building, take the following steps:

Step 1.   Determine the contribution of the noise that is propagated along each of the paths between the source and the listener. Detailed information describing methods of carrying out this and subsequent steps are given in Appendix 9.1.

Step 2.   Select a design goal.

Step 3.   Obtain the required noise reduction by taking the difference between the values determined in Steps 1 and 2.

Step 4.   Evaluate the various options that are available for achieving the required noise reduction determined in Step 3. In arriving at an economical solution, both the direct costs and the indirect costs should be considered.

In the example of Fig. 9.9a, the walls, ceiling, and floor are bare and reflective. To provide work conditions that are acceptable at the position of the listener, the following noise control measures can be applied, as illustrated in Fig. 9.9b, where the numbers correspond to those in the following list:

1. Replace the present copying machine with a newer, quieter model.
2. Surround the machine with a partial enclosure which is acoustically lined, of the type illustrated in Fig. 9.6.
3. Add ducts lined with sound-absorptive material to the ventilation openings for the machine.
4. Mount the machine on vibration isolators.
5. Install sound-absorptive materials in the room—for example, on the ceiling and one of the end walls, as shown in Fig. 9.6b.
6. Erect an acoustical barrier, *close to the listener,* to provide a measure of shielding from the airborne sound, as described earlier in this chapter.
7. Supply the listener with ear plugs.

Three possible solutions are considered in Table 9.2. As indicated, Solution 3, which consists of the application of Measures 3, 4, and 5, not only provides the most economical solution but also provides additional benefits.

TABLE 9.2   Results of Hypothetical Noise Control System Analysis of Fig. 9.9b

Solution	Control measure	Direct cost, dollars	Comments
1	1	10,000	New machine also more efficient but takes 6 months for delivery
2	2 + 3 + 4	6,000	Treatment of the ventilation openings and the housing may pose ventilation and access problems. Minimal vibration isolation is required
3	3 + 4 + 5 + 6	4,000	Satisfies all operational requirements and provides beneficial room absorption. Minimal treatment now required for ventilation openings. No treatment required for housing.

APPENDIX 9.1   OCTAVE-BAND ANALYSIS

The noise contribution along each of the paths between the noise source and the listener (shown in Fig. 9.9a) may be evaluated in terms of octave-band sound levels, as illustrated in Fig. 9.10. (In this

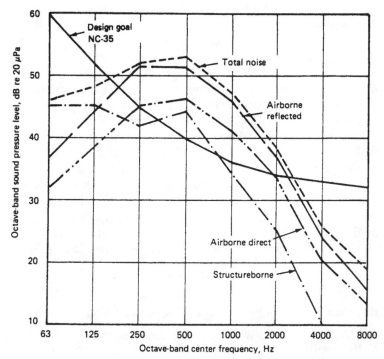

FIG. 9.10 Octave-band spectra for the noise control problem illustrated in Fig. 9.9.

example, it is assumed that the ambient noise is sufficiently low to be disregarded.)

In this illustration, *Total noise* represents the octave-band spectrum at the position of the listener when the equipment is in operation before any noise control measures are introduced, i.e., as in Fig. 9.9*a*.

Airborne reflected represents the octave-band spectrum at the position of the listener when both the "airborne direct" and the "structureborne" paths have been eliminated. The first of these two paths may be eliminated by temporarily installing a barrier which effectively shields the source from the listener; the second of these two paths may be temporarily eliminated by setting the copying machine on vibration isolators.

Airborne direct represents the octave-band spectrum, at the position of the listener, when sound transmission along the "airborne reflected" and "structureborne" paths have been eliminated. For example, the "airborne reflected" path may be eliminated by covering all surfaces of the room with a highly absorptive material; the "structureborne" path may be eliminated, as before, by temporarily setting the copying machine on vibration isolators.

Structureborne represents the octave-band spectrum, at the position of the listener, when all airborne paths have been eliminated. As an alternative to eliminating the airborne paths, vibration measurements on surfaces close to the listener can be used to estimate the contributions due to the structureborne path, from the relationship between surface vibration and the resultant sound radiation.[2]

Design goal defines the noise control objective; it represents the octave-band spectrum that is the objective to be achieved. Its value depends on the nature of the equipment, on the environment in which it is located, and on the nature of the requirements. In general, the design goal may be an octave-band noise spectrum that is required to meet (1) a government regulation, (2) a local noise ordinance, or (3) an accepted standard for comfort and speech communication. Here a design goal of NC 30 (selected from Table 7.12) is shown in Fig. 9.10.

REFERENCES

1. C. M. Harris (ed.), *Shock and Vibration Handbook,* 3d ed., McGraw-Hill, New York, NY 10020, 1988.
2. C. M. Harris (ed.), *Handbook of Acoustical Measurements and Noise Control,* 3d ed., p. 32.29, McGraw-Hill, New York, NY 10020, 1991.

Part 2: Selection and Applications of Vibration Isolators*

John J. Heintzel

Harry L. Hain

INTRODUCTION

Vibration isolators (also called *vibration mounts*) are used to control (1) *vibration,* such as that produced by rotation of a pump, and (2) *mechanical shock,* such as that produced by the impact of a punch press bolted to the floor of a building. Part 2 of Chap. 9 describes how to reduce significantly the vibratory energy that is imparted to a building structure by mechanical and electrical equipment. A brief description is given of: (1) the principles of vibration isolation, (2) the types and characteristics of vibration isolators, (3) the selection of isolators for the usual vibration problems encountered in buildings, and (4) practical considerations in the installation of isolators. An example is then given of the isolation of mechanical and electrical equipment.

Vibration isolators which are properly selected and installed can permit equipment to function as intended and can lengthen the life of the equipment. Isolation of machinery vibration also can provide a more comfortable environment within a building.

VIBRATION ISOLATION PRINCIPLES

Consider the motor shown in Fig. 9.11 which is mounted on vibration isolators. Mechanical imbalances of the rotating motor result in forces

---

*References for Part 2 appear at the end of Part 2.

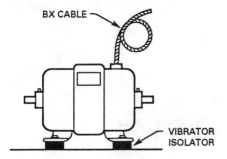

BX CABLE

VIBRATOR
ISOLATOR

FIG. 9.11   A motor mounted on vibration isolators.

which tend to move the motor. If the vibration isolators are properly selected, the forces which are transmitted in the vertical direction to the floor of the building will be significantly less than they would be if the motor were bolted directly to the floor. More complicated vibration problems in which there is significant horizontal motion, as well as rotation or rocking motion, are discussed in detail in Ref. 1.

Stiffness of a Vibration Isolator

Suppose a vibration isolator acts as an ideal spring, as is the case with many isolators over a limited range of motion. According to Hooke's law, if it is subject to a force F acting along its length, the change in length of the spring x is proportional to the force acting on it, that is:

$$F = k\,x \tag{9.1}$$

where k is a constant of proportionality called the *stiffness* (or *spring constant*) of the spring. In U.S. Customary units, the stiffness of an isolator is expressed in pounds per inch. In SI units, the stiffness of an isolator is expressed in newtons per meter or newtons per millimeter.

Static Deflection of an Isolator; Total Deflection

Figure 9.12*a* shows a schematic representation of a vibration isolator which has no load on it. Figure 9.12*b* shows the same isolator after a mass m has been placed on it. In this case, the isolator is compressed; the amount of compression is the *static deflection* δ_{st} given by

$$\delta_{st} = \frac{mg}{k} = \frac{W}{k} \tag{9.2}$$

where g represents the acceleration of gravity, and W is the weight of the mass on the isolator.

The total deflection (i.e., displacement) of a vibration isolator is the sum of the static deflection of the isolator and its deflection resulting

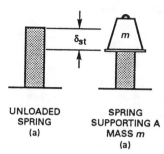

UNLOADED
SPRING
(a)

SPRING
SUPPORTING A
MASS m
(a)

FIG. 9.12 (*a*) A vibration isolator in the form of an ideal spring which has no load on it. (*b*) The same spring after a mass *m* has been placed on it. In this case, the spring is compressed by an amount δ_{st}—the static deflection.

from vibratory motion. The displacement of vibration isolators must be kept within acceptable limits. The displacement limit will depend on the characteristics of a given installation and on the type of isolators. If this limit is exceeded, rocking of the isolated equipment or premature failure of the vibration isolators may result. To prevent excessive motion, some vibration isolators incorporate *snubbers* which limit the motion of a vibration isolator. Snubbers which limit the motion in the vertical and horizontal directions are illustrated in Fig. 9.13. In the event of isolator failure (for example, as a result of a strong earthquake), a *fail-safe vibration isolator* provides support, in place, until the failed isolator can be replaced. This feature is provided by a positive metal-to-metal interlock.

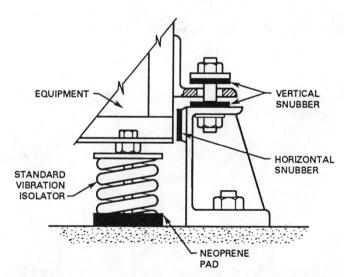

EQUIPMENT

VERTICAL
SNUBBER

HORIZONTAL
SNUBBER

STANDARD
VIBRATION
ISOLATOR

NEOPRENE
PAD

FIG. 9.13 A vibration isolator provided with auxiliary elastomeric "snubbers" to limit the motion of the isolator in the horizontal and vertical directions; these snubbers provide a "cushioned" stop to provide a lower shock force on the equipment than would be experienced with a metal-to-metal stop.

Natural Frequency of an Isolated Mass

Suppose the motor shown in Fig. 9.11 is at rest; then it is displaced from its position of equilibrium and released. It will then oscillate up and down about its equilibrium position with decreasing amplitude until it is once again at rest. The more rapid the decreasing amplitude (i.e., the more rapidly the motor comes to rest), the greater is said to be the *damping* in this moving system. The number of times per second the mass vibrates about its equilibrium position, after being displaced, is called its *natural frequency* f_n expressed in hertz (Hz) or cycles per second. In U.S. Customary units,

$$f_n = \frac{[k \ g/W]^{1/2}}{2\pi} \qquad (9.3a)$$

where k is the stiffness of the isolators in pounds per inch, W is the weight of the rigid body in pounds, and g is the acceleration of gravity in inches per second per second. In SI units:

$$f_n = \frac{[k_1/m]^{1/2}}{2\pi} = \frac{[k_2/(1000m)]^{1/2}}{2\pi} \qquad (9.3b)$$

where k_1 is the stiffness of the isolators in newtons per meter and k_2 is the stiffness in newtons per millimeter; m is the mass of the rigid body in kilograms. Substituting Eq. (9.2) in Eq. (9.3) yields

$$f_n = \frac{3.13}{(\delta_{st})^{1/2}} \qquad (9.4a)$$

where δ_{st} is the static deflection in inches. In SI units:

$$f_n = \frac{15.8}{(\delta_{st})^{1/2}} \qquad (9.4b)$$

where δ_{st} is the static deflection in millimeters. This relationship is shown graphically in Fig. 9.14.

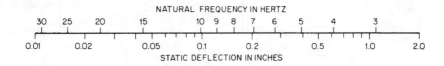

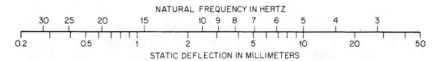

FIG. 9.14 Relation between natural frequency f_n and static deflection δ_{st} for a mass mounted on vibration isolators.

Transmissibility

Consider a rotating motor mounted on vibration isolators, as in Fig. 9.11. The *transmissibility* T of this system is equal to the ratio between: (a) the force transmitted to the floor when vibration isolation is employed and (b) the force which would be transmitted if the vibrating mass were rigidly attached to the floor. Where the damping is not significant, as is the case in many practical vibration problems, the transmissibility is given approximately by

$$T = \frac{1}{(f/f_n)^2 - 1} \qquad (9.5)$$

where f is the *forcing frequency* (also called the *disturbing frequency,* or *frequency of excitation*); f_n is the natural frequency of the vibrating system. Frequency is expressed in hertz (abbreviated Hz) or cycles per second (abbreviated cps). For example, if the static deflection of a mass on isolators is 0.066 inch (1.67 mm), then according to Eq. (9.4) or Fig. 9.14, its natural frequency is 12.2 Hz. If the forcing frequency is 30 Hz, then according to Eq. (9.5), the value of T is 0.2.

Vibration Isolation Efficiency

When vibration isolators are properly selected and applied, the value of the transmissibility T at the critical forcing frequencies is less than 1, so that the use of vibration isolators will be beneficial. Assuming that the vibration isolators rest on a rigid supporting structure, the vibration reduction (i.e., the isolation efficiency in percent) is given by

$$\text{isolation efficiency} = 100(1 - T) \qquad \text{percent} \qquad (9.6)$$

For example, if T is 0.2, the isolation efficiency is 80 percent. This equation shows that for an isolator system to be highly effective in reducing vibration, the value of T must be very much less than 1. A small value of T may be obtained by making the natural frequency f_n of the vibrating system low compared with the forcing frequency f. This is illustrated in Table 9.3, which shows the ratio of f/f_n that is required to achieve different isolation efficiencies. These values are obtained from Eqs. (9.5) and (9.6). Note that the ratio f/f_n must be greater than $(2)^{1/2}$ (that is, 1.41) in order to effect any reduction in vibration.

If the value of f/f_n is less than $(2)^{1/2}$, T will be greater than 1. Then, there is an *increase* in amplitude of vibration, rather than a reduction; also, the forces transmitted to the floor are *increased* instead of being reduced. If the ratio f/f_n is equal to 1, the amplitude of motion would be infinite if it were not for mechanical damping of the isolators; this condition is known as *resonance*. In this magnification region, damp-

TABLE 9.3   Ratio of (f/f_n) Required to Achieve Various
Values of Vibration Isolation Efficiency

Isolation efficiency, %	Maximum transmissibility	Required f/f_n
90	0.1	3.32
80	0.2	2.45
70	0.3	2.08
60	0.4	1.87
50	0.5	1.73
40	0.6	1.63
30	0.7	1.56
20	0.8	1.50
10	0.9	1.45
0	1.0	1.41

ing is particularly important in limiting the amplitude of motion. Resonance should be avoided by selecting the natural frequency f_n of the system, given by Eq. (9.3), so that it is much lower than the forcing frequency f; it should be lower by at least a factor of 2.

Vibration Isolation Efficiency Chart.   Figure 9.15 provides a means of determining vibration isolation efficiency graphically for a known value of either the natural frequency or static displacement of a mass on vibration isolators (shown along the horizontal axis). For example, if the static displacement is 0.066 inch, and the forcing frequency (shown along the vertical axis) is 30 Hz, then the isolation efficiency is 80 percent. The use of this chart is restricted to applications in which the structure supporting the vibration isolators is rigid.

Figure 9.15 also can be used to determine the required static deflection as follows: Enter the chart at the forcing frequency. Then project a horizontal line to the desired percentage reduction in vibration. From that intersection, project a vertical line to the required static deflection of the isolators.

Combinations of Vibration Isolators

Isolators in Parallel.   Consider the three vibration isolators shown in Fig. 9.16a. A number of vibration isolators are said to be in *parallel* if the load placed on the isolators is divided among them, as shown in Fig. 9.16b. If the stiffness of *each* of n isolators is represented by k, the stiffness of the combination is given by

$$\text{stiffness of } n \text{ isolators in parallel} = n\,k \qquad (9.7)$$

Thus, if a mass is supported on three identical isolators, as in Fig. 9.16b, the stiffness of this combination is 3 times the stiffness of a single isolator.

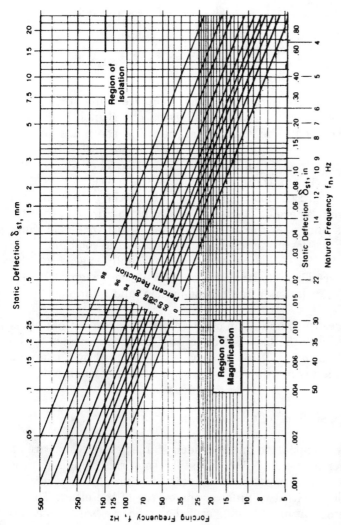

FIG. 9.15 Isolation efficiency chart. The vibration isolation efficiency is given as a function of natural frequency of the isolated system (along the horizontal axis) and the forcing frequency, i.e., the frequency of excitation (along the vertical axis). The use of this chart is restricted to applications where the vibration isolators are supported by a floor structure having a vertical stiffness of at least 15 times the total stiffness of the isolation system. This may require that the isolated structure be placed along the length of a floor beam or that an additional floor beam be added to the structure. (*Lord Corporation.*[4])

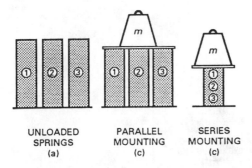

FIG. 9.16 Schematic diagram of: (a) Unloaded springs; (b) spring in parallel; (c) springs in series.

UNLOADED
SPRINGS
(a)

PARALLEL
MOUNTING
(c)

SERIES
MOUNTING
(c)

For example, suppose that when a mass is placed on a spring having a stiffness k, there is a static deflection of 0.3 inch (7.6 mm). According to Eq. (9.4), the natural frequency of the mass on this spring is 6 Hz. Now suppose this same mass is supported by three springs, each of stiffness k, as shown in Fig. 9.16b. They are equally spaced in relation to the center-of-gravity of the mass, so that each carries only one-third the load. According to Eq. (9.7), their combined stiffness is 3 times as great. Therefore, according to Eq. (9.2), the static deflection is only one-third as great, that is, 0.1 inch (2.5 mm). From Fig. 9.14, the resulting natural frequency of the combination is approximately 10 Hz. If the isolators are not equally spaced in relation to the center-of-gravity, then the motion of the system will be a combination of translation (straight-line motion) and rotation.

Isolators in Series. A combination of a number of vibration isolators is said to be in *series* if the load is transmitted from one isolator to the next as illustrated in Fig. 9.16c. If a mass is supported by n isolators in series, each having a stiffness k, the stiffness of the combination is given by

$$\text{stiffness of } n \text{ isolators in series} = \frac{k}{n} \qquad (9.8)$$

Thus, if a mass is supported on three identical isolators which are on top of each other as in Fig. 9.16c, the stiffness of this combination is one-third the stiffness of a single isolator. It is for this reason that many people sleep with two pillows, one on top of the other. This is because this combination is half as stiff (i.e., twice as "soft") as a single pillow.

For example, suppose that when a mass is placed on a spring having a stiffness k, there is a static deflection of 0.3 inch (7.6 mm). According to Eq. (9.4), the natural frequency of the mass on this spring is 6 Hz. Now suppose this same mass is supported by three identical springs which are on top of each other. According to Eq. (9.7), their combined stiffness is one-third as great. Therefore, according to Eq. (9.2), the static deflection is 3 times as great, i.e., 0.9 inch (23 mm). From Fig. 9.14, the resulting natural frequency of the combination is approximately 3.3 Hz. Similarly, suppose that when a mass is placed on a rubber pad (which entirely supports it), there is static deflection δ_{st}. If the mass is now supported on three such pads, one on top of the other (or if the pad is 3 times as thick), the static deflection will now be $3\delta_{st}$. According to Eq. (9.8), their combined stiffness is one-third as great.

TYPES OF AND CHARACTERISTICS OF VIBRATION ISOLATORS

Vibration isolators are available in a variety of materials, shapes, sizes, and load-carrying capacities. The best material for the fabrication of a vibration isolator depends, to a large extent, on the physical characteristics required of the isolator; it also depends on *environmental conditions,* including the *ambient temperature,* which may affect the expected life and performance of the vibration isolator.

Hundreds of types of vibration isolators are available for use in isolating equipment which is installed in buildings. The most widely used vibration isolators usually fall into one of three classifications: elastomeric isolators, metal coil springs, or resilient pad isolators (or some combination thereof). A number of these types are illustrated in Fig. 9.17.

Elastomeric Isolators

An *elastomeric material* is one which has rubber-like properties, such as natural rubber or neoprene. In general, the maximum deflection of a vibration isolator which incorporates an elastomer is about $1/2$ inch (12.7 mm).

Elastomeric material that is subject to sunlight, corrosive chemicals such as oil or gasoline, or severe mechanical shock may lose its physical integrity or experience a change in its operating characteristics.

The performance of vibration isolators also may be affected by extremes in temperature. At low temperatures, elastomers become harder and stiffer and are more highly damped. At high temperatures, they become softer, have a lower stiffness, and exhibit less damping. Furthermore, exposure of most natural rubber and common synthetic elastomers to temperatures below 20°F (−7°C) or above 120°F (49°C) for prolonged periods may affect the life of the material.

Metal Coil Springs

Coil springs (also called *helical springs*) are springs that are commonly used where the static deflection required is large, for very heavy

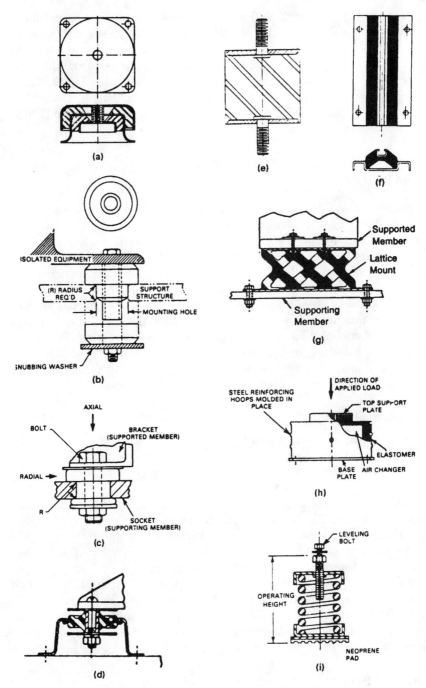

FIG. 9.17

FIG. 9.17 Typical examples of the large number of types of commercially available vibration isolators: (a) Unbonded cup-type isolator. *Features:* A fail-safe design that can be used in tension, compression, or shear with equal performance; load ratings from 8 to 1800 lb (3.6 to 816 kg); natural frequency at the rated load, as low as 12 Hz. (b) Semi-bonded general-purpose isolator. *Features:* A fail-safe design that can be used in all attitudes; load ratings from 40 to 4600 lb (18 to 2090 kg); natural frequency at the rated load, as low as 10 Hz; radial-to-axial dynamic stiffness ratio approximately equal to 1. (c) General-purpose, center-bonded isolator. *Features:* A low-cost, compact one-piece construction of fail-safe design; load ratings from 75 to 2100 lb (34 to 954 kg); natural frequency at the rated load, as low as 9 Hz; radial-to-axial dynamic stiffness ratio approximately equal to 1. (d) Bonded plate-form isolator. *Features:* A low-cost fail-safe isolator that is provided with a snubber; load ratings from 0.5 to 310 lb (0.2 to 140 kg); natural frequency at rated load, as low as 7 Hz. (e) Sandwich-type isolator; cylindrical or rectangular shapes available. *Features:* A low-cost isolator which is easy to install; fabricated with threaded studs or internal threads; load ratings from 1 to 1680 lb (0.45 to 763 kg) in shear, and 7 to 13,400 lb (3 to 6084 kg) in compression; natural frequency at the rated load, as low as 4 Hz in shear, and as low as 10 Hz in compression. (f) Elastomeric channel-type isolator. *Features:* Bonded construction with built-in vertical snubbers; load rating from 50 to 400 lb (23 to 182 kg); natural frequency at the rated load, down to 7 Hz. (g) Elastomeric lattice-type isolator. *Features:* Bonded construction; load ratings from 300 to 4000 lb (136 to 1816 kg); natural frequency at the rated load, as low as 3.2 Hz; low stiffness in vertical direction combined with lateral stability. (h) General-purpose elastomeric pneumatic isolator. *Features:* A compact design which provides automatic leveling and zero static deflection under load; load ratings from 25 to 19,200 lb (11 to 8700 kg); natural frequency at the rated load, as low as 3 Hz; nearly constant natural frequency over rated load range; radial-to-axial dynamic stiffness ratio of 1. (i) Metal coil spring isolator. *Features:* A low-cost isolator, usually with a leveling bolt, that can provide large static displacements; load ratings from 10 to 12,400 lb (4 to 5630 kg); natural frequency at the rated load, as low as 2.5 Hz; often is provided with an elastomeric pad to improve vibration isolation at high frequencies.

loads, and where the temperature or other environmental conditions make elastomers unsuitable. An example of this type of spring is shown in Fig. 9.17i; the load is applied along the axis of the coil. This is the most widely used vibration isolator in buildings for heavy loads. Systems using such springs (fully-loaded) commonly have natural frequencies as low as 2 Hz; the static deflection of such a system is about 2.4 inches (61 mm). For such a large static deflection, the spring must have adequate lateral stability or the mounted equipment will tip to one side. For a given natural frequency, the degree of lateral stability depends on the ratio of coil diameter to working height. Coil springs can transmit high-frequency energy along the metal coils. For this reason, they are usually used in combination with an elastomeric pad which provides the required high-frequency attenuation, as illustrated in Fig. 9.13.

Resilient Pads

Resilient pads are usually cut from a resilient material (such as neoprene or cork) and are used flat. For example, cork is often used to support relatively large concrete foundations. Fiberglass, of density which is appropriate for the load imposed on it, also is used for this purpose (see Floating Floors, Chap. 6). Numerous other materials compounded in slab form are used under machinery for vibration isolation.

HOW TO SELECT VIBRATION ISOLATORS

Vibration Isolator Selection Process

Step 1. Required isolation efficiency. First, indicate the percentage of isolation efficiency that is desired. In general, an efficiency of 70 to 90 percent is desirable and is usually possible to attain.

Step 2. Transmissibility. From Eq. (9.6) or Table 9.3, determine the maximum transmissibility T of the system at which the required vibration isolation efficiency of Step 1 will be provided.

Step 3. Forcing frequency. Determine the value of the lowest forcing frequency f (i.e., the frequency of vibration excitation). For example, in the case of a motor, the forcing frequency depends on the rotational speed, given in revolutions per minute (rpm); the rotational speed must be divided by 60 seconds/minute to obtain the forcing frequency in Hz (cycles per second). The *lowest* forcing frequency is used because this is the worst condition, resulting in the lowest value of f/f_n. If a satisfactory value of isolation efficiency is attained at this frequency, the vibration reduction at higher frequencies will be even greater.

Step 4. Natural frequency. From Eq. (9.5), find the natural frequency f_n of the isolated system (i.e., the mass of the equipment supported on isolators) required to provide a transmissibility T (determined in Step 2) for a forcing frequency of f Hz (determined in Step 3).

Step 5. Static deflection. From Eq. (9.4) or Fig. 9.14, determine the static deflection δ_{st} required to provide a natural frequency f_n of Step 4.

Step 6. Stiffness of isolation system. From Eq. (9.3), calculate the stiffness k required to provide a natural frequency f_n determined in Step 4.

Step 7. Stiffness of the individual vibration isolators. Determine the stiffness of each of the n isolators from Eq. (9.7) or Eq. (9.8) depending on whether the vibration isolators are in parallel or in series. In general, they are in parallel so that the required stiffness of each vibration isolator is $(1/n)$ times the value obtained in Step 6— assuming that all isolators share the load equally.

Step 8. Total load to be supported by all vibration isolators. Determine the total load that must be supported by the isolators.

Step 9. Load on individual vibration isolators. Now calculate the load on each individual isolator. In most practical vibration isolation problems in buildings, the isolators are in parallel and the total load of Step 8 is divided equally among all isolators. Then, the load per isolator is equal to the total load (Step 8) divided by the number of isolators. Do not specify isolators having a significantly greater load-carrying capacity than required. *Overspecification* is the practice of arbitrarily specifying much more severe requirements than will be met in actual practice, for example, specifying that the vibration isolators must be able to carry a much greater load than will ever be imposed on them. Such overspecification may be done under the false assumption that it is desirable to provide a high margin of safety regarding maximum load capacity of the isolators. If this is done, the vibration isolators will be much too stiff, so that the static deflection of the isolators will be too small, thereby resulting in less vibration reduction than required.

Step 10. Isolator selection. From a manufacturer's catalog, select a vibration isolator which meets the stiffness requirement determined in Step 7 and which has a load-carrying capacity (i.e., load rating) equal to the value obtained in Step 9. The preferred approach is to use the same type and size isolator at all points of support; choose isolator locations such that static loads (and thus deflections) are equalized. If this is not practical, isolators of different load ratings may be required at different support points on the equipment. If the vibration occurs only in one direction, usually a simple isolator can be selected; its characteristics need be specified along only one axis. In contrast, if the vibration is expected to occur along more than one direction, then the selected isolator must provide isolation along all the critical axes.

It is important to ensure that the building structure that supports the isolator is rigid. For example, if the roof of a building supports a "packaged rooftop air-conditioning unit," it is advisable to minimize the static deflection of the roof resulting from the load of this packaged unit by following the recommendations presented in Chap. 7, Part 1.

Example: Isolate an electric motor and pump which are rigidly mounted on a rectangular base. The weight of the assembly and base is 140 lb (63 kg). Four isolators are to support the load—one at each corner of the base. Here, the center-of-gravity is located near the base, directly below the center of the motor. The lowest forcing frequency is 1800 rpm, but there also are higher forcing frequencies due to magnetic forces and pump forces. Although there is vibration excitation in both the horizontal and vertical directions, the isolators permit movement primarily in the vertical direction. The objective in this example is to reduce the amount of vibration transmitted to the floor by 80 percent, i.e., to achieve an isolation efficiency of 80 percent.

solution

Step 1. A vibration isolation efficiency of 80 percent has been specified.

Step 2. From Eq. (9.6), a transmissibility T of 0.2 is needed to achieve a vibration isolation of 80 percent at the lowest forcing frequency.

Step 3. The value of the lowest forcing frequency in hertz (cycles per second) is obtained by dividing 1800 rpm by 60 seconds/minute, yielding a value of $f = 30$ Hz.

Step 4. Next, from Eq. (9.5), using $T = 0.2$ and $f = 30$ Hz, the natural frequency f_n equals 12.2 Hz.

Step 5. From Eq. (9.4), a static deflection δ_{st} of 0.066 inch (1.67 mm) is required to provide a natural frequency f_n of 12.2 Hz. The same results may be obtained by using the isolation efficiency chart, Fig. 9.15, as follows. Find the point at which the horizontal line for a forcing frequency $f = 30$ Hz intersects the diagonal line for a isolation efficiency of 80 percent. From the point of intersection, project a vertical line to read the values of $\delta_{st} = 0.066$ inch (1.67 mm) and $f_n = 12.2$ Hz.

Step 6. From Eq. (9.3), the spring constant k for the combination of four isolators which is required to provide a natural frequency f_n (of the total mass on the isolators) is equal to 2120 lb/inch (371 newtons/mm).

Step 7. Since there is one isolator at each corner of the base of the supported mass, the isolators are in parallel, with $n = 4$ in Eq. (9.7). This yields a value of $k_i = 530$ lb/inch (92.8 newtons/mm) for the stiffness of each individual isolator.

Step 8. The total load has been specified as 140 pounds (63 kg).

Step 9. In this example, the load is divided equally among the four identical isolators. Therefore, the load supported by each isolator is $W = 35$ lb (15.8 kg).

Step 10. Select an isolator having a spring constant of 530 lb/inch (92.8 newtons/mm) and the capacity to support a static weight of approximately 35 lb (15.8 kg).

PRACTICAL CONSIDERATIONS IN VIBRATION ISOLATOR INSTALLATION

There are usually two primary causes for unsatisfactory performance of an isolation system: (1) the isolator has been selected improperly or some important system parameter has been overlooked and (2) the isolator has been installed improperly. The following criteria can help obviate problems that can otherwise cause poor performance:

■ Do not overload the isolator, i.e., do not exceed the loading specified by the manufacturer. Overloading may shorten isolator life and affect performance.

■ In the case of coil-spring isolators: There should be adequate space between coils at normal static load so that adjacent coils do not touch, with no possibility of bottoming at the maximum load.

■ In the case of elastomeric compression-type isolators: The isolator should not be overloaded so that it bulges excessively—the ratio of deflection at the static load to the original rubber thickness should not exceed 0.15. As indicated earlier, overloading an isolator may affect its performance. An elastomeric element loaded in compression has a nonlinear stiffness. Therefore, its effective dynamic stiffness (i.e., its effective stiffness when it is vibrating) will be higher than the published value. This raises the natural frequency and reduces its efficiency of isolation.

- In the case of an elastomeric shear-type isolator: The ratio of the static deflection in shear (i.e., with metal plates moving parallel to one another) to the original thickness usually should not exceed 0.30.

- To minimize rocking of the equipment and the resultant high stress in the isolators, the distance between the isolator plane and the center-of-gravity should be equal to or less than one-third of the minimum spacing between isolators.

Inertia Blocks

In certain applications, it is neither desirable nor feasible to mount a machine directly on vibration isolators. Instead, the machine is attached to a relatively heavy and rigid block (usually concrete or reinforced concrete) which is then supported by suitable isolators; the use of such a mass (called an *inertia block*) is desirable for the following reasons:

1. If a very large and massive machine generates relatively large forces during its operation, the overall movement of the machine on its isolation system tends to become excessive unless its effective mass is substantially increased. This increase in effective mass can be achieved by rigidly attaching the machine to an inertia block and then mounting the inertia block on isolators.

2. In applications in which the forcing frequency is low, the natural frequency of the system must be very low to provide low transmissibility and therefore good vibration isolation. A problem often arises with a machine intended to be mounted only at its base because a low-stiffness base-mounted system tends to be unstable and to allow excessive motion. Effective isolation may be difficult to achieve.

3. Some types of equipment do not operate properly unless supported by a rigid structure. This applies to certain types of machine tools that are not inherently rigid and therefore need a rigid support to maintain the prescribed accuracy. In other types of machinery consisting of articulated components, a rigid support may be needed to maintain the proper alignment of working parts.

Isolators employed to support the block may be fabricated of an elastomer such as rubber or neoprene, steel springs, or other resilient material. The required size of the inertia block depends on the reason for its use and on the type and size of equipment. The purpose of the inertia block may be to provide rigidity; the size is determined by the momentum available for transfer to the block and by the permissible motion of the machine. The desired natural frequency for the isolation system usually is established by the operating characteristics of the mounted equipment and the isolation required.

Figure 9.18 shows an inertia block supported above floor level (also see Fig. 8.11). Here, commercially available isolators are used to support the inertia block. Isolators having a height adjustment feature will facilitate leveling of the block. The inertia block shown in this illustration may be poured without a form, using the floor to close the lower side of the frame and covering the floor with plastic sheeting before pouring the concrete. Upon hardening of the concrete, the inertia block is lifted from the floor by turning the lifting screws.

Figure 9.19 shows how resilient pads can be used in constructing an inertia block below floor level. A concrete pit of the required size is lined with a resilient pad. The pad should be covered with plastic sheeting to protect it from concrete which is poured to form an inertia block. The desired natural frequency can be obtained by using resilient pads of the appropriate thickness and area.

If the isolators are located substantially below the center-of-gravity of the inertia block, there will be a tendency toward instability—an effect which becomes more pronounced if the machine generates large horizontal forces during normal operation. This limitation can be

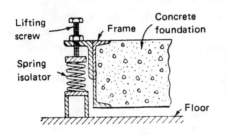

FIG. 9.18 An inertia block supported on vibration isolators composed of a combination of metal coil springs on neoprene pads.

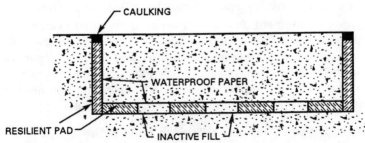

FIG. 9.19 An independent foundation, flush with the floor level, that is supported by a resilient pad. The foundation may be poured directly on plastic sheeting placed over the pad. Caulking at floor level, around the perimeter of the pad, prevents water or moisture from entering the resilient pad and damaging it.

minimized by installing the isolators in positions closer to the upper surface of the inertia block, supported on abutments extending inward from the walls of the pit. A more refined version of this concept is the T-shaped inertia block illustrated in Fig. 9.20. With such a design it is possible to place the isolators in the same horizontal plane as the center-of-gravity.

When the natural frequency of an inertia block on coil springs is relatively low, the possibility of instability is always present; this is because the only horizontal constraint is that provided by the horizontal spring constant of the load-carrying springs. If there are doubts concerning stability, additional springs should be added to provide horizontal stability.

If the static deflection of the isolators is the same with or without an inertia block (i.e., stiffer isolators are used when a machine is mounted on an inertia block), then the addition of the inertia block *does not* reduce the vibratory forces transmitted from the vibrating machine to its supporting structure via its isolators; however, the aforementioned benefits remain.

Flexible Conduit and Tubing

The advantages provided by the use of vibration isolators may be nullified by bridging (short-circuiting) if equipment mounted on isolators is attached to a structure by means of rigid piping or conduit. Instead, flexible conduit or tubing should be used (1) to permit the mounted equipment to move, (2) to prevent the transmission of vibration to the structure, and (3) to prevent failure of the conduit or a fitting due to metal fatigue resulting from vibration.

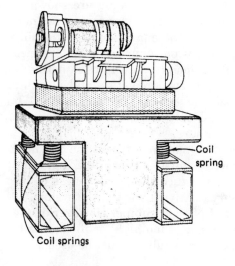

Coil spring

Coil springs

FIG. 9.20 An independent foundation supported by metal coil springs. This arrangement permits the center-of-gravity of the isolated mass to be located in the same plane as the vibration isolators, thereby providing good stability.

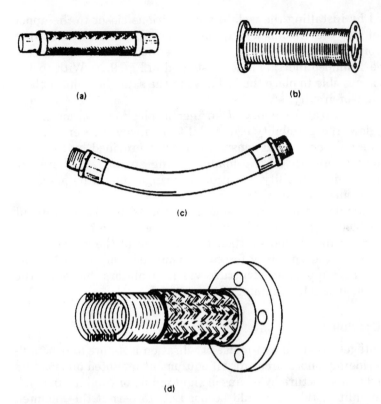

FIG. 9.21 Flexible tubing and hoses: (*a*) Corrugated tubing with metal braid covering; (*b*) corrugated tubing; (*c*) rubber hose; (*d*) detail of corrugated tubing with braid covering.

Common types of flexible conduit, hoses, and tubing are shown in Fig. 9.21. Flexible conduit as obtained from the manufacturer is normally equipped with integral fittings at the ends. Lengths of tubing are available in standard sizes or to custom dimensions determined by the application. Corrugated tubing for pressure lines is normally enclosed within a flexible braid to prevent elongation and ultimate bursting of the tubing (the braid being attached to the end fittings). It is acceptable for use without a braid only for such applications as transmitting air or gas under low pressure.

To obtain effective isolation, relative motion between the mounted equipment and its supporting structure must be permitted. Rigid conduit attached to this equipment can reduce the effectiveness of the isolators by restricting the necessary relative motion in the system.

Rubber hose often is used instead of rigid tubing. However, if the temperature is too great, if the pressure is too high, or if chemically active fluids are transmitted, metal hose or tubing must be used.

The use of flexible conduit or tubing can prevent the transmission of vibration through the conduit or tubing, but not the transmission of vibration through the fluid which it may contain. Thus flexible conduit can be very effective in electrical systems and air distribution systems; it is generally less effective in fluid systems.

In the installation of flexible conduit or tubing, the following design principles are important:

1. Attach the conduit to the mounted machine near the point of minimum vibratory movement in order to minimize the transmission of vibration through the conduit; the opposite end of the conduit should be attached to the most massive structure available in order to reduce the influence of transmitted vibration on this structure. If necessary, this principle can be effected by running a length of rigid conduit from the point of minimum movement to the location where the flexible portion can best be installed. The rigid part of the connection is then carried by the machine without affecting isolation.

2. Relatively large loops of flexible hose should be employed in the conduit where one end experiences a large displacement relative to the other end or where a very low conduit stiffness is required. Usually the vibration amplitude is small and the flexible portion of the conduit can be installed straight but with sufficient play to avoid vibration transmission.

3. Electrical connections to motors or fans which are mounted on vibration isolators should be made with a flexible connection such as BX cable; the cable should be long enough to minimize the transmission of vibration along its length. Such an illustration is shown in Fig. 9.11, where a loop of flexible BX cable provides an electrical connection to a motor.

4. If a loop is used, it is recommended that the flexible conduit be installed so that the vibratory motion is essentially distributed over the full length of the loop. If the movement occurs only adjacent to the ends of the conduit, excessive wear resulting from stress concentration at the end connections may shorten the life of the conduit.

REFERENCES

1. C. M. Harris (ed.), *Shock and Vibration Handbook,* 3d ed., McGraw-Hill, New York, 1988.
2. C. M. Harris (ed.), *Handbook of Acoustical Measurements and Noise Control,* 3d ed., McGraw-Hill, New York, 1991.
3. C. M. Harris (ed.), *Handbook of Utilities and Services for Buildings,* McGraw-Hill, New York, 1990.
4. *Designer's Guide,* Publication no. PB-8000e, Lord Corporation, Erie, PA, 1989.

10

Noise Control in Buildings

A. C. C. Warnock
J. D. Quirt

INTRODUCTION

The basic building components used to control noise in buildings are described in Chaps. 5 and 6. This chapter discusses problems that may arise when these components are combined for the solution of typical noise problems in major categories of buildings.

SOUND INSULATION CRITERIA

The criteria by which a noise is judged by a listener depends on the listener's activities and environment. In the occupancies considered here, the problem usually involves "background noise" which is accepted as part of the listener's environment, and the possible intrusion of disturbing sounds from neighboring occupancies. The requirements for sound insulation between offices are based on the need to prevent intelligible speech from being transmitted since speech usually is the most important intrusive sound. Between dwellings there is a wide variety in people's activities, in the noises they make and in their desire for quiet. Sound insulation requirements for multi-family dwellings are usually based on experience and social surveys that have been conducted in various countries.

Several interacting factors are important in determining whether noise from neighbors bothers an occupant of a multi-family dwelling:

- The airborne sound transmission and impact sound transmission characteristics of party walls and floors
- The noise level in the adjoining space
- The background noise level in the occupant's own dwelling
- The sensitivity of the occupant

TABLE 10.1   Minimum Requirements for Airborne Sound Insulation of Walls and Floors Separating Specific Categories of Rooms;* Expressed in Terms of Sound Transmission Class (STC)

Separated spaces	Bedrooms A	Living, dining, family rooms B	Kitchen, bathroom, ancillary spaces C
A Bedrooms	55		
B Living, dining, family rooms	55	50	
C Kitchen, bathroom, hallway, foyer, storage, utility space	55	50	50
D Service spaces common to two or more dwelling units:			
(a) Typically quiet, e.g., corridors, stairways, storage spaces	50	50	45
(b) Typically noisy, e.g., garages, garbage disposal areas (including garbage chutes), mechanical equipment rooms, furnace rooms, laundries, squash courts, party rooms	70	70	60

*If two or more of the categories are combined in one unpartitioned space, the higher requirement shall govern.

The last two factors vary widely. The sound insulation value of a wall or floor partition must be selected to provide protection for most, but not all, situations. Guidelines for acceptable noise levels in various occupancies are given in Table 7.12. Tables 10.1 and 10.2 give minimum values of effective sound insulation which are recommended for walls and floors to provide a decent living environment. Airborne sound insulation (for walls and floors) is expressed in terms of sound transmission class (STC), described in Chap. 5.

Impact sound insulation (for floors) is expressed in terms of impact insulation class (IIC), described in Chap. 6. These insulation ratings may be higher than those commonly required in some national or municipal jurisdictions but are similar to those used in many European countries.

The insulation requirements recommended in Tables 10.1 and 10.2 represent completed constructions with normal connections between walls, floors, and ceilings. Selection of building components which meet these ratings does not guarantee that the recommended insulation will be obtained in the finished building. This is because *flanking transmission* at the junctions of the construction components can reduce noise insulation drastically, as described in a later section. Field testing[1,2] of sound insulation at an early stage while the con-

TABLE 10.2 Minimum Requirements for Impact Insulation of Floors Separating Specific Categories of Rooms;* Expressed in Terms of Impact Insulation Class (IIC)

Room where source is located	Room where listener is located		
	Bedrooms	Living, dining, family rooms	Kitchen, bathroom ancillary spaces
	I	II	III
I. Bedrooms	55	55	50
II. Living, dining, family rooms	55	55	50
III. Kitchen, bathroom, hallway, foyer, storage, utility space	55	55	50
IV. Service spaces common to two or more dwelling units:			
(a) Typically quiet, e.g., corridors, stairways, storage spaces	55	55	50
(b) Typically noisy, e.g., garages, garbage disposal areas (including garbage chutes), mechanical equipment rooms, furnace rooms, laundries, squash courts, party rooms	70	65	55

*If two or more of the categories are combined in one unpartitioned space, the higher requirement shall govern.

struction is still in progress may allow changes to be made before the construction is completed.

The IIC ratings in Table 10.2 apply to floors without carpeting or other resilient coverings. Some floors that are tested covered with carpet and underlayment padding provide quite high IIC ratings, but only because of the presence of the carpet and underlayment. Although apartments may be originally furnished with such carpeted floors, tenants may remove the carpeting and install parquet or some other hard surface. Footstep noise is then quite unacceptable. For this, and the reasons discussed in Chap. 6, IIC criteria in building regulations should refer only to bare floors.

INFLUENCE OF BUILDING LAYOUT ON SOUND INSULATION REQUIREMENTS

A simple means of controlling noise in buildings is to separate noisy areas from quiet areas as far as possible. For example, consider units in a typical apartment: The noise levels vary widely from one room to another. Kitchens are often noisy; living rooms are sometimes the source of speech or sounds from radios or TV sets. If an area where quiet is required (such as a bedroom) is located next to a noisy machine room, a high value of noise reduction will be required to achieve a quiet environment in the bedroom. Thus, a carefully chosen layout reduces the required noise reductions between spaces and therefore reduces the sound insulation needed for the building components. This variation in activity and noise levels between rooms is taken into account in the recommendations given in Tables 10.1 and 10.2.

The following guidelines are recommended in designing a building layout:

- Place machinery rooms, refuse chutes, elevator shafts, central HVAC systems, water circulating pumps, and other noisy mechanical equipment as far as possible from sensitive living or sleeping areas.

- Place relatively quiet areas, such as bedrooms, next to each other to minimize the noise reduction requirements for occupant satisfaction.

- Use utility spaces, such as corridors and vestibules, as buffer spaces between noisy and quiet areas.

In Fig. 10.1, the bedroom (BR) in the poor layout is likely to be noisy because of the adjacent elevator shaft (E) and kitchen (K). The bedroom in the good layout is shielded from these major sources of noise in the apartment.

Corridors serve as buffer zones between apartments but can also be a source of noise. In Fig. 10.2, it is likely that noise will intrude not only from the corridor but also from adjacent apartments by way of

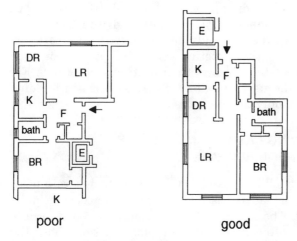

poor   good

FIG. 10.1 Comparison between two floor layouts for an apartment: K = kitchen, F = foyer, DR = dining room, LR = living room, BR = bedroom, E = elevator.

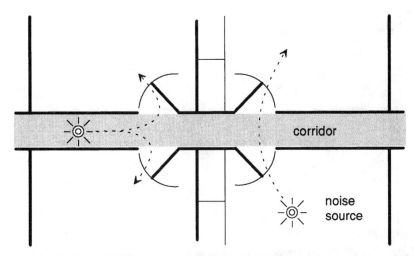

FIG. 10.2 Doors facing each other provide an easy path for sound to travel from one room to another especially if the doors have poor sound insulation, are not well weatherstripped, or have louvered panels for ventilation. The arrows show possible sound paths.

the doors. This is especially true if the doors provide little sound insulation, are poorly sealed with large gaps at the bottom, or contain louvered panels for ventilation.

A vestibule that can be closed off between the corridor and the living areas, as shown in Fig. 10.3, helps to reduce noise intrusion. This is commonly done in hotels in Europe and greatly reduces the intrusive noise from corridors. This technique can be put to good use in a restaurant to keep kitchen noise out of the dining area. Offset doors, carpeting, and an acoustical ceiling to absorb sound in the corridors

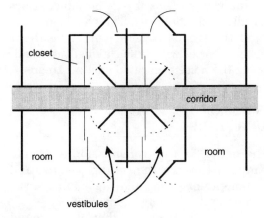

FIG. 10.3 A vestibule increases the noise reduction between the corridor and adjacent rooms.

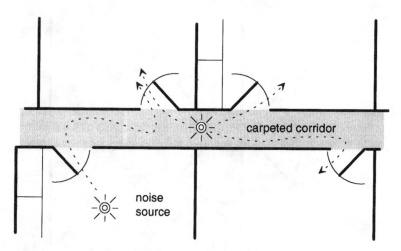

FIG. 10.4 Adding a sound-absorptive material in the corridor (for example, carpeting and an acoustic ceiling) and offsetting the doors reduce noise transmission between rooms. The arrows show possible sound paths.

are other ways of reducing noise transmission between apartments by way of the doors, as illustrated in Fig. 10.4. This approach is not as effective in reducing the intrusion of noise from the corridor as that shown in Fig. 10.3.

If noise reduction between apartments and corridors is high, then fire alarms placed in the corridors may not be loud enough to waken occupants sleeping in the apartments; they may not even be audible in the bedrooms of the apartments. More sophisticated systems linked together are required with alarms installed inside the apartments.

It is good practice to avoid the placement of stairs adjacent to areas where quiet conditions are required, and, as far as possible, stairs should be isolated from the walls of the building. The treads and the structure should be stiff, and the treads covered with a resilient material to reduce footstep noise. Carpet with underlayment is usually the best material for reducing the noise generated on stair treads.

PATHS FOR SOUND TRANSMISSION
BETWEEN ROOMS; FLANKING PATHS

In buildings, there are many paths for the transmission of sound. Sound energy can be transmitted through the ceilings, walls, and floors of the structure to reach adjacent rooms and cause annoyance; partitions other than the common partition may be involved.

A *flanking path* is a path for sound transmission that allows sound to circumvent the element that is intended to be the only significant

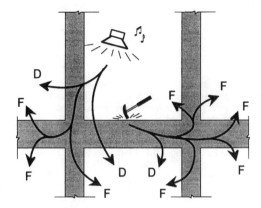

FIG. 10.5 Some of the possible paths for sound in a monolithic building structure. Arrowheads marked with D represent "direct" transmission through the common partition; those marked with F represent "flanking" paths where paths other than that through the common partition are involved.

sound path between two spaces. Figure 10.5 shows examples of several types of flanking paths in a building where all components are rigidly connected. Another example (shown in Fig. 5.19b) is the path through a hollow metal frame around a sound-retardant door; if the interior of the frame is not fully grouted or otherwise treated, there can be significant sound transmission through the frame.

Once sound has entered a structure and is propagating as vibration, it can travel for considerable distances; the energy lost in traveling from one point to another depends on the material and on the details of the construction. Flanking paths usually have much more serious consequences for structureborne sound transmission than for airborne sound transmission. This is because structureborne noise is inherently more difficult to control than airborne noise, particularly at low frequencies. For example, a source that is rigidly connected to the building structure will be heard much more easily in adjacent spaces than a source that is resiliently connected or rests on a resilient pad.

To provide the maximum possible sound attenuation in buildings, energy transmission along flanking paths should be reduced to a minimum by introducing structural breaks (such as isolation joints) and resilient connections in the construction. In an apartment building, ideally, each apartment should be an independent, resiliently supported unit within the building.

Where a floor is rigidly connected to the adjoining and supporting walls, sound transmission along flanking paths can be a serious problem. Resiliently suspending the ceiling below the floor as in Fig. 10.6 reduces the sound transmission for the path directly through the floor. It does not, however, reduce flanking transmission to the adjacent rooms on the same level or flanking transmission down the walls. A much better way (but usually more costly) to reduce sound transmission from the floor to the flanking paths is to use a "floating

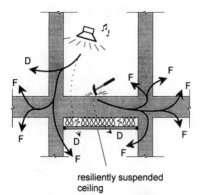

resiliently suspended
ceiling

FIG. 10.6 The resiliently suspended ceiling reduces the direct transmission through the floor (dotted lines and arrowheads marked with D) but has no influence on the transmission along flanking paths (arrowheads marked with F).

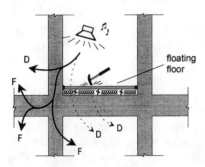

floating floor

FIG. 10.7 The floating floor reduces impact sound at the source and reduces direct (arrowheads marked with D) and flanking paths (arrowheads marked with F) through the floor.

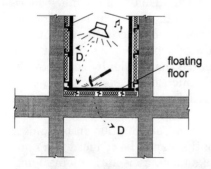

floating floor

FIG. 10.8 The floating floor and resiliently suspended walls in the upper room reduce transmission along all direct (arrowheads marked with D) and flanking paths.

floor" shown in idealized form in Fig. 10.7. (Practical floating floor constructions are illustrated in Figs. 6.2 through 6.5.) Figure 10.8 illustrates the use of resiliently suspended walls and a floating floor to reduce the transmission of noise along the remaining direct and flanking paths from the room containing the noise sources to the adjacent rooms. This kind of construction approximates the ideal condition in a building; each room is not connected to the structure at all or at least only resiliently. Note that sound insulation measures act in both directions, i.e., the room containing the noise sources is also protected against noise coming from the adjacent rooms.

CONSTRUCTION DETAILS TO AVOID FLANKING

The details of the construction where a wall and floor join greatly influence the sound insulation that the wall provides. This is because the floor may act as a flanking path. Flanking paths, construction elements having poor sound insulation, and/or sound leaks must be avoided in wall construction since they all reduce the sound insulation provided by the wall.

Consider the construction shown in Fig. 10.9. The wall and the floor should both provide very good sound insulation, yet, because of the flanking transmission along the upper surface of the floor, the sound insulation is poor between the two sides of the wall. The wall is "short-circuited" by the concrete slab. A similar problem can exist with the construction shown in Fig. 10.10a. Sound is transmitted along a flanking path (indicated by the arrow), thereby reducing the sound insulation provided by the wall. The problem may be circumvented by introducing a break in the floating slab as shown in Fig. 10.10b. If the floating slab is unable to support the weight of the wall structure, the construction shown in Fig. 10.10c can be used.

The introduction of a structural discontinuity reduces or prevents the passage of vibration along light-weight layers in the construction. A break in construction can be introduced to prevent such flanking in

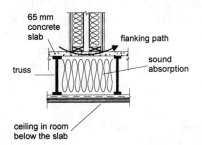

FIG. 10.9 A floor section illustrating flanking transmission along a continuous concrete slab supported on trusses. The sound insulation provided by this double-wall construction is reduced about 10 dB because of transmission of energy along the slab, thereby short-circuiting the double wall.

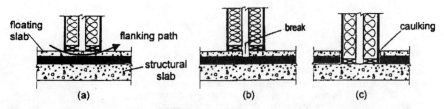

FIG. 10.10 (a) The continuous floating slab allows flanking sound to propagate along the slab and under the wall. (b) A break in the floating slab reduces the flanking transmission. (c) This type of construction can be used if the floating slab cannot support the wall structure as illustrated in (b).

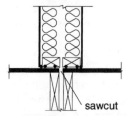

sawcut

FIG. 10.11 In wood stud construction a saw-cut in the floor provides a structural break which reduces flanking transmission. If the applicable fire code requires that the gap must be sealed, there should not be a rigid connection across the saw-cut.

wood joist construction by making a saw-cut in the floor (as illustrated in Fig. 10.11), or by constructing the two leafs of the double-stud party wall so that they are independent. In some jurisdictions, such construction breaks cannot be employed because of the applicable building code or because they will destroy the structural integrity of the building.

Figure 10.12*a* shows how flanking transmission may occur where party walls meet external walls. This situation is improved in the construction in Fig. 10.12*b* where a break is made in the path along the outer wall. The construction shown in Fig. 10.12*c* also breaks this path and provides a continuous inner surface to control vapor migration. The detail in Fig. 10.12*c* shows a gap left between the gypsum board sheets that is caulked to preserve a continuous vapor barrier while providing a construction break to eliminate flanking transmission.

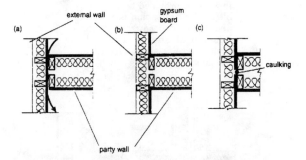

FIG. 10.12 (*a*) A detail showing the joining of a party wall with an external wall whose internal face is a continuous layer of gypsum board; here flanking transmission can occur as shown by the arrow. (*b*) A gap in the gypsum-board construction eliminates flanking along the lightweight gypsum board. (*c*) Sealing the gap with flexible tape or sealant provides a continuous vapor barrier while continuing to reduce flanking transmission.

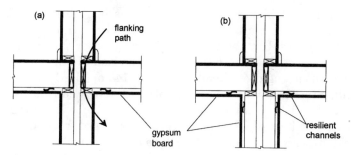

FIG. 10.13 (*a*) Section showing a flanking path from a room above to the room below, as shown by the arrows. (*b*) Same as (*a*), but here mounting the gypsum board on resilient metal channels in the rooms below reduces the flanking transmission.

An example, in wood-stud wall construction, illustrating how flanking sound can propagate down walls to reach the room below is shown in Fig. 10.13*a*. The resilient metal channels reduce flanking sound transmission from the apartments above as shown in Fig. 10.13*b*. Additional information on the installation of such light-frame constructions to preserve their sound insulation is given in Ref. 3.

Mounting bathroom cabinets back to back on a party wall can cause excessive noise transmission (i.e., through the cabinet in one apartment, out the adjacent cabinet into the next apartment), as illustrated in Fig. 10.14*a*. This type of flanking transmission through a party wall can be avoided by surface-mounting the cabinets on the party wall, as

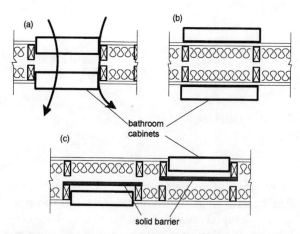

FIG. 10.14 (*a*) Back-to-back bathroom cabinets provide potential leakage paths or areas of strong sound transmission as shown by the arrows. (*b*) Surface mounting of the cabinets reduces noise transmission between the two sides of the wall. (*c*) Offsetting solidly backed recesses along the wall avoids surface mounting and reduces noise transmission.

shown in Fig. 10.14*b*. Cabinets may be recessed as in Fig. 10.14*c* if they are offset along the wall and backed by a solid barrier. The sound-absorptive material in the cavity absorbs much of the sound that leaks around the cabinets into the cavity. The risk of annoyance due to the impact of closing doors in either Fig. 10.14*b* or Fig. 10.14*c* is relatively small. Similar considerations apply to kitchen cupboards, but in this case the risk of annoyance to neighbors from slamming cupboard doors is significantly greater since they are used frequently. Therefore, avoid attaching kitchen cupboards to the party wall.

Ventilation ducts provide another potential path for the "cross transmission" of sound between rooms. Figure 10.15*a* shows a poor arrangement where sound can easily pass between rooms. The rearranged layout in Fig. 10.15*b* has branch ducts lined internally with sound-absorptive material. Commercial sound attenuators may also be necessary in some cases, as described in Chap. 7.

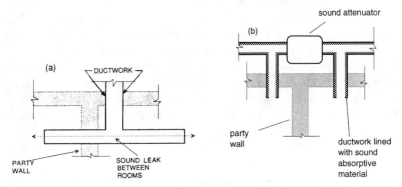

FIG. 10.15 Plan views showing: (*a*) Serious sound leak created by incorrect arrangement of ductwork; (*b*) improved version with longer paths for sound along ducts lined with sound-absorptive material. The sound attenuator (i.e., sound trap) shown may not be required.

INCREASING SOUND INSULATION IN EXISTING STRUCTURES

Improvement of Existing Walls

Attempts to increase sound insulation between two rooms or homes should be made only after careful investigation to determine the reason for the poor insulation. Common reasons for poor sound insulation include: (1) sound leaks, (2) flanking paths, and (3) a common partition having a value of sound insulation that is too low. The common partition is not always the principal sound path. All three faults may be present in any situation. All leaks should be repaired before making any structural changes; the sound insulation should then be re-evaluated. Before structural changes are made, the major sound paths between the rooms should be identified. This might be done by careful listening in one of the rooms to a noise source in the other. Examination of construction details in the building plans might reveal faults, but, in many cases, professional help will be needed to determine if the poor sound insulation is due to the party wall, due to the floor, or the result of flanking.

Where the sound insulation of a partition is to be improved, it is better from the point of view of the acoustical consultant to change the construction to one of the better constructions described in Chap. 5. This may require partial dismantling of the existing construction which is often found to be too costly and other methods may have to be used.

NOISE AND VIBRATION FROM ELEVATORS AND REFUSE CHUTES

Office buildings, apartment buildings, and individual homes contain a variety of mechanical devices that create noise. The importance of their location relative to quiet spaces is discussed in an earlier section, "Influence of Building Layout on Sound Insulation Requirements." The control of noise produced by air-conditioning systems is described in Chap. 7, plumbing noise in Chap. 8, and mechanical and electrical equipment noise in Chap. 9. This section describes two additional major sources of noise in buildings: elevators and refuse chutes.

Elevator Installations

Figure 10.16 shows an example of an elevator installation designed to minimize noise generation. Note the following noise control measures:

- The motor and winch are supported on an inertia block, which is mounted on vibration isolators.

- The internal surfaces of the elevator room that encloses the elevator equipment are lined with sound-absorptive material.

- Openings between the elevator room and the elevator shaft are minimized, using cover plates where necessary.

- The guide rails for the cab and counterweight are mounted resiliently. Resilient rollers could also be used.

- Electrical controls, signals and bells are vibration isolated from the building structure.

- The noise generated by the closing of the elevator doors is minimized by rubber buffers.

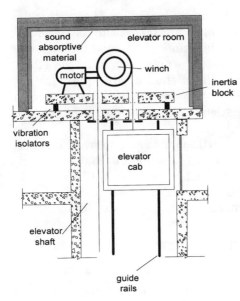

FIG. 10.16 Methods of noise control to reduce elevator noise.

Refuse Chutes

Refuse chutes (i.e., trash chutes and garbage chutes) should be surrounded by a heavy double-wall construction to minimize noise transmission to adjacent living spaces as a result of impacts generated by trash as it drops down the chute. Figure 10.17 shows an example of

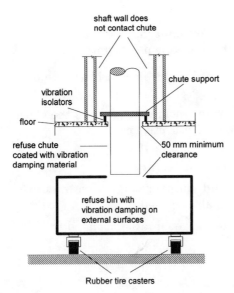

FIG. 10.17 Example of a well-designed refuse chute system.

an installation for a refuse chute designed to minimize the effects of impact noise. In such a construction, the following measures should be taken:

- Support the metal refuse chute on a resilient material to prevent impact energy from being transmitted into the building structure.
- Avoid any contact between the refuse chute and the walls of the shaft.
- Apply vibration-damping material to the metal walls of the refuse chute.
- Provide generous clearance [2 inches (5 cm)] between the refuse chute and the surrounding walls and between the refuse chute and the refuse bin.
- Apply vibration damping on the metal refuse bin, and support the bin on soft rubber casters.

SPEECH PRIVACY IN OFFICE BUILDINGS

Where an office building contains a number of independent occupancies, speech originating in an office must be easily understood within it but should be unintelligible in adjacent areas. Providing speech privacy between offices is a matter of selecting partitions with adequate sound insulation and ensuring their correct installation.

Selection of Partitions for Offices

The amount of airborne sound insulation required between offices depends on their use. *Normal privacy* exists when intrusive speech is audible, partially intelligible, but not disturbing. *Confidential privacy* exists when intrusive speech is unintelligible. *Inaudibility* is an even more stringent requirement.

The degree of speech privacy between two rooms depends on:

- The sound level of the talker's speech
- The noise reduction between the two rooms
- The background noise level in the listener's room
- The total sound absorption in each room

Table 10.3 gives the minimum sound transmission class (STC) ratings partitions must have to provide confidential privacy between various types of offices. These STC ratings take account of typical variations in voice level, room size, total room absorption, and background noise in the room. To use the table, proceed as follows:

TABLE 10.3   Minimum Values of Sound Transmission Class Required to Provide Confidential Privacy between Different Types of Occupancies

	Occupancy	A	B	C
A	Large conference room	55	55	50
B	Small conference room, senior executive office	55	50	50
C	Small office	50	50	45
D	Landscaped office	50	50	45

Step 1. Select the type of one of the rooms from the "Occupancy" column, and note its letter designation.

Step 2. Select the type of the second room from the "Occupancy" column, and note its letter designation.

Step 3. Move along the row corresponding to the first room and read the required STC under the letter corresponding to the second room.

Example: To provide confidential acoustical privacy between a large conference room (Occupancy A) and an adjacent small office (Occupancy C), the STC (from row A and column C) should be at least 50.

Installation Requirements for Partitions in Offices

The values of sound insulation for partitions given in the tables of Chaps. 5 and 6 assume that all peripheral cracks are carefully sealed on both sides. To obtain these ratings in office buildings, all openings, holes, cracks, etc. must be sealed, and flanking paths must be eliminated. To obtain sound transmission class (STC) values greater than 40:

- The partition should abut heavy surrounding structures to avoid the flanking transmission shown in Fig. 10.12. The partition should be properly sealed around the periphery. For example, the partition should rest on the structural floor slab rather than on carpet or on light-weight false floor. Similarly, the partition should extend from the floor to the structural slab above (or to a substantial ceiling that does not bridge across the partition).

- There should be no holes or cracks in the partition; a hole amounting to 0.1 percent of the wall area limits the sound insulation value to about STC 30.

- There should be no penetrations of the partition by continuous, lightly covered or open cavities such as heating strips, lighting troffers, short ducts, back-to-back service openings in the partition, or light-weight sidewalls with connecting cavities that bridge across the partition.

Flanking Transmission through Ceiling Plenums in Offices

In most modern commercial office buildings, partitions usually extend from the floor only to the underside of the suspended ceiling; a plenum is in the space above. The space above the suspended ceiling usually is left open for building services such as electrical services, piping, and air-conditioning ducts. As a result, flanking sound is transmitted (a) from one office into the plenum, (b) along the plenum, and (c) from the plenum down through the ceiling of an adjacent office, as illustrated in Fig. 3.7. The magnitude of the airborne sound transmitted from one side of the partition to the other side depends primarily on (1) the characteristics of the ceiling, (2) the openings through the ceiling to handle airflow, and (3) the blocking (if any) of the plenum space above the suspended ceiling.

If the space above the suspended ceiling is used as a return air plenum, sound transmitted through the airflow openings provides another significant path for sound transmission. The sound transmitted through typical air return openings [about 1 square foot (0.1 m²) per office] limit the effective sound insulation of the suspended ceiling/partition system to an STC rating of about 30. Although this rating is better than the typical separation between work-stations in an open-plan office, it is not adequate for speech privacy, and it may result in significant occupant dissatisfaction.*

Blocking Plenum Openings to Reduce Flanking. Blocking the plenum space to prevent the transmission of sound through it is difficult because of the supply services in the space. Barrier materials (such as mass-loaded vinyl) are commercially available, but they seldom provide a noise reduction of more than 10 dB because of the many gaps where building services penetrate the barrier.

One method of reducing sound transmitted via the suspended ceiling and plenum is to construct a barrier from a slightly compressed

---

*Specific test procedures have been developed for sound transmission through the ceiling, along the plenum, and down through the ceiling again into the adjacent space.[4] Ceiling attenuation class (CAC) is the rating that results from the test. It may be used to rank and compare ceiling systems. Typical ceilings have CAC ratings from about 20 to 45.

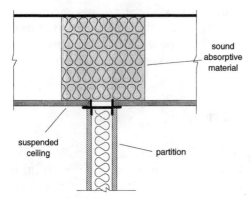

FIG. 10.18   Filling the space above a partition and suspended ceiling with sound-absorptive material to increase sound attenuation between offices.

stack of insulation batts extending from the top of the partition to the slab above, as shown in Fig. 10.18. These batts tend to puff out to fill the gaps where pipes and ducts pass through, and thus reduce the sound leakage. If the plenum space serves as an air return, paths for return airflow can readily be incorporated in the stack of batts (and perform essentially as lined ducts with little effect on the noise reduction). In general, a sound-absorptive material provides relatively poor sound insulation. However, if the path through the sound-absorptive material is sufficiently long [say, 4 feet (1.2 m)], there is substantial attenuation of high-frequency sound and therefore a reduction of speech intelligibility in the office. Used with typical suspended ceilings, it can provide a sound transmission class (STC) in the range from 35 to 50.

OPEN-PLAN OFFICES

An open-plan office is a large space that accommodates many seated workers separated by barriers [typically at least 5 feet (1.5 m) high] that provide visual separation between work positions. The barriers may be free-standing or integrated into the furniture. Open-plan offices are economical to construct, provide flexibility, and may have advantages for groups of individuals whose activities are functionally related.

An open-plan office can function reasonably well if it is carefully designed as a system, and when adjacent activities are compatible and are not too close together. Note, however, that even in a well-designed open-plan office, privacy between adjacent work positions is less than that available in a well-constructed fully partitioned office. Special facilities must be provided for noisier devices such as printers and copying machines—for example, by grouping them in a central area behind high, sound-absorptive barriers or in fully partitioned rooms. Properly designed, fully partitioned conference rooms should be provided for activities which require low background noise levels and high privacy. The sound from one work position reflects from common surfaces (ceiling, walls, and windows) and bends over or around the edges of the barrier, as illustrated in Figs. 10.19a and b. To achieve acceptable privacy, sound reflection from horizontal and vertical surfaces must be minimized, and the dimensions of the barri-

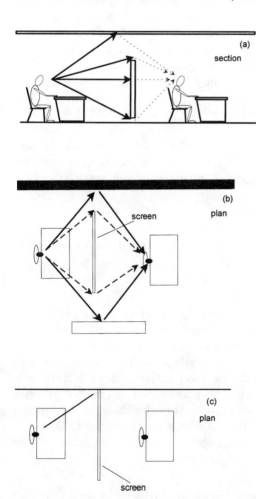

FIG. 10.19 Transmission of sound between work positions in an open office. (a) Paths in the vertical plane for sound traveling between work stations: reflections from ceiling, and floor, bending around the top and bottom of the barrier, and transmission through the body of the barrier or leaks in its structure. (b) Paths in the horizontal plane: reflections from walls and furniture. (c) Butting a barrier against a wall eliminates the reflected and diffracted paths for sound around one side of the barrier.

ers must be large enough to reduce the level of the sound that bends around them.† Requirements for the various elements that make up the open-plan office are considered in the following sections.

Barriers for Open-Plan Offices

Barriers (also called *screens, partial-height partitions,* and *office dividers*) are placed between work positions to provide some sound attenuation and visual privacy, at least between seated persons. Systems furniture is furniture that combines the functions of the barrier and other office equipment into a single unit which may include storage compartments, desk or work surfaces, as well as built-in lighting, and power and communications wiring. Systems furniture, used in many open offices to save space, may be interconnected in groups. When used in an open-plan office, those parts of the system furniture that act as barriers between work positions should meet the physical requirements for barriers given below. The sound attenuation provided by an office barrier can be measured using a standard test[7] which rates the barriers using articulation class (AC) as a measure of their effectiveness.‡ Barriers should meet the following minimum requirements:

- *Height:*   At least 5 feet (1.7 m)
- *Width:*   At least 6 feet (1.8 m)
- *Distance of Bottom Edge from Floor:*   Less than 4 inches (100 mm)
- *Sound Transmission Class (STC):*   Greater than 20
- *Noise Reduction Coefficient:*   Greater than 0.8

The greater the dimensions of a barrier, the better the sound insulation it will provide. Maximum dimensions are usually limited by physical convenience, possible interference with airflow, and preservation of the "open look." Barrier units usually can be joined to increase the effective length. If the attenuation of a high barrier is desired but visual openness must be maintained, a plate of glass or transparent plastic at least 1 foot (30 cm) may be fitted to the top of a barrier to increase its height. Sound which is transmitted through a barrier should be negligible compared with the sound which bends around it if the requirement of STC 20 is satisfied.

---

†The degree of speech privacy in an existing open office or a mock-up of a proposed office may be evaluated using a standard test procedure.[5] Testing provides the opportunity to evaluate problem situations or proposed changes in design.

‡Articulation class (AC),[2–5] is the sum of the weighted sound attenuations (in the one-third-octave frequency bands from 200 to 5000 Hz) measured in a real or simulated open-plan office by radiating sound from a loudspeaker at a talker position and measuring levels at the talker and a listener position. The higher this number, the better.

Open-plan office barriers often are fabricated of a sound-absorptive material such as fiberglass 1 inch (25 mm) thick which covers both faces of a central impermeable core. This combination is then covered with a porous upholstery fabric. Such a barrier has a noise reduction coefficient (NRC) of about 0.8.

The gap between the bottom edge of the barrier and the floor should be as small as is practical; otherwise, sound can be reflected under the barrier to the opposite side. However, sound reflected under the barrier tends to be diffused or absorbed by furniture and carpeting.

Ceilings in Open-Plan Offices

As illustrated in Fig. 9.7, the ceiling in an open-plan office is the principal surface which reflects sound from one side of a barrier to the other. To ensure that the full benefit of the barriers between workstations is obtained, the ceiling must be highly sound-absorptive—a noise reduction coefficient (NRC) of at least 0.9. A specific test procedure is available to evaluate ceiling systems for use in an open-plan office[8]; it simulates the situation shown in Fig. 10.19a.

To illustrate the importance of ceiling absorption, Table 10.4 shows the attenuation for sound propagating between work positions for ceilings having different absorption coefficients and for two barrier heights. Only for ceilings having "average sound absorption coefficients" greater than 0.9 does the attenuation reach an acceptable value, providing attenuations of about 20 dB(A). This value is in contrast to values of 30 to 50 dB(A) easily attainable in conventional partitioned offices.

The number of flat, plastic luminaries in the ceiling system should be kept to a minimum or they should not be used since they reflect considerable sound and seriously reduce sound insulation between adjacent work positions. Open-grid fixtures or fixtures that scatter sound are preferred. Small lamps (task lighting) can provide additional illumination at individual desks as necessary.

TABLE 10.4 **Attenuation in Decibels (A-Weighted) for Sound Propagating between Work Positions: For Two Heights of Office Barriers and Various Average Sound Absorption Coefficients of the Ceiling**

(Averages of Coefficients at 1000, 2000, and 4000 Hz.)

Barrier height	For an average sound absorption coefficient of			
	0.05	0.60	0.85	Over 0.90
5 feet (1.5 m)	14	15	16	22
6 feet (1.8 m)	14	15	17	24

Sound-Absorptive Treatment on Walls and Other Vertical Surfaces in Open-Plan Offices

As shown in Fig. 10.19b, walls and other vertical surfaces can reflect sound around barriers and thus reduce the attenuation provided by a barrier. To minimize this, exposed flat vertical surfaces (such as walls, office barriers, columns, backs of cabinets and systems furniture, and bookcases) should be covered with sound-absorptive material where it is practical to do so. Products that reduce reflections from vertical surfaces of open office components may be rated in terms of articulation class using standard test procedures.[10] Where such test information is not available, select wall materials having a noise reduction coefficient (NRC) of 0.7 or higher. In practice, this usually requires a thickness of 1 inch (25 mm) or more of fiberglass covered with porous decorative fabric. Carpeting usually has a low sound absorption if applied directly to a hard surface so it is unsuitable for this purpose; if the carpeting has a porous backing, the carpeting may be used as a covering for an acoustical board.

A simple way of reducing wall reflections is to avoid gaps between the wall and barriers. Figure 10.19c shows that, in comparison with b, the sound reflecting from the wall and bending around the barrier is blocked when there is no gap between the wall and the barrier.

It is difficult to prevent sound from one work position reflecting from windows to adjacent desks where such reflections may be a source of disturbance. Drapes which cover the windows will reduce these reflections, but the drapes must be heavy—not sheer (e.g., see Fig. 3.30). Most slatted or venetian blinds do not reduce the reflection of sound from the windows.

Masking Sound Systems for Open-Plan Offices

In many open-plan offices, large quantities of sound-absorptive material reduce background noise to a very low level, thereby making it easier to overhear one's neighbors. Hence speech privacy is reduced. To provide greater privacy, a masking sound system may be installed in the ceiling to increase the background noise level, thereby making it more difficult for persons in adjacent work areas to overhear conversations. Such a system should generate a more or less uniform level of noise throughout the open office area.§ An array

---

§The level, spectral content, and spatial distribution of masking sound require careful adjustment for occupant acceptance. The following octave-band levels ±3 dB have been found to be acceptable at work positions: 63 Hz, 59 dB; 125 Hz, 55 dB; 250 Hz, 51 dB; 500 Hz, 46 dB; 1000 Hz, 41 dB; 2000 Hz, 35 dB; 4000 Hz, 29 dB. This is equivalent to a sound level of 48 dB(A). Higher background noise levels usually will induce the occupants to complain and tend to defeat the purpose of the masking sound since the

of loudspeakers that radiates the masking sound is usually above the ceiling panels; transmission through the ceiling panels affects the uniformity of the masking sound in the office below. Transmission through luminaries and other elements can lead to "hot" spots below and occupant complaints. Masking sound systems should only be installed by professionals who are experienced in such work.

RATING INSULATION AGAINST OUTDOOR NOISE; OUTDOOR-INDOOR TRANSMISSION CLASS (OITC)

Within a building, the insulation against outdoor sound depends on the following factors:

- *Area of the Components:* For example, if most sound is transmitted into the room through the window, the resulting noise indoors depends on the type of window and on its size. Doubling the size doubles the transmitted sound energy and increases the average indoor sound level.

- *Total Sound Absorption in the Room:* This includes the absorption provided by room furnishings such as carpets, heavy drapes, and upholstered furniture. The more absorptive the furnishings, the lower the average indoor sound level.

- *Character of the Outdoor Sound:* In passing from outdoors to indoors, the relative loudness of the high- and low-frequency sounds is altered because the noise reduction provided by typical building components is less at low frequencies than at high frequencies. For example, the low-frequency roar of a truck is only slightly reduced in transmission through an external wall. In contrast, a high-frequency whistle that is very loud outdoors may be inaudible indoors.

Sound transmission class (STC) (described in Chap. 5) is a single-number rating of the airborne sound insulation provided by indoor partitions, with respect to noises such as speech that have little sound energy at low frequencies. In contrast, outdoor noise sources such as road traffic have strong low-frequency content. For such noises, the perceived insulation provided by the external walls of build-

---

occupants will then compensate for this higher level of masking noise level by talking in louder voices. Ventilation systems create some masking sound, but usually it varies considerably from position in the office; furthermore, such masking sound may vary with time. A prime requirement of a masking noise system is that the noise it generates should not be obtrusive. Spatial and temporal variations[11] should be no greater than 3 dB; otherwise, the office occupants will complain.

TABLE 10.5 Correction to Be Added to Difference between Outdoor and Indoor Sound Levels, to Obtain Required Sound Transmission Class (STC) for the Combined Exterior Surfaces of the Room
(This Correction Depends on the Source of the Outdoor Noise and Room Furnishings.)

Source of outdoor noise	Room furnishings	Exterior surface area as percent of room floor area										
		20	25	32	40	50	63	80	100	125	160	200
Aircraft or railway wheels	Hard	−1	0	+1	+2	+3	+4	+5	+6	+7	+8	+9
	Standard	−3	−2	−1	0	+1	+2	+3	+4	+5	+6	+7
	Soft	−5	−4	−3	−2	−1	0	+1	+2	+3	+4	+5
Road traffic	Hard	+1	+2	+3	+4	+5	+6	+7	+8	+9	+10	+11
	Standard	−1	0	+1	+2	+3	+4	+5	+6	+7	+8	+9
	Soft	−3	−2	−1	0	+1	+2	+3	+4	+5	+6	+7
Diesel locomotive or road traffic screened by barrier	Hard	+3	+4	+5	+6	+7	+8	+9	+10	+11	+12	+13
	Standard	+1	+2	+3	+4	+5	+6	+7	+8	+9	+10	+11
	Soft	−1	0	+1	+2	+3	+4	+5	+6	+7	+8	+9

Notes: Hard room furnishings comprise sound-reflective walls, floor, and ceiling without upholstered furniture, carpets, or other sound-absorptive treatment. *Standard room furnishings* comprise carpet or absorptive acoustical ceiling, with some upholstered furniture. *Soft room furnishings* comprise carpet and absorptive acoustical ceiling with drapes and upholstered furniture.

ings tends to be less than the sound transmission class indicates. To compensate for this, the following procedure is applicable.

The *composite sound transmission class* rating for the external wall system (including windows, doors, etc.) is related to the difference between the A-weighted sound level outdoors $L_{outdoors}$ and the maximum acceptable A-weighted sound level inside a room $L_{indoors}$, as follows:

$$\text{composite STC} = L_{outdoors} - L_{indoors} + \text{correction} \qquad (10.1a)$$

or

$$L_{outdoors} - L_{indoors} = \text{composite STC} - \text{correction} \qquad (10.1b)$$

where the correction term in decibels is selected from Table 10.5, as described below.

Recommended maximum acceptable A-weighted sound levels are given in Table 7.12 for a variety of residential and commercial uses. Normally $L_{indoors}$ represents the average sound level throughout the room. (The sound level near an open window is higher than at more distant positions from the window; even with closed windows, the sound levels vary noticeably within a typical room.)

Table 10.5 gives appropriate values to correct for these three factors for typical outdoor noise sources.

The *outdoor-indoor transmission class* (OITC) is a single-number rating[12] that evaluates fenestration products with respect to their effectiveness in attenuating transportation noise.

Sound is usually transmitted into a room through several components including walls, windows, doors, and roof. Equation (10.1) applies to the composite sound transmission class for the complete surface exposed to outdoor noise, which might include wall(s), roof, windows, and/or door(s).

Many common wall and roof constructions have much higher STC ratings than typical windows or doors, as discussed in Chap. 5.

REFERENCES[§]

1. ASTM E336, "Standard Test Method for Measurement of Airborne Sound Insulation in Buildings."
2. ASTM E597, "Standard Practice for Determining Single-Number Rating of Airborne Sound Isolation for Use in Multi-unit Building Specifications."
3. ASTM E497, "Standard Practice for Installation of Fixed Partitions of Light Frame Type for the Purpose of Conserving Their Sound Insulation Efficiency."

§ASTM (American Society for Testing Materials) standards are available from the headquarters of ASTM, 1916 Race Street, Philadelphia, PA 19103-1187.

4. ASTM E1414, "Standard Test Method for Airborne Sound Attenuation between Rooms Sharing a Common Ceiling Plenum."
5. ASTM E1130, "Standard Test Method for Objective Measurement of Speech Privacy in Open Offices Using Articulation Index."
6. ASTM E1110, "Standard Classification for Determination of Articulation Class."
7. ASTM E1179, "Standard Specification for Sound Sources Used for Testing Open Office Components and Systems."
8. ASTM E1111, "Standard Test Method for Measuring Interzone Attenuation of Ceiling Systems."
9. ASTM E1375, "Standard Test Method for Measuring the Interzone Attenuation of Furniture Panels Used as Acoustical Barriers."
10. ASTM E1376, "Standard Test Method for Measuring the Interzone Attenuation of Sound Reflected by Wall Finishes and Furniture Panels."
11. ASTM E1041, "Standard Guide for Measurement of Masking Sound in Open Offices."
12. ASTM E1332, "Classification for Determination of Outdoor-Indoor Transmission Class."

Index

ABOUT THE EDITOR IN CHIEF

Cyril M. Harris is Professor Emeritus of Architecture at Columbia University and is currently Special Lecturer in the Graduate School of Architecture, Planning, and Preservation, where he was Chairman of the Division of Architectural Technology for ten years. He is also the Charles Batchelor Professor Emeritus of Electrical Engineering at Columbia and has served as the S. Charles Lee Visiting Professor of Architecture at U.C.L.A. Dr. Harris has received the AIA Medal of the American Institute of Architects, the gold Medal and the Sabine Medal of the Acoustical Society of America, the Franklin Medal of the Franklin Institute, and the gold Medal of the Audio Engineering Society. He is a member of both the National Academy of Sciences and the National Academy of Engineering. He has received international recognition for his work in auditorium design and noise control. He was the acoustical consultant for the John F. Kennedy Center for the Performing Arts and the National Academy of Sciences Auditorium in Washington; the Metropolitan Opera House in New York City; Orchestra Hall in Minneapolis; Symphony Hall in Salt Lake City; Powell Symphony Hall in St. Louis; the National Centre for the Performing Arts in Bombay; and many other performing arts halls. He received his Ph.D. in physics from M.I.T. and has been awarded honorary doctorates by Northwestern University and the New Jersey Institute of Technology. Books written or edited by Dr. Harris include *Acoustical Designing in Architecture, Illustrated Dictionary of Historic Architecture*, and the following McGraw-Hill publications: *Handbook of Utilities and Services for Buildings, Handbook of Acoustical Measurements and Noise Control, Dictionary of Architecture and Construction*, Second Edition, and *Shock and Vibration Handbook*.